TEACHER'S EDITION

Common Core
Progress™

Mathematics

3

For additional online resources, access your state-specific Teacher Toolbox.
Go to www.SadlierConnect.com and enter the Teacher's Access Code:

State	Access Code	State	Access Code
Alabama	CCPM01AL3P	Mississippi	CCPM28MS3E
Arizona	CCPM04AZ3T	Missouri	CCPM29MO3B
Arkansas	CCPM05AR3N	New Jersey	CCPM34NJ3W
California	CCPM06CA3E	North Carolina	CCPM37NC3U
Colorado	CCPM08CO37	Ohio	CCPM39OH34
Connecticut	CCPM09CT3N	Oklahoma	CCPM40OK3M
Florida	CCPM12FL36	Pennsylvania	CCPM42PA3L
Georgia	CCPM13GA3P	South Carolina	CCPM45SC3K
Illinois	CCPM17IL38	Tennessee	CCPM47TN3H
Kentucky	CCPM21KY3J	Texas	CCPM48TX3A
Louisiana	CCPM22LA3X	Wisconsin	CCPM55WI31
Massachusetts	CCPM25MA3M	Other States	CCPMNA2300
Michigan	CCPM26MI3W		

Sadlier School

TEACHER'S EDITION

Common Core

Progress™

Mathematics

Cover: *Series Design:* Studio Montage;
Title design: Quarasan, Inc.

Photo Credits: *Cover:* Getty Images/Jill Fromer: *right;*
P Gadomski Michael: *right;* tioloco: *top left;* ULTRA.F:
bottom left. Used under license from Shutterstock.com:
RoboLab: *background. Interior:* Corbis/Rob Lewine:
T12; Ocean: T15 and T17; Dann Tardiff: T09. Used
under license from Shutterstock.com/wavebreakmedia:
T03. Alamy/Novastock: 140 *top.* Blend Images/Marc
Romanelli: 78 *top.* Dreamstime.com/Yuri Arcurs: 254
top; Steve Allen: vi *bottom left;* Lowlihjeng: 255;
Njnightsky: vi *top right.* Getty Images/Digital Vision: 79;
Jupiter Images: 8 *top;* Tony Metaxas: 216 *top;* tioloco:
vi *center.* Masterfile/Royalty Free: 9. Used under license
from Shutterstock.com/Ilya Akinshin: vi *bottom right;*
april70: 141 *background;* Jana Guothova: 8 *bottom,* 78
bottom, 140 *bottom,* 216 *bottom,* 254 *bottom;*
koosen: vi *top left;* Dan Kosmayer: 141; RoboLab: 1, vi
background; Ivan Ryabokon: vi *top left.* SuperStock/
Exactostock/Andy Sotiriou: 217.

Illustration Credit: Dave Titus

William H. Sadlier, Inc.
9 Pine Street
New York, NY 10005-4700

Printed in the United States of America.
ISBN: 978-1-4217-3163-6
1 2 3 4 5 6 7 8 9 WEBC 18 17 16 15 14

Contents

Student Worktext Contents T4

Introducing *Common Core Progress* T7

Implementing *Common Core Progress* T9

Print and Digital Resources T10

Correlating Assessment and Instruction T12

Overview of the Student Worktext T14

Overview of the Teacher's Edition T19

Suggested Planning and Pacing Guide T25

Common Core State Standards for Mathematics T26

Integrating the Standards for Mathematical Practice T30

Access Your Digital Resources

Get Started

1. Go to www.SadlierConnect.com.

2. Log in

Don't have a username and password? Self register! Teachers click "Get Started!" in the Teacher Registration section.

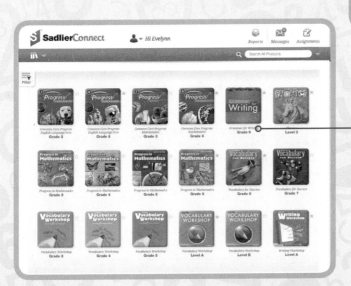

3. Select your program to begin accessing content.

With one username and password, you now have access to all your Sadlier Mathematics and English Language Arts content.

Contents

Unit 1   Focus on Operations and Algebraic Thinking

Progress Check/Home Connect 7

Unit 1 Planner 9A–9B

Unit 1 Learning Progressions 9C

Essential Question 9

Lesson 1   Interpret Products of Whole Numbers 10   3.OA.1

Lesson 2   Interpret Quotients of Whole Numbers 18   3.OA.2

Lesson 3   Problem Solving: Multiplication/Division
and Equal Groups 26   3.OA.3

Lesson 4   Problem Solving: Multiplication/Division and Arrays   34   3.OA.3

Lesson 5   Find Unknown Numbers in Multiplication
and Division Equations 42   3.OA.4

Lesson 6   Apply Commutative and Associative Properties
to Multiply 50   3.OA.5

Lesson 7   Apply the Distributive Property to Multiply 58   3.OA.5

Lesson 8   Divide by Finding an Unknown Factor 66   3.OA.6

Common Core Review 74

Performance Task . . . . ONLINE

Unit 2   Focus on Operations and Algebraic Thinking/ Number and Operations in Base Ten

Progress Check/Home Connect 77

Unit 2 Planner 79A–79B

Unit 2 Learning Progressions 79C

Essential Question 79

Lesson 9   Multiply and Divide Fluently within 100 80   3.OA.7

Lesson 10   Problem Solving: Two-Step Problems 88   3.OA.8

Lesson 11   Problem Solving: Use Equations 96   3.OA.8

Lesson 12   Identify and Explain Arithmetic Patterns 104   3.OA.9

Lesson 13   Round Whole Numbers to the Nearest 10 or 100 . . . 112   3.NBT.1

Lesson 14   Add and Subtract Fluently within 1,000 120   3.NBT.2

Lesson 15   Multiply One-Digit Whole Numbers by
Multiples of 10 128   3.NBT.3

Common Core Review 136

Performance Task . . . . ONLINE

continued next page

Contents

COMMON CORE
STATE STANDARDS

CCSS

Unit 3 **Focus on Number and Operations–Fractions**

Progress Check/Home Connect 139
Unit 3 Planner 141A–141B
Unit 3 Learning Progressions 141C
Essential Question 141
Lesson 16 Understand Unit Fractions as Quantities 142   3.NF.1
Lesson 17 Understand Fractions as Quantities 150   3.NF.1
Lesson 18 Understand Fractions on the Number Line 158   3.NF.2a; 3.NF.2b
Lesson 19 Understand Equivalent Fractions 166   3.NF.3a
Lesson 20 Write Equivalent Fractions 174   3.NF.3b
Lesson 21 Relate Whole Numbers and Fractions 182   3.NF.3c
Lesson 22 Compare Fractions: Same Denominator 190   3.NF.3d
Lesson 23 Compare Fractions: Same Numerator 198   3.NF.3d
Common Core Review 206
Performance Task . . . . (ONLINE)

Unit 4 **Focus on Measurement and Data**

Progress Check/Home Connect 215
Unit 4 Planner 217A–217B
Unit 4 Learning Progressions 217C
Essential Question 217
Lesson 24 Problem Solving: Time 218   3.MD.1
Lesson 25 Problem Solving: Liquid Volumes and Masses 226   3.MD.2
Lesson 26 Draw Graphs to Represent Categorical Data 234   3.MD.3
Lesson 27 Generate and Graph Measurement Data 242   3.MD.4
Common Core Review 250
Performance Task . . . . (ONLINE)

continued next page

Contents

Unit 5 | **Focus on Measurement and Data/Geometry**

Progress Check/Home Connect 253

Unit 5 Planner 255A–255B

Unit 5 Learning Progressions 255C

Essential Question 255

Lesson 28 Understand Concepts of Area Measurement 256   3.MD.5a; 3.MD.5b; 3.MD.6

Lesson 29 Find Areas of Rectangles: Tile and Multiply 264   3.MD.7a; 3.MD.7b

Lesson 30 Find Areas of Rectangles: Use the
Distributive Property 272   3.MD.7c

Lesson 31 Find Areas: Decompose Figures into Rectangles . . . 280   3.MD.7d

Lesson 32 Problem Solving: Measurement 288   3.MD.2; 3.MD.7 3.OA.3

Lesson 33 Problem Solving: Perimeter 296   3.MD.8

Lesson 34 Problem Solving: Compare Perimeter and Area . . . 304   3.MD.8

Lesson 35 Understand Shapes and Attributes 312   3.G.1

Lesson 36 Partition Shapes to Make Equal Areas 320   3.G.2

Common Core Review 328

Performance Task . . . . (ONLINE)

Performance Task 1 209

Performance Task 2 331

Foundational Skills Handbook 337

Problem-Solving Model 343

Common Core State Standards for
Mathematical Practice 346

Glossary 347

Index 351

Program Overview

Common Core Progress Mathematics is a streamlined, yet comprehensive K-8 supplemental mathematics program that follows the structure of the Common Core State Standards for Mathematics and integrates the Standards for Mathematical Practice into every lesson. The program systematically addresses all of the Common Core State Standards for Mathematics across the Domains: Operations and Algebraic Thinking, Number and Operations in Base Ten, Number and Operations–Fractions, Measurement and Data, and Geometry, which helps prepare students for the rigor of Common Core standardized assessments and enables them to develop key college and career readiness skills.

In *Common Core Progress*, students will:

- Build understanding of key mathematical concepts using multiple representations of a skill.

- Model mathematics with real-world problems to make sense of math and apply their knowledge.

- Share their thinking and reason mathematically while developing academic vocabulary.

- Use higher-level thinking skills and apply levels of Webb's Depth of Knowledge (DOK) with rigorous, cognitively-demanding independent practice items.

- Regularly use the Standards for Mathematical Practice so that they become habits of mind.

With the support of a comprehensive Teacher's Edition, teachers will be able to:

- Scaffold student learning with easy-to-use, comprehensive lesson plans.

- Use student assessment data, both observational and formal, to inform and redirect instruction.

- Understand the progression of Common Core Mathematics requirements across grade levels and tailor instruction to Common Core grade-level standards.

- Support diverse learners, including English language learners, struggling learners, and those needing extended learning opportunities.

- Access online and professional development resources to enhance instruction.

Founded on the Common Core Standards

Sadlier's *Common Core Progress Mathematics* was designed to effectively implement the three instructional shifts (focus, coherence, and rigor) that are necessary to teach the Common Core State Standards (CCSS) and fully addresses the shifts that were reorganized by Student Achievement Partners and the Publisher's Criteria to fall under rigor: fluency, deep understanding, application, and dual intensity.

Shifts in Mathematics Common Core Standards		
Shift	**Requirement**	**How Addressed in *Common Core Progress***
Focus	Class time and energy spent on a deeper focus on the key concepts as prioritized by the standards.	*Common Core Progress* is designed to focus on the major work of the grade per the CCSS.
Coherence	Learning within and across grade levels is carefully connected in order to build students' understanding.	Learning Progression charts that describe how the standards are developed across the grade levels are provided for each unit.
Rigor as Fluency	Students are expected to have speed and accuracy with simple calculations; teachers structure class or homework time for students to memorize through repetition.	Fluency Practice is provided (online) with references to the extra practice included at point of use in the Teacher's Edition.
Rigor as Deep Understanding	Students deeply understand and can operate easily within a math concept before moving on.	The structure of the lesson allows the student to develop a deep understanding of the concept being covered, with the Guided Instruction and Guided Practice portions of the lesson establishing the conceptual understanding.
Rigor as Application	Students use math and choose appropriate concept for application–not only when prompted.	While working independently on the independent practice and the performance tasks, students must determine which skills, strategies, and practices best serve to solve the problems and tasks at hand.
Rigor as Dual Intensity	Students are practicing and understanding with intensity.	As students work through the scaffolded Independent Practice exercises, teachers can gauge student understanding of the concepts by referencing the Common Error Analysis guidance provided in the Teacher's Edition. Through both direct instruction and practice students work toward a deep understanding of the concept.

Flexible Program Use

Common Core Progress fully aligns to the Common Core State Standards, serving as a flexible resource for supporting schools in meeting the full breadth and rigor of these standards. Lessons focus on the key concepts addressed in the Common Core and combine solid content with a pedagogically-sound lesson design that simplifies the instructional process.

***Common Core Progress* can be used as:**

- Supplemental lessons to fill Common Core gaps in a current core Mathematics program.
- Targeted preparation materials for Common Core standardized assessments.
- Support for individual or small group instruction on a particular Common Core standard.

Diverse Grouping Models

The *Common Core Progress* program employs diverse grouping and instructional models to help teachers provide effective instruction in the Common Core State Standards.

Guided Instruction For standard instruction, the program uses **whole-class** instruction to provide direct skill instruction and think-aloud modeling while the students follow along with the teacher, helping students conceptualize skills and concepts through modeling and reasoning.

Guided Practice For scaffolded practice of the standard, students work through problems of increasing complexity, independently or in small groups, as the teacher circulates around the classroom to gauge understanding of the concepts and skill being learned.

Independent Practice For application of the standards, lessons offer independent practice requiring students to use their critical-thinking skills and apply their math knowledge.

Foundational Skill Support and Fluency Practice

Foundational skills lessons and fluency practice are provided in the following ways in *Common Core Progress*.

- A comprehensive Foundational Skills Handbook, located in the back of this guide as well as in the student edition, provides a review of *all* prerequisite mathematics needed to understand the concepts and skills of Grade 3.
- Fluency practice is available online providing students with the opportunity to build their skills of performing calculations and solving problems quickly and accurately in order to meet the grade level fluency expectations specified by the Common Core State Standards.
- Problem-Solving Model offers students a four-step model as an approach to solving problems.

Print Components

Student Worktext

Organized around the Common Core Domains, the standards-based instruction includes clearly-stated models, multiple representations of skills, a focus on the critical areas of each grade level, and connections between topics to meet all Common Core State Standards. ▶

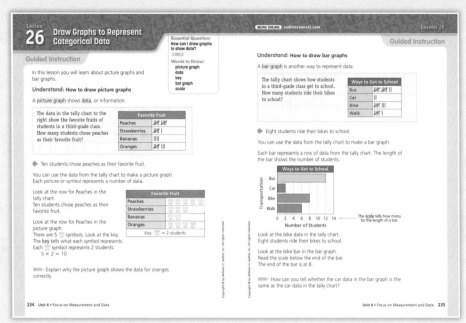

Grade 3 Pages 234–235

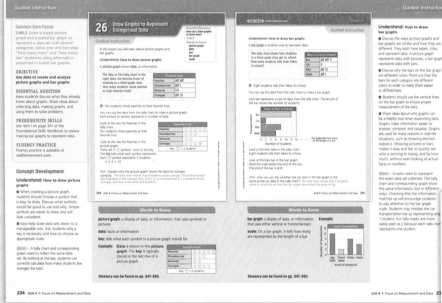

Grade 3 Teacher's Edition Pages 234–235

◀ Teacher's Edition

Teacher-friendly lesson plans with targeted standards instruction and supportive features suitable for both novice and experienced teachers. Supports instruction for all Common Core State Standards!

Progress Monitor

Four comprehensive Benchmark Assessments to identify instructional needs as benchmarked against the grade level's full set of Common Core State Standards. ▶

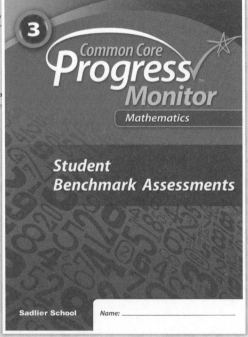

Grade 3 Progress Monitor

Digital Components

A rich array of online digital components supports program implementation and extends learning.

- **Home Connect Activities** support family member involvement and help create associations with math in real-world situations
- **Student Book Performance Tasks 1 and 2 Resources** allow students to apply their learning and provide teachers with robust evaluation support
- Downloadable **Unit Performance Tasks** provide practice opportunities for Performance Tasks related to the program's instructional units
- **Additional Practice** downloadables offer opportunities to augment program practice
- **Fluency Practice** downloadables provide opportunities for students to improve speed and accuracy with simple calculations
- **Teacher Resources**, such as a professional development training video support teachers in implementing the program

iProgress Monitor (Optional Purchase)

This dynamic online assessment system is available to help monitor student progress on the Common Core standards in real time and customize assignments based on individual needs through it's built-in test generator feature. See page T13 of this guide for more information.

Online State-Specific Teacher Toolbox

Tailored to your state, and to each grade level, K-8, the online State-Specific Teacher Toolbox has everything you need to seamlessly incorporate *Progress* into your core Math programs!

Find answers to critical questions on structure and pacing to assessment to professional development and much more! Learn how *Progress…*

- Relates to your state's Common Core **implementation plan**.
- Aligns with the **structure and pacing** of your state's model curriculum.
- Correlates to your **state's standards**.
- Supports your state's **assessment** plan.
- Helps to implement a **Common Core curriculum**.
- Provides embedded **Professional Development**

Interactive Edition

The Interactive Edition of Common Core Progress is a web-based version of the complete program through **www.SadlierConnect.com**, with access to rich media and an abundance of resources for teachers, students, and parents.

Core Digital Components

Digital **Student Worktext** Digital version of the Student Worktext, accessible online to all students.

Digital **Teacher's Edition** Digital version of the Teacher's Edition, available 24/7 to teachers at home or at school without the need to carry a heavy text! Incorporates links to all online resources as well as iProgress Monitor.

Digital Components

Exclusive to the Interactive Edition!

- **Interactive Whiteboard Tools** provide support for teaching key skills and concepts.
- *Domain- and Lesson-Specific Videos* support student learning of Commom Core State Standards.
- **iProgress Monitor** gives students access to:
  - Independent Practice
  - Common Core Reviews
  - Performance Tasks

Plus, access program assessment in a digital format or build your own!

Plus all the Digital Components included with the Print Edition!

Common Core Progress contains many formative and summative assessment opportunities to help teachers gather evidence of students' progress toward mastering the Common Core State Standards and prepare for the new Common Core assessments.

Integrated, Ongoing Assessment Opportunities

Observational Assessment opportunities are a routine part of each Lesson Plan in the Teacher's Edition. Common Errors and Teaching Tips features at point of use help teachers identify student misconceptions and provide strategies for solutions. ▶

Teaching Tips

Item 16
Students may have difficulty solving the problem because they do not draw the array correctly. Provide grid paper for those who have difficulty aligning rows and columns.

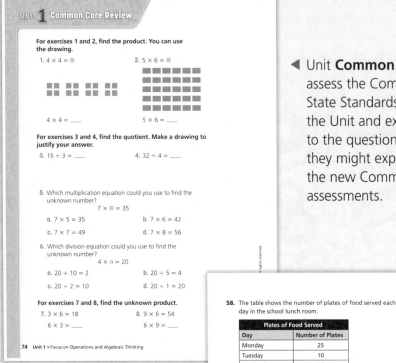

Grade 3 Page 74

◀ Unit **Common Core Reviews** assess the Common Core State Standards taught within the Unit and expose students to the question types that they might experience on the new Common Core assessments.

◀ Benchmark Assessments in **Progress Monitor** (an optional purchase) provide four comprehensive assessments that can be administered periodically throughout the school year to evaluate students' knowledge and skill level relative to the grade level's set of Common Core State Standards.

Grade 3 Progress Monitor Benchmark Assessment

Correlating Assessment and Instruction

Performance Tasks 1 and 2

provide benchmark Performance Tasks that parallel the tasks in standardized assessments to be used as guided practice opportunities. The tasks assess conceptual understanding of the content standards and show evidence of the Standards for Mathematical practice through application, modeling, and written arguments. They are also available online at **www.SadlierConnect.com**. These Performance Tasks can also be used for mid-year and end-of-year assessment purposes. These Performance Tasks play a vital role in helping you determine if students are able to integrate the standards being taught and apply them in solving real-world problems. ▶

Grade 3 Pages 210–211

Downloadable **Unit Performance Tasks**, available online at **www.SadlierConnect.com**, provide practice opportunities for students to solve real-world problems that integrate the standards within each Domain, connect to the Standards for Mathematical Practice, and often require students explain and justify their solutions.

iProgress Monitor (Optional Purchase)

Augment your assessment resources with customized assignments and test-building power!

- **Independent Practice, Unit Common Core Reviews, and Benchmark Assessment** items can be assigned to individual learners with reports that capture student progress. Includes additional items beyond those in the print program. Items can be accessed according to standard/lesson. Responses are automatically scored and reported in a grade book.

- The **Build a Test** feature enables teachers to customize assignments/assessments by a particular standard with items beyond those provided in the Student Worktext.

T13

Student Worktext

With a full-color, engaging design the Student Worktext, also available in an ebook format, provides students with the opportunity to

- Develop proficiency in mathematics through the integration of the Common Core State Standards and the Standards for Mathematical Practice
- Build conceptual understanding of mathematical content following a gradual release of responsibility model of instruction
- Reason and communicate mathematically
- Develop mathematical arguments and model real world problems

Organized around the Common Core Domains, the lessons in the Student Worktext address all of the Common Core State Standards and focus on the major work of each grade level.

A Unit Introduction That Focuses on Standards

Grade 3 Page 7

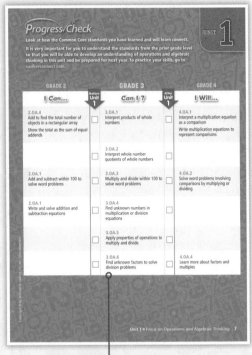

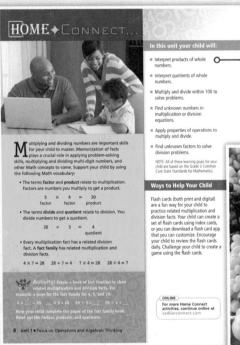

Grade 3 Page 8

Home Connect activities for each unit provide families a window into their child's learning and encourage them to take an active role.

Progress Check at the beginning of each unit allows students to focus on the unit's key standards, self-assess before learning, and reflect on progress at the end of the unit.

Grade 3 Page 9

An **Essential Question** sets the focus and identifies the big idea for each unit, enhanced with vivid images featuring engaging and relevant content that helps students make connections between math and the real world.

Gradual Release of Responsibility

Each standard is taught using a gradual release of responsibility instructional model. By gradually decreasing the level of support within each lesson, students can develop the conceptual understanding necessary for solving complex problems and tasks independently.

This gradual release of responsibility instructional model starts with **Guided Instruction**, helping students conceptualize skills and concepts through modeling and reasoning. The Standards for Mathematical Practice (MP) are embedded in all instructional presentations.

Guided Instruction

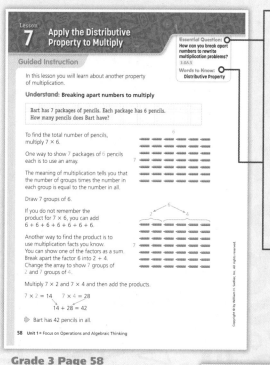

Grade 3 Page 58

Each lesson begins with an **Essential Question** to prompt students' thinking and classroom discussion to help define the lesson objective.

Key **academic vocabulary** is highlighted and used strategically when teaching the lesson.

The **Understand** instructional presentations break down the Common Core State Standards into simpler chunks of content to help students build their knowledge of the complete standard being addressed.

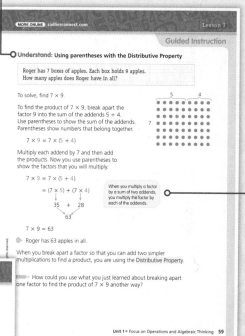

Grade 3 Page 59

The **Connect** and **Understand** presentations, together, help build knowledge to answer the lesson's Essential Question.

Opportunities for classroom discussion integrate the Standards for Mathematical Practice and build student confidence with the new material being learned.

Notes provided throughout the instruction provide scaffolding of concepts so students can go back and review each step.

Grade 3 Page 60

Gradual Release of Responsibility

The structure of the lesson continues the gradual release of responsibility model with **Guided Practice,** which allows the opportunity for students to work through problems with the teacher's supervision and assistance.

Guided Practice

Grade 3 Page 61

Scaffolding is gradually removed as students work through the problems on the page(s). This allows students more independence in applying and developing strategies and skills necessary to solve the problems.

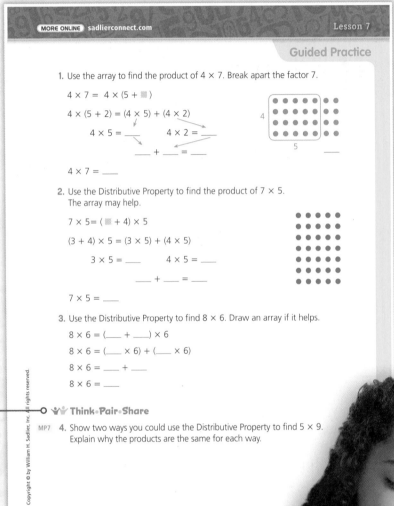

MORE ONLINE sadlierconnect.com

Lesson 7

Guided Practice

1. Use the array to find the product of 4×7. Break apart the factor 7.

$4 \times 7 = 4 \times (5 + \blacksquare)$

$4 \times (5 + 2) = (4 \times 5) + (4 \times 2)$

$4 \times 5 = \underline{\quad}$ $4 \times 2 = \underline{\quad}$

$\underline{\quad} + \underline{\quad} = \underline{\quad}$

$4 \times 7 = \underline{\quad}$

2. Use the Distributive Property to find the product of 7×5. The array may help.

$7 \times 5 = (\blacksquare + 4) \times 5$

$(3 + 4) \times 5 = (3 \times 5) + (4 \times 5)$

$3 \times 5 = \underline{\quad}$ $4 \times 5 = \underline{\quad}$

$\underline{\quad} + \underline{\quad} = \underline{\quad}$

$7 \times 5 = \underline{\quad}$

3. Use the Distributive Property to find 8×6. Draw an array if it helps.

$8 \times 6 = (\underline{\quad} + \underline{\quad}) \times 6$

$8 \times 6 = (\underline{\quad} \times 6) + (\underline{\quad} \times 6)$

$8 \times 6 = \underline{\quad} + \underline{\quad}$

$8 \times 6 = \underline{\quad}$

Think•Pair•Share

MP7   4. Show two ways you could use the Distributive Property to find 5×9. Explain why the products are the same for each way.

Unit 1 ■ Focus on Operations and

Think-Pair-Share opportunities encourage students to think independently about mathematics and then discuss, model, and explain their reasoning while learning from one another, serving to establish reliance on the Standards for Mathematical Practice.

Think•Pair•Share

T16

Gradual Release of Responsibility

The gradual release of responsibility model culminates with **Independent Practice,** which requires students to use their critical-thinking skills, apply their math knowledge, and respond to problems leveled to Webb's Depth of Knowledge. These independent practice pages can be used independently at home or in class.

Independent Practice

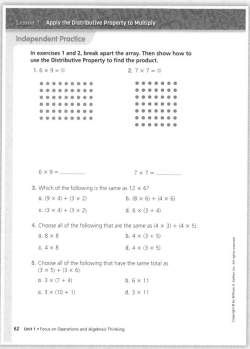

Grade 3 Page 62

As the level of scaffolding decreases and students' knowledge and confidence with the material increases, the exercises become more difficult and require higher-order thinking as well as justification of answers.

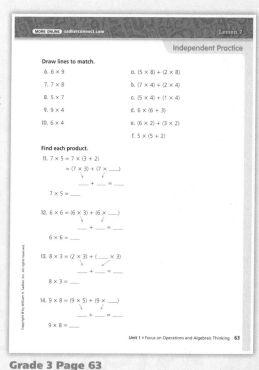

Grade 3 Page 63

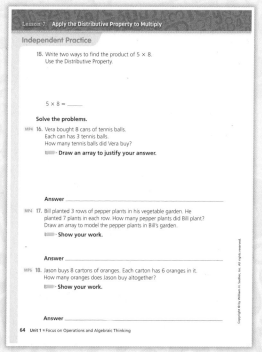

Grade 3 Page 64

Students have ample opportunities to model, reason, and justify their answers and apply all of the Standards for Mathematical Practice.

Grade 3 Page 65

Built-In Common Core Assessment Practice

Every unit concludes with a **Common Core Review** that provides practice with items similar to those students will encounter on Common Core standardized assessments. Covering all of the standards presented in the unit, the reviews allow teachers to monitor student progress and understanding of each standard.

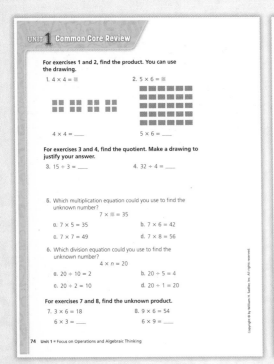

UNIT **1** Common Core Review

For exercises 1 and 2, find the product. You can use the drawing.

1. $4 \times 4 = \blacksquare$ 2. $5 \times 6 = \blacksquare$

$4 \times 4 =$ ____ $5 \times 6 =$ ____

For exercises 3 and 4, find the quotient. Make a drawing to justify your answer.

3. $15 \div 3 =$ ____   4. $32 \div 4 =$ ____

5. Which multiplication equation could you use to find the unknown number?

$7 \times \blacksquare = 35$

a. $7 \times 5 = 35$ b. $7 \times 6 = 42$

c. $7 \times 7 = 49$ d. $7 \times 8 = 56$

6. Which division equation could you use to find the unknown number?

$4 \times n = 20$

a. $20 \div 10 = 2$ b. $20 \div 5 = 4$

c. $20 \div 2 = 10$ d. $20 \div 1 = 20$

For exercises 7 and 8, find the unknown product.

7. $3 \times 6 = 18$ 8. $9 \times 6 = 54$

$6 \times 3 =$ ____ $6 \times 9 =$ ____

74   Unit 1 ▪ Focus on Operations and Algebraic Thinking

Grade 3 Page 74

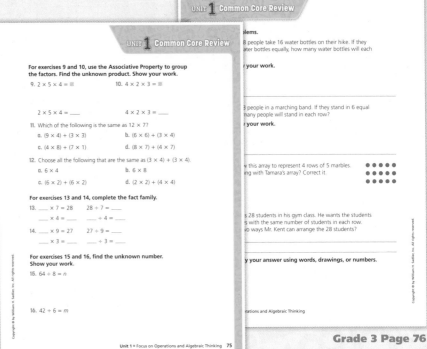

UNIT **1** Common Core Review

For exercises 9 and 10, use the Associative Property to group the factors. Find the unknown product. Show your work.

9. $2 \times 5 \times 4 = \blacksquare$ 10. $4 \times 2 \times 3 = \blacksquare$

$2 \times 5 \times 4 =$ ____ $4 \times 2 \times 3 =$ ____

11. Which of the following is the same as 12×7?

a. $(9 \times 4) + (3 \times 3)$ b. $(6 \times 6) + (3 \times 4)$

c. $(4 \times 8) + (7 \times 1)$ d. $(8 \times 7) + (4 \times 7)$

12. Choose all the following that are the same as $(3 \times 4) + (3 \times 4)$.

a. 6×4 b. 6×8

c. $(6 \times 2) + (6 \times 2)$ d. $(2 \times 2) + (4 \times 4)$

For exercises 13 and 14, complete the fact family.

13. ____ $\times 7 = 28$ $28 \div 7 =$ ____

____ $\times 4 =$ ____   ____ $\div 4 =$ ____

14. ____ $\times 9 = 27$ $27 \div 9 =$ ____

____ $\times 3 =$ ____   ____ $\div 3 =$ ____

For exercises 15 and 16, find the unknown number. Show your work.

15. $64 \div 8 = n$

16. $42 \div 6 = m$

Unit 1 ▪ Focus on Operations and Algebraic Thinking   75

Grade 3 Page 75

UNIT **1** Common Core Review

...blems.

...8 people take 16 water bottles on their hike. If they ...water bottles equally, how many water bottles will each

...y your work.

...8 people in a marching band. If they stand in 6 equal ...many people will stand in each row?

...y your work.

...w this array to represent 4 rows of 5 marbles. ...ng with Tamara's array? Correct it.

...s 28 students in his gym class. He wants the students ...s with the same number of students in each row. ...o ways Mr. Kent can arrange the 28 students?

...y your answer using words, drawings, or numbers.

...erations and Algebraic Thinking

Grade 3 Page 76

Performance Task 1

Rows of Radishes

1. Ms. Galindo counts 24 tiny radish plants. The radish plants are in rows. Each row has the same number of plants.

   a. Draw two different arrays to show how the radish plants might be growing.

   b. Write a multiplication fact for each array.

   c. Explain how each of your arrays relates to the multiplication fact.

210   Performance Task 1

Grade 3 Page 210

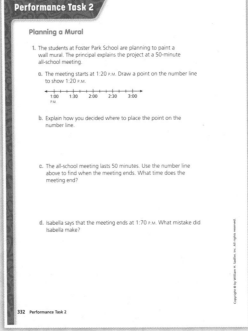

Performance Task 2

Planning a Mural

1. The students at Foster Park School are planning to paint a wall mural. The principal explains the project at a 50-minute all-school meeting.

   a. The meeting starts at 1:20 P.M. Draw a point on the number line to show 1:20 P.M.

   1:00   1:30   2:00   2:30   3:00
   P.M.

   b. Explain how you decided where to place the point on the number line.

   c. The all-school meeting lasts 50 minutes. Use the number line above to find when the meeting ends. What time does the meeting end?

   d. Isabella says that the meeting ends at 1:70 P.M. What mistake did Isabella make?

332   Performance Task 2

Grade 3 Page 332

Performance Tasks provide opportunities for students to demonstrate their understanding of content standards and to show evidence of the Standards for Mathematical Practice through application, modeling, and written arguments.

Teacher's Edition

Teacher-friendly, easy-to-use lesson plans support teachers in providing systematic instruction, practice, and application of Common Core State Standards. The Teacher's Edition is also available in an eBook format.

At-a-Glance Unit Introduction Pages

Unit introduction pages, featuring student self-assessment, a home connection, a planner for understanding key concepts at a glance, and learning progressions provide an at-a-glance reference for busy educators!

Each unit begins with support for student self-assessment and connecting to home. The **Progress Check** provides students with a visual roadmap identifying how the standards are developed and linked across grade levels, emphasizing coherence.

Home Connect activities for each unit encourage families to take an active role in their child's learning and connect math to real-world situations.

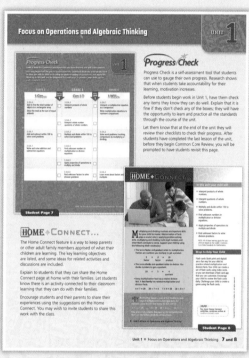

Grade 3 Teacher's Edition Pages 7 and 8

Unit Planner

The **Unit Planner** outlines everything a teacher needs to know to gather unit resources, and identify all lesson objectives, essential questions, and vocabulary.

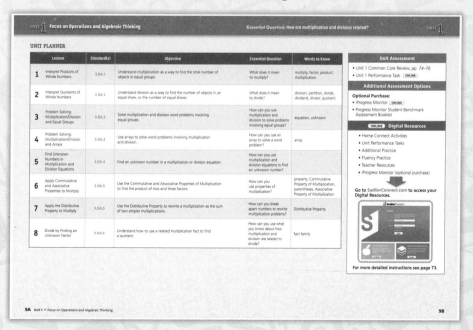

Grade 3 Teacher's Edition Pages 9A and 9B

Learning Progressions

Learning Progressions provide context and background knowledge for the Common Core State Standards by showing what students learned in the previous grade and connections to what they will learn in the next grade, building coherence within and across grade levels.

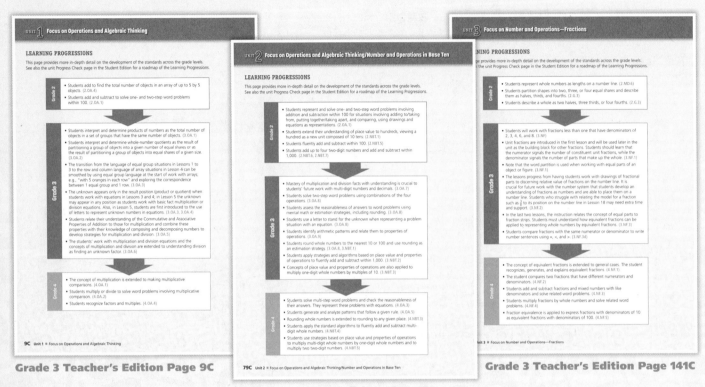

Grade 3 Teacher's Edition Page 9C

Grade 3 Teacher's Edition Page 79C

Grade 3 Teacher's Edition Page 141C

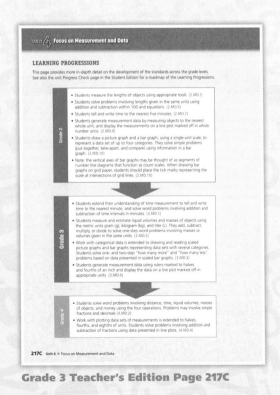

Grade 3 Teacher's Edition Page 217C

Grade 3 Teacher's Edition Page 255C

On-the-Spot Lesson Support Makes Teachers Common Core Experts!

Lesson plans featuring instruction built around key standards cover ALL Common Core standards.

Guided Instruction

Clearly stated objectives provide the focus for each lesson.

Resources available to support all learners and encourage fluency practice are listed at point-of-use.

The standards are broken down to help students build the concept and gain full understanding.

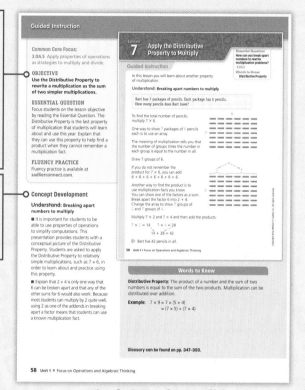

Grade 3 Teacher's Edition Page 58

The Guided Instruction culminates with the **Connect** feature building the students' understanding of the mathematical concept being taught.

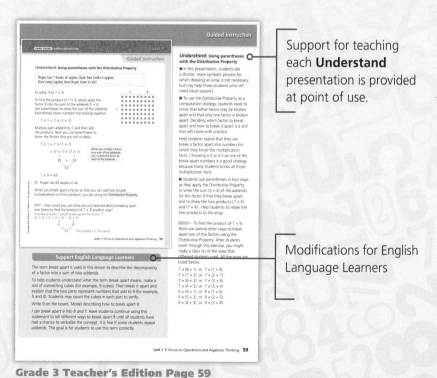

Support for teaching each **Understand** presentation is provided at point of use.

Modifications for English Language Learners

Grade 3 Teacher's Edition Page 59

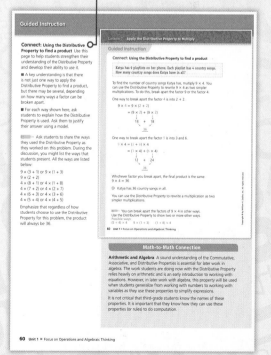

Grade 3 Teacher's Edition Page 60

Successive Increase of Student Responsibility Leads to Success

Guided Practice

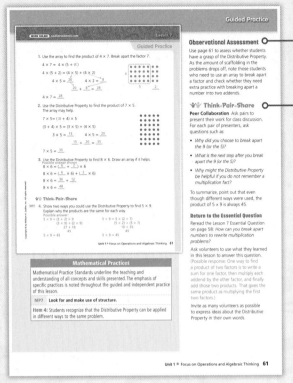

Grade 3 Teacher's Edition Page 61

Observational Assessment
The Guided Practice pages offer teachers an opportunity for formative assessment to gauge student progress.

Think-Pair-Share
Support for this peer collaboration activity helps teachers to encourage students to work together.

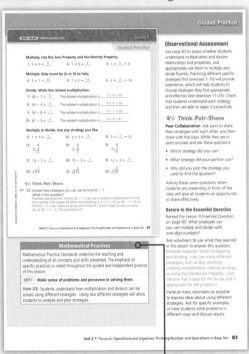

Grade 3 Teacher's Edition Page 83

Return to the Essential Question
In order to help solidify understanding, before students begin to work independently, teachers encourage them to return to the Essential Question of the lesson, allowing them to explain what they have learned in their own words.

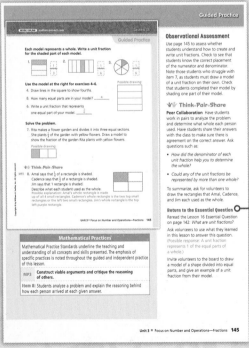

Grade 3 Teacher's Edition Page 145

Mathematical Practices
Detailed explanations of the Standards for Mathematical Practice and their application to exercises are detailed throughout the lesson as an at-a-glance reference for teachers.

Scaffolded Practice Make Independent Application of Skills Accessible

Common Core Progress provides ample opportunity for rigorous independent practice allowing students to develop procedural fluency together with conceptual understanding.

Independent Practice

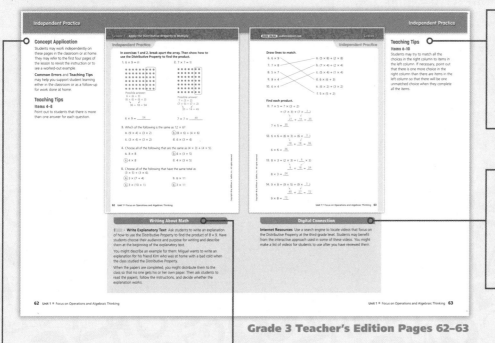

Grade 3 Teacher's Edition Pages 62–63

Teaching Tip Point-of-use teaching strategies and Common Error analyses provide help to identify potential areas of confusion or misconceptions.

Digital Connections give suggestions for helping students find online resources to enhance their understanding of mathematical concepts.

Concept Application Teachers direct students to work independently on increasingly cognitive demanding exercises and tasks.

Writing About Math Teacher-directed suggestions for helping students to make connections between concepts and integrate ELA skills in their math lessons.

Mathematical Practices Chart The Standards for Mathematical Practice are seamlessly correlated to items throughout the program.

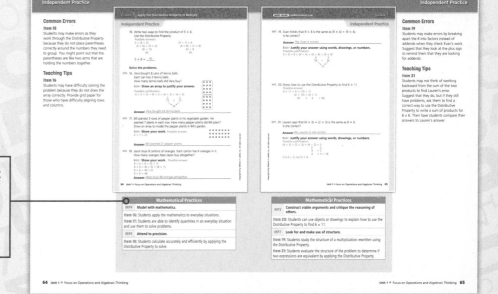

Grade 3 Teacher's Edition Pages 64–65

Assessment Tools Make Grading Simple

Common Core Progress supports busy teachers by offering easy-to-use rubrics for grading and results charts that outline next steps after grading or assessment.

Grade 3 Teacher's Edition Pages 74–75

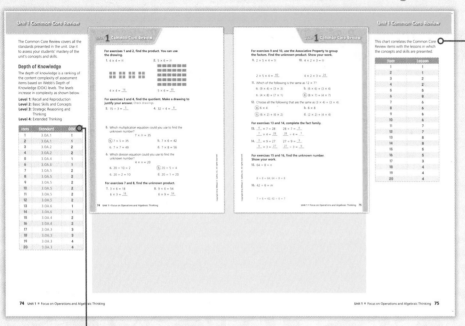

A correlation is provided for each item in the Common Core Review, identifying the lesson in which the concepts or skills are presented providing teachers with a quick reference should students require a review of the concepts.

Each item is identified by the DOK level, allowing teachers to quickly identify the level of understanding of each student.

Grade 3 Teacher's Edition Page 336

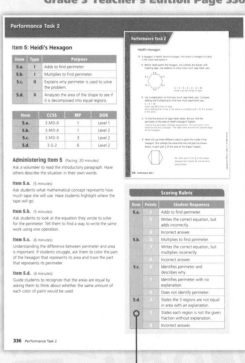

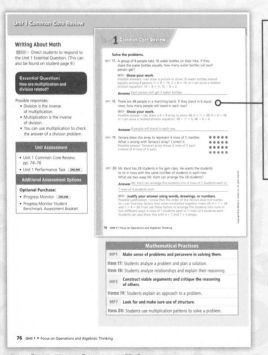

The reviews culminate with higher-order thinking problems and require students to justify their answers in writing.

Additional Assessment options are referenced at point-of-use.

Grade 3 Teacher's Edition Page 76

Performance Task Rubrics provide clear and thorough guidance on how to evaluate the assessment.

For more specific suggestions on planning and pacing, please see the Teacher Toolbox.

Weeks	Student Worktext	Online Resources to Enrich, Support, and Assess
1-6	Unit 1: Focus on Operations and Algebraic Thinking Lessons 1–8; pp. 7–76	Unit 1 Performance Task; Additional Practice; Fluency Practice; Teacher Resources Optional purchase: iProgress Monitor
7-12	Unit 2: Focus on Operations and Algebraic Thinking/ Number and Operations in Base Ten Lessons 9–15; pp. 77–138	Unit 2 Performance Task; Additional Practice; Fluency Practice; Teacher Resources Optional purchase: iProgress Monitor
13-18	Unit 3: Focus on Number and Operations – Fractions Lessons 16–23; pp. 139–208	Unit 3 Performance Task; Additional Practice; Fluency Practice; Teacher Resources Optional purchase: iProgress Monitor
19	Performance Task 1 pp. 209–214	Performance Task 1
20-23	Unit 4: Focus on Measurement and Data Lessons: 24–27; pp. 215–252	Unit 4 Performance Task; Additional Practice; Fluency Practice; Teacher Resources Optional purchase: iProgress Monitor
24-29	Unit 5: Focus on Measurement and Data/Geometry Lessons: 28–36; pp. 253–330	Unit 5 Performance Task; Additional Practice; Fluency Practice; Teacher Resources Optional purchase: iProgress Monitor
30	Performance Task 2 pp. 331–336	Performance Task 2

Suggested Pacing

To achieve optimum student results, it is suggested that *Common Core Progress* become an integral part of your math instruction. The multi-part lesson structure provides you with the flexibility you need in order to focus on a particular Common Core State Standard each day.

Suggested Timeline	Day 1	Day 2	Day 3	Day 4	Day 5
Lesson Structure	Guided Instruction	Guided Practice	Independent Practice	Independent Practice	• Additional Practice Online • iProgress Monitor Customized Assignments

Progress Monitor Student Benchmark Assessments, an optional purchase, is a workbook containing four comprehensive Benchmark Assessments that you may administer throughout the school year to track and assess students' mastery of the Common Core State Standards.

The lessons in this book are built upon the progression of the Grade 3 Common Core State Standards for Mathematical Content (CCSS). These Standards identify the mathematical concepts that students need to learn.

The focus of each *Common Core Progress* lesson is identified with a Common Core State Standard abbreviation without the topic label. For example, Grade 3 Lesson 1 focuses on Operations and Algebra standard 1 and is referenced as 3.OA.1, not 3.OA.A.1. Note: Topic abbreviations are not used in these references.

Operations and Algebraic Thinking   3.OA

Represent and solve problems involving multiplication and division.

3.OA.1   Interpret products of whole numbers, e.g., interpret 5 × 7 as the total number of objects in 5 groups of 7 objects each. *For example, describe a context in which a total number of objects can be expressed as 5 × 7.*

3.OA.2   Interpret whole-number quotients of whole numbers, e.g., interpret 56 ÷ 8 as the number of objects in each share when 56 objects are partitioned equally into 8 shares, or as a number of shares when 56 objects are partitioned into equal shares of 8 objects each. *For example, describe a context in which a number of shares or a number of groups can be expressed as 56 ÷ 8.*

3.OA.3   Use multiplication and division within 100 to solve word problems in situations involving equal groups, arrays, and measurement quantities, e.g., by using drawings and equations with a symbol for the unknown number to represent the problem.

3.OA.4   Determine the unknown whole number in a multiplication or division equation relating three whole numbers. *For example, determine the unknown number that makes the equation true in each of the equations 8 × ? = 48, 5 = ☐ ÷ 3, 6 × 6 = ?.*

Understand properties of multiplication and the relationship between multiplication and division.

3.OA.5   Apply properties of operations as strategies to multiply and divide. *Examples: If 6 × 4 = 24 is known, then 4 × 6 = 24 is also known. (Commutative property of multiplication.) 3 × 5 × 2 can be found by 3 × 5 = 15, then 15 × 2 = 30, or by 5 × 2 = 10, then 3 × 10 = 30. (Associative property of multiplication.) Knowing that 8 × 5 = 40 and 8 × 2 = 16, one can find 8 × 7 as 8 × (5 + 2) = (8 × 5) + (8 × 2) = 40 + 16 = 56. (Distributive property.)*

3.OA.6   Understand division as an unknown-factor problem. *For example, find 32 ÷ 8 by finding the number that makes 32 when multiplied by 8.*

Multiply and divide within 100.

3.OA.7   Fluently multiply and divide within 100, using strategies such as the relationship between multiplication and division (e.g., knowing that 8 × 5 = 40, one knows 40 ÷ 5 = 8) or properties of operations. By the end of Grade 3, know from memory all products of two one-digit numbers.

Solve problems involving the four operations, and identify and explain patterns in arithmetic.

3.OA.8   Solve two-step word problems using the four operations. Represent these problems using equations with a letter standing for the unknown quantity. Assess the reasonableness of answers using mental computation and estimation strategies including rounding.

3.OA.9   Identify arithmetic patterns (including patterns in the addition table or multiplication table), and explain them using properties of operations. *For example, observe that 4 times a number is always even, and explain why 4 times a number can be decomposed into two equal addends.*

Number and Operations in Base Ten   3.NBT

Use place value understanding and properties of operations to perform multi-digit arithmetic.

3.NBT.1   Use place value understanding to round whole numbers to the nearest 10 or 100.

3.NBT.2   Fluently add and subtract within 1000 using strategies and algorithms based on place value, properties of operations, and/or the relationship between addition and subtraction.

3.NBT.3   Multiply one-digit whole numbers by multiples of 10 in the range 10–90 (e.g., 9 x 80, 5 x 60) using strategies based on place value and properties of operations.

Number and Operations—Fractions   3.NF

Develop understanding of fractions as numbers.

3.NF.1   Understand a fraction 1/b as the quantity formed by 1 part when a whole is partitioned into b equal parts; understand a fraction a/b as the quantity formed by a parts of size 1/b.

3.NF.2   Understand a fraction as a number on the number line; represent fractions on a number line diagram.

    3.NF.2a   Represent a fraction 1/b on a number line diagram by defining the interval from 0 to 1 as the whole and partitioning it into b equal parts. Recognize that each part has size 1/b and that the endpoint of the part based at 0 locates the number 1/b on the number line.

    3.NF.2b   Represent a fraction a/b on a number line diagram by marking off a lengths 1/b from 0. Recognize that the resulting interval has size a/b and that its endpoint locates the number a/b on the number line.

3.NF.3   Explain equivalence of fractions in special cases, and compare fractions by reasoning about their size.

    3.NF.3a   Understand two fractions as equivalent (equal) if they are the same size, or the same point on a number line.

    3.NF.3b   Recognize and generate simple equivalent fractions, e.g., 1/2 = 2/4, 4/6 = 2/3. Explain why the fractions are equivalent, e.g., by using a visual fraction model.

3.NF.3c   Express whole numbers as fractions, and recognize fractions that are equivalent to whole numbers. *Examples: Express 3 in the form 3 = 3/1; recognize that 6/1 = 6; locate 4/4 and 1 at the same point of a number line diagram.*

3.NF.3d   Compare two fractions with the same numerator or the same denominator by reasoning about their size. Recognize that comparisons are valid only when the two fractions refer to the same whole. Record the results of comparisons with the symbols >, =, or <, and justify the conclusions, e.g., by using a visual fraction model.

Measurement and Data   3.MD

Solve problems involving measurement and estimation of intervals of time, liquid volumes, and masses of objects.

3.MD.1   Tell and write time to the nearest minute and measure time intervals in minutes. Solve word problems involving addition and subtraction of time intervals in minutes, e.g., by representing the problem on a number line diagram.

3.MD.2   Measure and estimate liquid volumes and masses of objects using standard units of grams (g), kilograms (kg), and liters (l). Add, subtract, multiply, or divide to solve one-step word problems involving masses or volumes that are given in the same units, e.g., by using drawings (such as a beaker with a measurement scale) to represent the problem.

Represent and interpret data.

3.MD.3   Draw a scaled picture graph and a scaled bar graph to represent a data set with several categories. Solve one- and two-step "how many more" and "how many less" problems using information presented in scaled bar graphs. *For example, draw a bar graph in which each square in the bar graph might represent 5 pets.*

3.MD.4   Generate measurement data by measuring lengths using rulers marked with halves and fourths of an inch. Show the data by making a line plot, where the horizontal scale is marked off in appropriate units— whole numbers, halves, or quarters.

Geometric measurement: understand concepts of area and relate area to multiplication and to addition.

3.MD.5   Recognize area as an attribute of plane figures and understand concepts of area measurement.

    3.MD.5a   A square with side length 1 unit, called "a unit square," is said to have "one square unit" of area, and can be used to measure area.

    3.MD.5b   A plane figure which can be covered without gaps or overlaps by *n* unit squares is said to have an area of *n* square units.

3.MD.6   Measure areas by counting unit squares (square cm, square m, square in, square ft, and improvised units).

3.MD.7   Relate area to the operations of multiplication and addition.

    3.MD.7a   Find the area of a rectangle with whole-number side lengths by tiling it, and show that the area is the same as would be found by multiplying the side lengths.

    3.MD.7b   Multiply side lengths to find areas of rectangles with whole-number side lengths in the context of solving real world and mathematical problems, and represent whole-number products as rectangular areas in mathematical reasoning.

    3.MD.7c   Use tiling to show in a concrete case that the area of a rectangle with whole-number side lengths a and $b + c$ is the sum of $a \times b$ and $a \times c$. Use area models to represent the distributive property in mathematical reasoning.

    3.MD.7d   Recognize area as additive. Find areas of rectilinear figures by decomposing them into non-overlapping rectangles and adding the areas of the non-overlapping parts, applying this technique to solve real world problems.

Geometric measurement: recognize perimeter as an attribute of plane figures and distinguish between linear and area measures.

3.MD.8   Solve real world and mathematical problems involving perimeters of polygons, including finding the perimeter given the side lengths, finding an unknown side length, and exhibiting rectangles with the same perimeter and different areas or with the same area and different perimeters.

Geometry   3.G

Reason with shapes and their attributes.

3.G.1   Understand that shapes in different categories (e.g., rhombuses, rectangles, and others) may share attributes (e.g., having four sides), and that the shared attributes can define a larger category (e.g., quadrilaterals). Recognize rhombuses, rectangles, and squares as examples of quadrilaterals, and draw examples of quadrilaterals that do not belong to any of these subcategories.

3.G.2   Partition shapes into parts with equal areas. Express the area of each part as a unit fraction of the whole. *For example, partition a shape into 4 parts with equal area, and describe the area of each part as 1/4 of the area of the shape.*

The eight Standards for Mathematical Practice identified in the Common Core State Standards set the expectations for the ways students should approach the study of, and practice with, the subject of mathematics. These Mathematical Practices are fully embedded within the instruction and practice, labeled as MP , and encourage students to develop the habit of reliance on the practices when approaching problems.

Mathematical Practices in *Common Core Progress*

Additionally, the emphasis of specific practices is noted throughout the guided and independent practice of the lessons.

1. **Make sense of problems and persevere in solving them.**
   The Guided Instruction provided in the program offers stepped out approaches to solving problems, helping students develop strategies to use when approaching new problems.

2. **Reason abstractly and quantitatively.**
   Concepts are introduced using the Understand and Connect structure to help students break down the components of the standard and develop the reasoning skills necessary for deep conceptual understanding.

3. **Construct viable arguments and critique the reasoning of others.**
   Whether justifying their reasoning in writing or participating in group discussions about a Think-Pair-Share exercise, there are opportunities in every lesson for students to practice the skills of developing and defending mathematical arguments and communicating their ideas clearly.

4. **Model with mathematics.**
   In addition to the models of real world situations presented to the students throughout the program to introduce new concepts, students are encouraged to develop their own models when working through the exercises.

5. **Use appropriate tools strategically.**
   Having a solid understanding of the tools available and practicing with those tools during Guided Instruction and Guided Practice, fosters familiarity and fluency using the tools when working independently.

6. **Attend to precision.**
   Students are encouraged to be precise and accurate during each stage of the problem solving process, from using the correct vocabulary to communicate ideas to attending to the units used to express their answers.

7. **Look for and make use of structure.**
   Presenting concepts and skills in a way that reveals mathematical structures, allows students to seek out these patterns on their own.

8. **Look for and express regularity in repeated reasoning.**
   As students work through cognitively-demanding exercises they develop an awareness of repeated reasoning which promotes their ability to apply similar reasoning in real world situations.

Progress Check

UNIT 1

Look at how the Common Core standards you have learned and will learn connect.

It is very important for you to understand the standards from the prior grade level so that you will be able to develop an understanding of operations and algebraic thinking in this unit and be prepared for next year. To practice your skills, go to sadlierconnect.com.

GRADE 2			GRADE 3		GRADE 4
I Can...	Before Unit 1		**Can I ?**	After Unit 1	**I Will...**
2.OA.4 Add to find the total number of objects in a rectangular array Show the total as the sum of equal addends	☐		**3.OA.1** Interpret products of whole numbers	☐	**4.OA.1** Interpret a multiplication equation as a comparison Write multiplication equations to represent comparisons
			3.OA.2 Interpret whole number quotients of whole numbers	☐	
2.OA.1 Add and subtract within 100 to solve word problems	☐		**3.OA.3** Multiply and divide within 100 to solve word problems	☐	**4.OA.2** Solve word problems involving comparisons by multiplying or dividing
2.OA.1 Write and solve addition and subtraction equations	☐		**3.OA.4** Find unknown numbers in multiplication or division equations	☐	
			3.OA.5 Apply properties of operations to multiply and divide	☐	
			3.OA.6 Find unknown factors to solve division problems	☐	**4.OA.4** Learn more about factors and multiples

Unit 1 ■ Focus on Operations and Algebraic Thinking

Student Page 7

Progress Check

Progress Check is a self-assessment tool that students can use to gauge their own progress. Research shows that when students take accountability for their learning, motivation increases.

Before students begin work in Unit 1, have them check any items they know they can do well. Explain that it is fine if they don't check any of the boxes; they will have the opportunity to learn and practice all the standards through the course of the unit.

Let them know that at the end of the unit they will review their checklists to check their progress. After students have completed the last lesson of the unit, before they begin Common Core Review, you will be prompted to have students revisit this page.

HOME ◆ CONNECT...

In this unit your child will:

- Interpret products of whole numbers.
- Interpret quotients of whole numbers.
- Multiply and divide within 100 to solve problems.
- Find unknown numbers in multiplication or division equations.
- Apply properties of operations to multiply and divide.
- Find unknown factors to solve division problems.

NOTE: All of these learning goals for your child are based on the Grade 3 Common Core State Standards for Mathematics.

Ways to Help Your Child

Flash cards (both print and digital) are a fun way for your child to practice related multiplication and division facts. Your child can create a set of flash cards using index cards, or you can download a flash card app that you can customize. Encourage your child to review the flash cards daily. Challenge your child to create a game using the flash cards.

Multiplying and dividing numbers are important skills for your child to master. Memorization of facts plays a crucial role in applying problem-solving skills, multiplying and dividing multi-digit numbers, and other Math concepts to come. Support your child by using the following Math vocabulary:

- The terms **factor** and **product** relate to multiplication. Factors are numbers you multiply to get a product.

$$5 \times 4 = 20$$
factor   factor   product

- The terms **divide** and **quotient** relate to division. You divide numbers to get a quotient.

$$20 \div 5 = 4$$
quotient

- Every multiplication fact has a related division fact. A **fact family** has related multiplication and division facts.

$$4 \times 7 = 28 \quad 28 \div 7 = 4 \quad 7 \times 4 = 28 \quad 28 \div 4 = 7$$

Activity: Create a book of fact families to show related multiplication and division facts. For example, a page for the fact family for 4, 5, and 20:

$$4 \times \_\_ = 20 \quad \_\_ \times 5 = 20 \quad 20 \div 5 = \_\_ \quad 20 \div 4 = \_\_$$

Help your child complete the pages of the fact family book. Point out the factors, products, and quotients.

ONLINE
For more Home Connect activities, continue online at sadlierconnect.com

Student Page 8

HOME ◆ CONNECT...

The Home Connect feature is a way to keep parents or other adult family members apprised of what their children are learning. The key learning objectives are listed, and some ideas for related activities and discussions are included.

Explain to students that they can share the Home Connect page at home with their families. Let students know there is an activity connected to their classroom learning that they can do with their families.

Encourage students and their parents to share their experiences using the suggestions on the Home Connect. You may wish to invite students to share this work with the class.

UNIT PLANNER

	Lesson	Standard(s)	Objective
1	Interpret Products of Whole Numbers	3.OA.1	Understand multiplication as a way to find the total number of objects in equal groups.
2	Interpret Quotients of Whole Numbers	3.OA.2	Understand division as a way to find the number of objects in an equal share, or the number of equal shares.
3	Problem Solving: Multiplication/Division and Equal Groups	3.OA.3	Solve multiplication and division word problems involving equal groups.
4	Problem Solving: Multiplication/Division and Arrays	3.OA.3	Use arrays to solve word problems involving multiplication and division.
5	Find Unknown Numbers in Multiplication and Division Equations	3.OA.4	Find an unknown number in a multiplication or division equation.
6	Apply Commutative and Associative Properties to Multiply	3.OA.5	Use the Commutative and Associative Properties of Multiplication to find the product of two and three factors.
7	Apply the Distributive Property to Multiply	3.OA.5	Use the Distributive Property to rewrite a multiplication as the sum of two simpler multiplications.
8	Divide by Finding an Unknown Factor	3.OA.6	Understand how to use a related multiplication fact to find a quotient.

Essential Question	Words to Know
What does it mean to multiply?	multiply, factor, product, multiplication
What does it mean to divide?	division, partition, divide, dividend, divisor, quotient
How can you use multiplication and division to solve problems involving equal groups?	equation, unknown
How can you use an array to solve a word problem?	array
How can you use multiplication and division equations to find an unknown number?	
How can you use properties of multiplication?	property, Commutative Property of Multiplication, parentheses, Associative Property of Multiplication
How can you break apart numbers to rewrite multiplication problems?	Distributive Property
How can you use what you know about how multiplication and division are related to divide?	fact family

Unit Assessment

- Unit 1 Common Core Review, *pp. 74–76*
- Unit 1 Performance Task   ONLINE

Additional Assessment Options

Optional Purchase:

- iProgress Monitor   ONLINE
- Progress Monitor Student Benchmark Assessment Booklet

ONLINE   Digital Resources

- Home Connect Activities
- Unit Performance Tasks
- Additional Practice
- Fluency Practice
- Teacher Resources
- iProgress Monitor (optional purchase)

Go to SadlierConnect.com to access your Digital Resources.

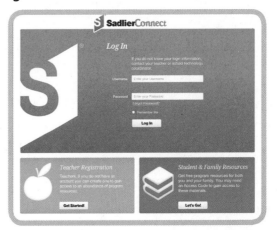

For more detailed instructions see page T3.

LEARNING PROGRESSIONS

This page provides more in-depth detail on the development of the standards across the grade levels. See also the unit Progress Check page in the Student Edition for a roadmap of the Learning Progressions.

Grade 2

- Students add to find the total number of objects in an array of up to 5 by 5 objects. (2.OA.4)
- Students add and subtract to solve one- and two-step word problems within 100. (2.OA.1)

Grade 3

- Students interpret and determine products of numbers as the total number of objects in a set of groups that have the same number of objects. (3.OA.1)
- Students interpret and determine whole-number quotients as the result of partitioning a group of objects into a given number of equal shares or as the result of partitioning a group of objects into equal shares of a given size. (3.OA.2)
- The transition from the language of equal group situations in Lessons 1 to 3 to the row and column language of array situations in Lesson 4 can be smoothed by using equal group language at the start of work with arrays; e.g., "with 5 oranges in each row" and exploring the correspondence between 1 equal group and 1 row. (3.OA.3)
- The unknown appears only in the result position (product or quotient) when students work with equations in Lessons 3 and 4; in Lesson 5 the unknown may appear in any position as students work with basic fact multiplication or division equations. Also, in Lesson 5, students are first introduced to the use of letters to represent unknown numbers in equations. (3.OA.3, 3.OA.4)
- Students relate their understanding of the Commutative and Associative Properties of Addition to those for multiplication and combine these properties with their knowledge of composing and decomposing numbers to develop strategies for multiplication and division. (3.OA.5)
- The students' work with multiplication and division equations and the concepts of multiplication and division are extended to understanding division as finding an unknown factor. (3.OA.6)

Grade 4

- The concept of multiplication is extended to making multiplicative comparisons. (4.OA.1)
- Students multiply or divide to solve word problems involving multiplicative comparison. (4.OA.2)
- Students recognize factors and multiples. (4.OA.4)

Focus on Operations and Algebraic Thinking

Essential Question:
How are multiplication and division related?

Activity

Materials: 1-inch grid paper
Tell students that there are at least 12 pears or parts of pears in the photograph. They may count to verify.

Explain that there are several ways to share the 12 pears into smaller equal groups. Ask each student to make a drawing on the grid paper showing one way to do this. Suggest that students use a circle or other easy-to-draw shape to represent each pear.

Have a whole-class discussion in which students share and explain their work. Students may generate 12 groups of 1 pear, 6 groups of 2 pears, 4 groups of 3 pears, 3 groups of 4 pears, or 2 groups of 6 pears. Elicit the idea that skip counting can be used to find the total number. If possible, repeat the activity for other numbers, such as 16 or 18.

Essential Question:
How are multiplication and division related?

As students become involved with the Essential Question they will use properties of multiplication and the inverse relationship between multiplication and division as strategies to develop a deep understanding of the two operations.

Conversation Starters

Have students discuss the photograph. Ask questions such as: *What fruits and vegetables do you see? Which fruit or vegetable has the most pieces? Which has the least? How can you tell?*

Ask students to look at the green peppers just above the tomatoes. *Suppose you have these green peppers. How can you find the total number of them?* (count them)

Have students look at the bunches of green grapes just above the pears. *Suppose you have all these bunches of grapes and want to know how many grapes there are in all. Why would it be hard to count them?* (You may skip a number or lose count because there are so many grapes.) *If you put the grapes in groups of 10, how can you find the total number of grapes without adding 10 + 10 + 10 over and over?* (Skip count by tens.)

Let students work in pairs to discuss how to find the total number of pieces of other fruits or vegetables. Lead them to see that choosing a group size and skip counting by the number of items in the group is a good strategy to find the total number.

Common Core Focus:
3.OA.1 Interpret products of whole numbers.

OBJECTIVE
Understand multiplication as a way to find the total number of objects in equal groups.

ESSENTIAL QUESTION
Tell students that sometimes they can use multiplication to find how many in all. Use this as an opportunity to discuss the differences between addition and multiplication. Reinforce the terminology of equal groups and the number of objects in each group throughout the lesson.

PREREQUISITE SKILLS
Use Item A on page 337 of the Foundational Skills Handbook to review addition facts and the concept of repeated addition.

FLUENCY PRACTICE
Fluency practice is available at **sadlierconnect.com**.

Concept Development

Understand: What multiplication means

■ Students will develop an understanding of multiplication and multiplication strategies in Grade 3. This presentation uses repeated addition to demonstrate equal groups and the number of objects in each group.

■ Be sure students develop a good understanding of factors and products. If they know the number of equal groups (factor) and the number of objects in each group (factor), they can multiply to find the total number of objects (product). Students will use the multiplication skills they have acquired to learn similar division strategies in later lessons.

▨ Emphasize that multiplication is only possible in situations with equal groups. Ask students to explain why.

Lesson 1

Interpret Products of Whole Numbers

Guided Instruction

Essential Question:
What does it mean to multiply?
3.OA.1

Words to Know:
multiply
factor
product
multiplication

In this lesson you will learn when you can multiply and what happens when you multiply.

Understand: What multiplication means

> Bella buys 5 packages of juice boxes.
> Each package has 3 juice boxes.
> How many juice boxes does Bella buy?

One way to find how many juice boxes in all is to add.

There are 5 groups of 3 boxes each.

3 + 3 + 3 + 3 + 3 = 15

The sum of 5 threes is 15.

Each package has the same number of boxes, so the 5 groups are equal in size. When the groups are equal in size, you can multiply to find the number in all.

number of equal groups *times* number in each group *is equal to* number in all

   5 equal groups   ×   3 in each group   =   15

       5   ×   3   =   15 ◄── Read: 5 times 3 is equal to 15.

Each of the numbers you multiply is a **factor**.
The number in all is the **product**.

factor   ×   factor   =   product
  5   ×   3   =   15

Multiplying 5 × 3 is the same as adding 5 threes.

▶ Bella buys 15 juice boxes.

▬▬ Why do you think the product and the sum are the same?
Possible answer: Multiplying 5 times 3 is a short way to add 5 threes.

Words to Know

multiply: perform multiplication with two or more numbers

factor: each of the numbers being multiplied that will result in a product

product: the answer in multiplication

Example: factor × factor = product
             2   ×   3   =   6

Glossary can be found on pp. 347–350.

Understand: What a product means

> Max uses stickers to make a picture.
> He has 4 cards of dot stickers.
> Each card has 5 stickers.
> How many stickers are there in all?

4 cards
5 stickers on each card
4 fives equals 20.

factor → 4 × 5 = 20 ← product

the number of cards — the number of stickers on a card — the number of stickers in all

➡ There are 20 stickers in all.

A product is the result of multiplication. The product tells how many objects in all are in a number of equal groups of objects.

✏ Describe another example. Think of a number of groups of equal things. Draw or tell what they are and write the factors and the product. Possible answer: 3 boxes of 8 crayons; the factors are 3 and 8; the product is 24

Understand: What a product means

■ This presentation builds students' understanding of multiplication. Models are used to represent equal groups, but repeated addition is not shown. Students can skip count or use repeated addition to check the multiplication.

✏ Ask volunteers to present their examples without identifying the factors and the products. Have the rest of the class identify the factors and products in their classmates' examples.

■ Propose to students that Max has 6 cards of stickers instead of 4 cards. Ask students how to write the multiplication sentence for this situation. Ask students whether the number of groups or the number in each group changes. Observe which factor the students want to change.

■ Have students draw a model for 5 × 4 = 20. Reinforce that this equation represents 5 groups of 4 objects each. Have children draw 1 more object in each group. Ask children to tell if the factors and product change and explain why.

Words to Know

multiplication: a joining operation on two or more numbers to find a total for equal groups

Example:

number of equal groups	×	objects in each group	=	total number of objects
4	×	2	=	8

Glossary can be found on pp. 347–350.

Connect: **Using factors and products to describe problem situations** Use this page to help students strengthen their understanding of multiplication and situations where multiplication is used.

■ Remind students that multiplication describes the number of objects in equal groups. Ask students to identify the factors and explain how they can find the product.

■ Some students may benefit from using counters with this presentation. Ask students how they can check their work.

 ▸ After students have answered the question, explain why they were able to use multiplication to find the product.

■ Ask volunteers to share ideas about other situations in which 3 × 4 describes the total number of objects.

Connect: **Using factors and products to describe problem situations**

> Describe a situation for which 3 × 4 shows the total number of objects. Then ask and answer a question about the total number of objects.

To do this, you need to describe a number of equal groups of objects.

Step 1

Think: How many equal groups are there? __3__ groups

What could the groups be? The groups could be 3 nests.

Step 2

Think: How many objects are in each group? __4__ objects

What objects could be in each nest? Each nest could hold 4 eggs.

Step 3

Think: In what situation could there be 3 nests with 4 eggs?

My friends were in the park. They saw __3 nests__ in the trees.

In each nest, there were __4 eggs__.

Step 4

Think: What is a question about this situation? What is its answer?

➡ How many __eggs__ in all are in the 3 nests?

There are __12 eggs__ in the 3 nests.

 ▸ Explain why you can multiply to answer your question. Tell what the factors and product are. Possible answer: I need equal groups to multiply. The number in each group is the same, so the groups are equal. That means I can multiply to find a total. The factors are 3 and 4 and the product is 12.

12 Unit 1 ■ Focus on Operations and Algebraic Thinking

Support English Language Learners

Students will see and use the term *product* throughout this lesson, as well as in future lessons in this book. Explore with students the different meanings that the term *product* has, for example, something made or sold in stores. Relate to students that products are usually the result of something (consumer products being made by machines), and that it is similar in math (two factors make a product).

Write a multiplication sentence on the board, for example, 4 × 5 = 20. Ask the class to identify the product by using a sentence frame: When we multiply four times five, the product is twenty. Then have students write their own problems and repeat the sentence.

MORE ONLINE sadlierconnect.com Lesson 1

Guided Practice

Are all the groups equal? Write *yes* or *no*. Can you multiply to find the total number of stars? Write *yes* or *no*.

1.

2.

Are all the groups equal? _no_

Can you multiply to find the total? _no_

Are all the groups equal? _yes_

Can you multiply to find the total? _yes_

Find the number of groups. Tell how many are in each group. Then find how many there are in all.

3.

4. ■■■■■
■■■■■
■■■■■
■■■■■

5. ◆◆◆◆◆
◆◆◆◆◆
◆◆◆◆◆

_4_ groups

_2_ in each group

_8_ in all

$4 \times 2 = $ _8_

_4_ groups

_5_ in each group

_20_ in all

$4 \times 5 = $ _20_

_3_ groups

_6_ in each group

_18_ in all

$3 \times 6 = $ _18_

Look at this multiplication: $6 \times 7 = 42$.

6. Name the factors. _6_ _7_

7. Name the product. _42_

Think·Pair·Share

MP7 **8.** Draw 3 groups with the same number of things in each group. Explain how you can find the total number of things.

Drawings should show 3 groups of the same number of items. Possible answer: I can find the total by multiplying 3 times the number of things in each group.

Mathematical Practices

Mathematical Practice Standards underline the teaching and understanding of all concepts and skills presented. The emphasis of specific practices is noted throughout the guided and independent practice of this lesson.

MP7 **Look for and make use of structure.**

Item 8: Students draw groups with the same number of objects and then explain how to find the total number of objects.

Observational Assessment

Use page 13 to assess whether students have a grasp of when and how to use multiplication. As the amount of scaffolding in the problems drops off, note those students who are not correctly identifying the factors and the product. Discuss how the answer to item 3 could be 4 groups of 2, or 2 groups of 4. Have students explain their reasoning.

Think·Pair·Share

Peer Collaboration Have students apply their understanding of multiplication. Working in pairs, ask students to draw 3 groups with the same number of objects. Ask students to identify the number of objects in each group. Once students have drawn their groups, ask:

- *Which numbers are the factors?*
- *What does the product tell you?*
- *How do you know you can multiply to find the total number of objects?*

To summarize, explain that multiplication can be used to find the total number of objects in equal groups.

Return to the Essential Question

Reread the Lesson 1 Essential Question on page 10: *What does it mean to multiply?*

Ask volunteers to use what they learned in this lesson to answer this question. (Possible responses: You can multiply to find the total number of objects in equal groups. The numbers you multiply are the factors. The number in all is the product. Multiplication is another way to write repeated addition.)

Independent Practice

Concept Application

Students may work independently on these pages in the classroom or at home. They may refer to the first four pages of the lesson to revisit the instruction or to see a worked-out example.

Common Errors and **Teaching Tips** may help you support student learning either in the classroom or as a follow-up for work done at home.

Common Errors

Items 5–8

Pay special attention to students' drawings. Students may draw the wrong number of groups or the wrong number of objects in each group. Tell students that the first factor should be the number of groups, and the second factor should be the number of items in each group. Suggest that children check their drawings to make sure each group has the same number of items.

Teaching Tips

Items 1–4

Remind students that they can use repeated addition to help solve the problems or to check their work.

Independent Practice

Find the total number of objects and complete the multiplication. You can use the drawing.

1. $3 \times 3 = \underline{9}$

2. $6 \times 2 = \underline{12}$

3. $4 \times 2 = \underline{8}$

4. $4 \times 4 = \underline{16}$

For exercises 5–8, find each product. Use a drawing to justify your answer.

MP4 5. $3 \times 4 = \underline{12}$
Check students' drawings.

6. $2 \times 5 = \underline{10}$

7. $5 \times 6 = \underline{30}$

8. $7 \times 3 = \underline{21}$

Mathematical Practices
MP4   **Model with mathematics.**
Items 5–8: Students use a drawing to model the problem.

Lesson 1

Independent Practice

9. There are 6 boxes of 3 erasers each. Which choice shows how many erasers in all?

   a. 3   b. 6 + 3

   (c.) 6 × 3   d. 6

10. For which situation is the total number of marbles shown by 7 × 4?

   a. Joe has 7 marbles and gives Mike 4 marbles.

   (b.) Joe gives 4 marbles to each of 7 friends.

   c. Joe wins 4 marbles from Mike and 7 marbles from Sam.

   d. Joe has 4 friends and 7 marbles.

11. Make a drawing that shows the product of 3 × 8. Then find the product. Drawings should show 3 groups of 8 each.

   3 × 8 = __24__

12. Show that 20 is the same as 4 fives. Explain how you know.
Possible answer: I drew 20 squares. Then I made groups of 5 squares. There were 4 groups of 5 squares. So 20 is the same as 4 fives. Drawings should show 4 groups of 5 each.

Teaching Tips
Items 9–10
Encourage students to reword the problems using the terminology *number of groups* and *equal groups.* For example, in item 9 there are 6 equal groups with 3 objects in each group.

Writing About Math

▸ **Write Explanatory Text** Ask students to write a paragraph explaining to someone when multiplication can be used. Students should develop the topic with definitions and examples. Illustrations could also be used to help explain their ideas.

Ask volunteers to read their paragraphs aloud. Remind students that there are different ways to explain when multiplication can be used.

Independent Practice

Common Errors

Item 13

Students may be uncertain about the terms *factor* and *product*. Have students label a multiplication equation to remind themselves which number is the product.

Teaching Tips

Item 15

Some students may not know how to set up the problem since the groups are not specifically identified. Explain that a "row" of desks can also be considered a "group" of desks. So, 5 rows of 5 desks can be thought of as 5 groups with 5 desks in each group.

Item 16

Make sure students know that "pair" means 2.

Independent Practice

13. In multiplication, what does the product show?

    a. how many factors there are

    b. how many things are in a group

    c. how many groups there are

    d. how many things in all

MP6 14. Describe a situation where the total number of soccer balls is shown as 4×6. Include the total number of soccer balls in your answer.

Answer Possible answer: Four teams are practicing on the soccer field. Each team has 6 soccer balls. There are 24 soccer balls on the field.

Solve the problem.

MP6 15. There are 5 rows of desks in Jake's classroom. Each row has 5 desks. How many desks are in the classroom?

Show your work. Drawings should show 5 groups of 5 or the sum of five 5s.

Answer There are 25 desks.

MP4 16. Mia has 6 pairs of white socks. How many white socks does Mia have?

Use a drawing to justify your answer. $6 \times 2 = 12$; drawings should show 6 groups of 2 socks each.

Answer Mia has 12 white socks.

16   Unit 1 ■ Focus on Operations and Algebraic Thinking

Mathematical Practices	
MP4	**Model with mathematics.**
Item 16: Students use a drawing to model the problem.	
MP6	**Attend to precision.**
Items 14–15: Students communicate their understanding of how to solve the problem.	

Lesson 1

Independent Practice

MP3 **17.** The class library has 6 bookshelves. Each shelf has 5 books. Ann says that there are 11 books in all. Is she correct?

Answer No. There are 30 books; $6 \times 5 = 30$.

Justify your answer using words, drawings, or numbers.
Students may show an array of 6 fives or an equation.

MP2 **18.** The team needs 16 baseballs. There are 3 baseballs in each package. If Mr. Tam buys 6 packages of baseballs for the team, will there be enough baseballs?

Answer Yes; there will be enough baseballs.

Justify your answer using words, drawings, or numbers.
Mr. Tam will have 18 baseballs, which is more than 16 baseballs; $3 \times 6 = 18$, and 18 is more than 16.

MP5 **19.** The table shows totals for multiplying the number of groups by the number in each group. Complete the table.

	Number in Each Group								
×	1	2	3	4	5	6	7	8	9
2	2	4	6	8	10	12	14	16	18
3	3	6	9	12	15	18	21	24	27
4	4	8	12	16	20	24	28	32	36
5	5	10	15	20	25	30	35	40	45

(Row labels 2, 3, 4, 5 grouped under "Number of Groups")

Unit 1 ■ Focus on Operations and Algebraic Thinking **17**

Common Errors

Items 17–18

Some students may incorrectly identify the factors since they are given three numbers in the problem. Remind students that the factors tell the number of groups and the number of objects in each group. Suggest that they first identify the factors and use those numbers to find the product. After they find the product, they can compare it to the total number of objects in the problem to determine the answer.

Teaching Tips

Item 19

If needed, review how to use the rows and columns to complete the multiplication table. Point out that the numbers in the first column (the blue column) and the first row (the blue row) are the factors. The white boxes are for the products. Tell students they must complete the table by filling in the missing products.

Mathematical Practices

MP2	**Reason abstractly and quantitatively.**

Item 18: Students use words, drawings, or numbers to prove their answers.

MP3	**Construct viable arguments and critique the reasoning of others.**

Item 17: Students justify their answer using words, drawings, or numbers.

MP5	**Use appropriate tools strategically.**

Item 19: Students complete a multiplication table.

Common Core Focus:
3.OA.2 Interpret whole number quotients of whole numbers.

OBJECTIVE

Understand division as a way to find the number of objects in an equal share, or the number of equal shares.

ESSENTIAL QUESTION

Division is the opposite of multiplication. Starting with a given number of objects, students will use division to find the number of objects in an equal share or the number of equal shares.

FLUENCY PRACTICE

Fluency practice is available at **sadlierconnect.com**.

Concept Development

Understand: Using division to find how many in an equal share

■ This lesson shows students that division sometimes involves the partitioning or sharing of a number of objects so that the shares are equal. This presentation shows how to use a diagram as one way of partitioning objects. Illustrate the meaning of *partition* in context of partitioning a room. When you partition a room, you break it into parts. In this case, the parts are equal.

■ Discuss how this presentation is related to using equal groups to multiply. Students should realize that the divisor and the quotient in division are the factors of the related multiplication equation.

■ Some students may need to see objects partitioned in order to interpret the quotient. Providing materials such as counters or connecting cubes to model problems may be helpful.

Interpret Quotients of Whole Numbers

Essential Question:
What does it mean to divide?
3.OA.2

Words to Know:
division
partition
divide
dividend
divisor
quotient

Guided Instruction

In this lesson you will learn how to use division to find the number of objects in an equal share or to find the number of equal shares.

Understand: Using division to find how many in an equal share

> Three friends have 12 marbles for a game.
> They will share the marbles equally.
> How many marbles will each friend get?

To find how many marbles each friend will get, partition, or share, the marbles equally.

One way to share the marbles is to use a diagram. Draw 3 circles for the 3 friends. Next draw marbles in each circle, 1 at a time, until you have drawn all 12 marbles. Then count to see that there are 4 marbles in each circle.

Another way to share the marbles is to divide.

total number divided by number of groups is equal to number in each group
   12 in all   ÷   3 groups   =   number in each group
         $12 ÷ 3 = 4$ ← Read: 12 divided by 3 is equal to 4.

➧ Each friend will get 4 marbles.

Words to Know

division: an operation used when partitioning a group of objects to find either the number of equal shares or the number in each equal share

partition: separate into equal parts

divide: perform a division with two numbers

Glossary can be found on pp. 347–350.

Understand: Using division to separate

> Payten has 18 heart stickers. She can put 6 stickers on each page of her sticker book. How many pages will Payten fill?
>
>

To find the number of pages, separate the total number of stickers into equal groups of 6.

One way to find the number of pages is to draw a diagram. Draw 18 dots to represent the 18 stickers.

• • • • • • • • • • • • • • • • • •

Circle groups of 6 dots.

There are no stickers left over. Count to see that there are 3 groups.

Another way to find the number of pages is to divide.

total number	divided by	number in each group	is equal to	number of groups
18	÷	6	=	3
↑		↑		↑
dividend		divisor		quotient

The dividend is the total number.

The divisor is the number by which the dividend is divided.

The quotient is the result of the division.

> Each part of a division has a name.

➡ Payten fills 3 pages of her sticker book.

✏ Describe another example. Think of a number of things you can partition into equal shares. Draw or tell what they are and write the division. **Possible answer: Divide 12 pencils equally among 6 students so that each one gets 2 pencils. 12 ÷ 6 = 2**

Unit 1 ■ Focus on Operations and Algebraic Thinking   **19**

Understand: Using division to separate

■ In this presentation, students use illustrations to see how a number of objects can be separated into equal groups. Students are also introduced to the terminology for the parts of a division equation: *dividend, divisor,* and *quotient.* Students can practice labeling the parts of a division equation on the board.

■ Help students understand why groups of 6 dots were circled to solve the problem. Explain that there are 6 objects in each group (6 stickers per page) and they need to find the number of groups (number of pages).

■ Discuss how students could divide the 18 stickers if Payten put 2 stickers on each page. Encourage discussion about what it means to divide equally.

✏ After students have answered this question, ask volunteers to read their answers aloud. Explain that there are numerous things that can be divided into equal shares. Pay close attention to the students' illustrations as a way to show understanding.

Words to Know

dividend: the number to be divided

divisor: the number by which the dividend is divided

quotient: the answer in a division

Example: dividend ÷ divisor = quotient
                   15 ÷ 3 = 5

Glossary can be found on pp. 347–350.

Guided Instruction

Connect: Using equal shares to describe problem situations

Use this page to help students strengthen their understanding of how to divide objects into equal shares to determine the number of objects in each share.

■ Have students identify the divisor and the dividend in the division. Elicit a discussion about which is the whole and which is a part.

■ You may wish to have students write a multiplication sentence for the model in Step 3. In later lessons students will work with multiplication/division fact families to find the unknown factor in a division.

■ After students complete Step 4, write the final division equation: 35 ÷ 5 = 7. Reinforce the meaning of the mathematical symbols by having a volunteer read the equation aloud.

▨▸ Have students share the answer they wrote. Encourage students to use terms such as *divide, divisor, dividend, quotient,* and *partition* in their explanations.

To extend thinking, ask students to explain how they would find 35 ÷ 7. Discuss how the number of groups would change and how many would be in each group.

Additional Answer

Possible answer: I divided 35 by 5 to get 7. The 7 oranges in 1 bag is the number in an equal share because all 5 bags have the same number of oranges.

Guided Instruction

Connect: Using equal shares to describe problem situations

> Describe a situation for which 35 ÷ 5 shows the number in an equal share. Then ask and answer a question about the situation.

To do this, you need to describe a number of objects and the number of equal shares.

Step 1

Think: How many objects are there? __35__ objects

What could the objects be?
The objects could be 35 oranges.

Step 2

Think: What does the 5 represent?

Five represents the __number__ of shares.

What could be used to make the shares?
The shares could be 5 bags.

You can draw circles to represent the bags.

Step 3

Think: What situation tells about 35 oranges shared into 5 bags?

The Greenes pick __35 oranges__ in an orange grove. They divide them equally among __5 bags__.

Step 4

Think: What is a question about this situation? What is its answer?

▸ How many __oranges__ are in one bag?

There are __7 oranges__ in one bag.

▨▸ Explain how you answered the question. Tell why the number of oranges in one bag is the number in an equal share. See Additional Answers.

20 Unit 1 ■ Focus on Operations and Algebraic Thinking

Support English Language Learners

Read the terms and the definitions of Words to Know aloud and have students repeat them. Be sure to review the pronunciation of the Words to Know, particularly *quotient* and *partition*. Note that "qu" may have a different pronunciation in other languages. Some languages pronounce this as \k\ instead of \kw\. Provide additional examples of how to pronounce words that begin with "qu." Students might share examples of "qu" or "q" words and their pronunciation in their native language.

Guided Practice

Solve each problem. You can use the picture to the right of the problem.

1. The zookeeper has 15 bananas. If he shares the bananas equally among 3 monkeys, how many bananas will each monkey get?

   15 bananas
   3 monkeys

   There are __5__ bananas in each equal share.

   $15 \div 3 = \underline{5}$

   Each monkey will get __5__ bananas.

2. There are 12 flowers. If you put 6 flowers in each vase, how many vases will you need?

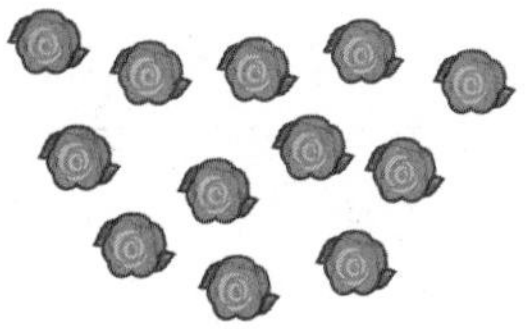

   12 flowers
   6 flowers in each vase

   You make __2__ equal groups of flowers.

   $12 \div 6 = \underline{2}$

   You will need __2__ vases.

3. Make a drawing to show $40 \div 5$. Then find the quotient.

   $40 \div 5 = \underline{8}$

   Students' drawings should show 40 items partitioned into 5 groups of 8 each or 8 groups of 5 each.

�················ Think·Pair·Share

MP1 4. Write two word problems for the division $42 \div 6 = 7$. In one, you have to find the number in each share. In the other, you have to find the number of equal shares.
   Possible answer: Number in each share: Six friends share 42 pennies equally. How many pennies does each friend get? 7 Number of shares: There are 42 soccer balls. Each team gets 6 balls. How many teams are there? 7

Unit 1 ▪ Focus on Operations and Algebraic Thinking **21**

Mathematical Practices

Mathematical Practice Standards underline the teaching and understanding of all concepts and skills presented. The emphasis of specific practices is noted throughout the guided and independent practice of this lesson.

MP1	**Make sense of problems and persevere in solving them.**

Item 4: Students write two word problems for a division equation and use concrete objects to plan out solutions.

Observational Assessment

Use page 21 to assess whether students are able to solve problems involving partitioning into equal groups. As scaffolding decreases, note if students can find the number of objects in each equal share, as well as the number of equal shares.

☼☼ Think·Pair·Share

Peer Collaboration Ask each student to write two word problems for the division equation. Students can work with a partner and share their word problems. One partner should read his or her problems and the other partner should write the division, properly identifying the number of groups and the number of objects in each group. Next, have partners switch roles. If some students are struggling, encourage them to draw an illustration to help them visualize the problem. As students work, ask questions such as:

- *What words in a word problem tell you if you are finding the number of equal shares or the number in each share?*

- *Why can the same division equation be used to model two different situations?*

To summarize, point out that division can be used to find the number of objects in an equal share or the number of equal shares.

Return to the Essential Question

Reread the Lesson 2 Essential Question on page 18: *What does it mean to divide?*

Ask volunteers to use what they learned in this lesson to answer this question. (Possible response: To divide means to partition a number of objects into equal shares or to find how many are in each equal share.)

Independent Practice

Concept Application

Students may work independently on these pages in the classroom or at home. They may refer to the first four pages of the lesson to revisit the instruction or to see a worked-out example.

Common Errors and **Teaching Tips** may help you support student learning either in the classroom or as a follow-up for work done at home.

Common Errors

Item 4

Students may confuse the divisor and the dividend when dividing the apples into equal groups. Ensure students understand that there are 42 apples in all and that they are being divided into 6 baskets. A depiction of the 6 baskets may help visual learners solve the problem.

Independent Practice

For exercises 1 and 2, use the drawing to find the quotient.

1.

   $27 \div 3 = \underline{\ 9\ }$

2. (● ● ● ● ● ● ●) (● ● ● ● ● ● ●) (● ● ● ● ● ● ●) (● ● ● ● ● ● ●)
   (● ● ● ● ● ● ●) (● ● ● ● ● ● ●) (● ● ● ● ● ● ●) (● ● ● ● ● ● ●)

   $56 \div 8 = \underline{\ 7\ }$

3. For which situation is the number in a share expressed as $36 \div 9$?

   a. Betty shares 36 tickets for the softball game among 4 friends.

   b. Mrs. Baker makes 9 big batches of 36 muffins each for the school picnic.

   c. Lizzie has 36 guppies and 9 goldfish in her aquarium.

   (d.) Ms. Juarez shares 36 boxes of copy paper among the 9 classrooms in her school.

MP6 4. Describe a situation where the number of apples in a basket is expressed as $42 \div 6$. Then ask a question about the situation.
   Possible answer: Jane picks 42 apples. She shares the apples equally among 6 baskets. How many apples were in each basket?

22   Unit 1 ■ Focus on Operations and Algebraic Thinking

Mathematical Practices

MP2	**Reason abstractly and quantitatively.**
Item 5: Students solve a division word problem.	
MP4	**Model with mathematics.**
Items 6–7: Students draw models to find the quotient and justify their thinking.	
MP6	**Attend to precision.**
Items 4, 8, 9, 10: Students describe a situation to model a division.	

Lesson 2

Independent Practice

MP2 **5.** Explain how to share 36 things equally among 4 groups. Then find the quotient.
Possible answer: I would put 36 things one by one in each of the 4 groups, until all 36 things are in a group. There are 9 things in each group. $36 \div 4 = 9$

Find each quotient. Make a drawing to justify your answer. Check drawings.

MP4 **6.** $25 \div 5 = \underline{\ 5\ }$

7. $14 \div 2 = \underline{\ 7\ }$

Find each quotient. Describe a situation that can be represented by the division.

MP6 **8.** $6 \div 3 = \underline{\ 2\ }$
Possible answer: 6 marbles shared by 3 friends

MP6 **9.** $32 \div 8 = \underline{\ 4\ }$
Possible answer: 32 markers shared by 8 students

MP6 **10.** $20 \div 4 = \underline{\ 5\ }$
Possible answer: 20 jars of paint shared by 4 artists

Teaching Tips

Items 6-7
Remind students that the first step to modeling the division equation could be drawing circles to show the number of groups.

Items 8-10
Have students develop a plan before describing each division situation. Suggest using an illustration to help visualize the problem. Refer students to the Connect Presentation if they need additional support.

Writing About Math

▶ **Compare and Contrast** Ask students to write a paragraph on what they have learned about multiplication and division. Students should include what it means to multiply and what it means to divide.

Independent Practice

Common Errors

Item 11

Students may read 24 boxes as the number of groups, not the total number of objects. Make sure students correctly identify what is given in the problem and what they need to find.

Teaching Tips

Item 12

Encourage students to represent the problems with illustrations in order to organize their thinking.

Independent Practice

11. There are 24 boxes of cereal at the food pantry. Each family will receive 3 boxes. Which choice shows how many families will receive boxes of cereal?

    a. 3

    b. 24 × 3

    c. 24 ÷ 3

    d. 24

12. Ms. Tucker has a package of 12 small notebooks. She makes a list to show how many she can give to different numbers of friends if she shares them equally. Complete the list.

    2 friends   Each friend will get __6__ notebooks.

    3 friends   Each friend will get __4__ notebooks.

    4 friends   Each friend will get __3__ notebooks.

    6 friends   Each friend will get __2__ notebooks.

Solve the problems.

MP6 13. Dan has 40 grapes. He wants to share the grapes equally among 5 fruit salads. How many grapes will Dan put in each fruit salad?

    ▶ **Show your work.**
    Possible answer: 40 ÷ 5 = 8

    Answer Dan will put 8 grapes in each fruit salad.

MP7 14. A toy store has 56 plush animals. The store clerk puts the plush animals on 7 shelves. Each shelf has the same number of plush animals. How many plush animals are on each shelf?

    ▶ **Show your work.**
    Possible answer: 56 ÷ 7 = 8

    Answer There are 8 plush animals on each shelf.

24   Unit 1 ■ Focus on Operations and Algebraic Thinking

Mathematical Practices	
MP6	**Attend to precision.**
Item 13: Students calculate accurately to solve the problem.	
MP7	**Look for and make use of structure.**
Item 14: Students evaluate the structure of the problem to aid in solving it.	

Lesson 2

Independent Practice

MP4 **15.** The 24 students in Mr. Lee's class will rent vans to go on a field trip. Six students and 1 adult will ride in each van. How many vans are needed?

Answer Four vans are needed.

▸ **Justify your answer using words, drawings, or numbers.**
Possible answer: 24 ÷ 6 = 4

MP3 **16.** Nicholas says that 10 ÷ 2 = 8. Is he correct?

Answer No; he is not correct.

▸ **Justify your answer using words, drawings, or numbers.**
Possible justification: 10 ÷ 2 = 5; Nicholas subtracted 10 − 2 to get 8.

MP2 **17.** Kara partitions 16 dimes into equal groups in 3 different ways. She puts more than 1 dime in each group. She makes 2 or more groups for each way. Describe the groups that Kara made.

Answer Kara makes 2 groups of 8 dimes each, 8 groups of 2 dimes each, and 4 groups of 4 dimes each.
▸ **Justify your answer using words, drawings, or numbers.**
Possible justification: 2 × 8 = 16; 8 × 2 = 16; 4 × 4 = 16

Unit 1 ■ Focus on Operations and Algebraic Thinking **25**

Common Errors

Item 15
Students may try to divide by 7. Point out to students that there is additional information about how many adults will ride in each van.

Item 17
Students may have trouble sorting out the various pieces of information given in this problem. Students can use manipulatives to physically illustrate the concepts if needed.

Teaching Tips

Item 16
Remind students that they can use multiplication to check division.

Mathematical Practices	
MP2	**Reason abstractly and quantitatively.**
Item 17: Students interpret mathematical language and solve a division problem involving money.	
MP3	**Construct viable arguments and critique the reasoning of others.**
Item 16: Students explain an approach to a problem and construct arguments by using drawings.	
MP4	**Model with mathematics.**
Item 15: Students model a real-world division problem.	

Common Core Focus:

3.OA.3 Use multiplication and division within 100 to solve word problems in situations involving equal groups, arrays, and measurement quantities.

OBJECTIVE

Solve multiplication and division word problems involving equal groups.

ESSENTIAL QUESTION

Have students give examples of word problems that can be solved using multiplication or division. Review multiplication and division strategies using illustrations. Discuss how similar diagrams can be used to show both strategies.

FLUENCY PRACTICE

Fluency practice is available at **sadlierconnect.com**.

Concept Development

Understand: Using multiplication to solve problems involving equal groups

■ Multiplication can be differentiated as multiplication of equal groups and multiplication using arrays. When multiplying equal groups, each factor fulfills a distinct role: one factor represents the number of groups, and the other factor represents the number of objects in each group. Therefore, the model representing 4 groups of 8 objects does not represent 8 groups of 4 objects. There is no such distinction when modeling by using arrays.

■ If students have difficulty understanding equal groups, have them use paper plates to model the groups and counters to represent the number of objects in each group. Emphasize that each group must contain the same number of objects in order to be equal.

Problem Solving: Multiplication/Division and Equal Groups

Essential Question:
How can you use multiplication and division to solve problems involving equal groups?

3.OA.3

Words to Know:
equation
unknown

Guided Instruction

In this lesson you will learn how to solve problems involving equal groups.

Understand: Using multiplication to solve problems involving equal groups

> Lindsay has 4 pencil cases. She wants to put 8 pencils in each case. How many pencils does Lindsay need?

The number of pencils Lindsay needs is represented by 4×8. Find the product 4×8.

One way to find 4×8 is to draw a diagram.

Draw 4 pencil cases with 8 pencils in each case.

You can count or add to find that there are 32 pencils.

Another way to find 4×8 is to multiply.

You can use a symbol for the unknown number to write a multiplication equation that relates the factors to the product. The unknown represents the number of pencils Lindsay needs. To find the value of the unknown number, solve the equation.

$4 \times 8 = \blacksquare$
$4 \times 8 = 32$

▷ Lindsay needs 32 pencils.

▷ Why can you multiply to solve this problem? Possible answer: There are equal groups, so you can multiply by the number of groups.

26 Unit 1 ■ Focus on Operations and Algebraic Thinking

Words to Know

equation: a number sentence that includes an equal sign

Example: $4 \times 8 = 32$

unknown: a value in a mathematical problem that is not known

Glossary can be found on pp. 347–350.

Lesson 3

Guided Instruction

Understand: Using division to find the number of equal groups

> Mr. Kane asks 21 students to form lines of 7 students each.
> How many lines can the students form?

To solve, separate the 21 students into equal groups.

One way is to use a number line diagram. Start at 21. Draw jumps to show equal groups of 7 until you reach 0.

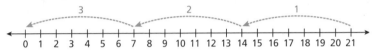

There are 3 equal groups of 7.

Another way is to divide.

$21 \div 7 = \blacksquare$
$21 \div 7 = 3$

➡ Mr. Kane's students can form 3 lines.

> **Remember!**
> Using division to separate:
> The number in all divided by the number in each group is equal to the number of groups.

Understand: Using division to find the number in each group

> Three children share 18 pieces of sidewalk chalk. How many pieces of chalk does each child get?

To solve, make 3 groups of equal shares.

One way is to use a diagram. Draw 3 boxes. Draw 1 line in each box, 1 at a time until you have drawn all 18 lines. Count the 6 lines in each box.

| | | | | | | | | | | | | | | | | | | | | | | | |

Another way is to divide.

$18 \div 3 = \blacksquare$
$18 \div 3 = 6$

➡ Each child gets 6 pieces of sidewalk chalk.

> **Remember!**
> Using division to share:
> The number in all divided by the number of groups is equal to the number in each group.

Unit 1 ■ Focus on Operations and Algebraic Thinking **27**

Understand: Using division to find the number of equal groups

■ In this presentation, students examine how to use a number line diagram to solve a division problem. Students can start by drawing a number line, and then using repeated subtraction to represent the problem. Each subtraction is shown as a jump equal to the number of objects in each group. The solution is the number of equal jumps it takes to reach 0.

Understand: Using division to find the number in each group

■ Students can also solve division word problems involving equal groups by using drawings. Drawings provide a visual context for discussing and applying the meaning of division in real-world situations.

■ Students may think they need to draw representations of the actual items when modeling division. Encourage students to use simple lines or shapes to represent the objects being shared.

■ Showing and practicing different ways to model and solve problems provides students flexibility in choosing strategies.

Support English Language Learners

English language learners may have difficulty using the multiplication and division terminology. Write a multiplication and a division equation on the board. Label each with the appropriate terms. As you label, read each term aloud as you point to the corresponding number. Then, have students repeat. Next, have students write a multiplication or division equation giving clues that use only the terms *factor, product, dividend, divisor,* and *quotient.* For example:

> Write an equation that has a *quotient* of 15 and a *divisor* of 5.
> Write an equation that has a *factor* of 4 and a *factor* of 7.

Students should label each part of the equation including the unknown number.

Connect: What you know about multiplication and division to solve problems Use this page to help students strengthen their understanding of how multiplication and division equations can be used to solve word problems.

■ Be sure students can differentiate between situations that represent multiplication and situations that represent division. Multiplication is used to join smaller equal groups of objects into one whole group. Division is used to separate one whole group of objects into smaller equal groups.

■ Remind students to use a symbol for an unknown number in an equation. It is important for students to make connections between models, symbols, and equations. Provide ample opportunity for students to practice verbalizing how to translate a visual model into a written equation.

✏️ ▸ Ask students to explain how each part of the diagram represents both multiplication and division. Students should realize that the total number of objects represents the product and also the dividend. The number of equal groups and the number of objects in each group represent the factors, or the divisor and quotient.

Lesson 3 Problem Solving: **Multiplication/Division and Equal Groups**

Guided Instruction

Connect: What you know about multiplication and division to solve problems

> Ms. Chavez uses the 4 windows in her bookstore to display 12 new books. She puts the same number of books in each window. How many books are in each window?

Step 1

Decide what information is known and what is unknown.

Known: the number of new books she has —12
the number of windows she uses —4

Unknown: the number of books in each window

Step 2

Use a diagram to represent the situation. First sketch the windows.

Now represent the 12 books in the 4 windows so that the same number of books is in each window.

Step 3

The diagram shows that you can write and solve a division equation to answer the question.

$12 \div 4 = $ ■

$12 \div 4 = \underline{\ 3\ }$

➡️ There are _____3 books_____ in each window.

✏️ ▸ What multiplication fact is represented by your diagram of the 12 books in the 4 windows? Explain why the diagram can show both multiplication and division. $4 \times 3 = 12$; possible explanation: The diagram can show both multiplication and division because I can see 4 groups of 3 books and I can see 12 books shared among 4 windows.

28 Unit 1 ▪ Focus on Operations and Algebraic Thinking

Math-to-Math Connection

Arithmetic and Algebra A strong understanding of the relationship between multiplication, division, and an unknown-factor problem will be helpful when students begin solving equations. Using a symbol, such as an empty circle or square, for an unknown number will build a basic understanding before transitioning to variables.

MORE ONLINE sadlierconnect.com

Lesson 3

Guided Practice

1. Tony is making a picture frame. He needs 4 pieces of wood, each 9 inches long. How many inches of wood does Tony need in all?

   4 times 9 inches equals how much?
   4 × 9 = ■

   Use the number line. Represent the 4 pieces of wood, each 9 inches long.

   Answer Tony needs __36__ inches of wood.

2. Una and her four friends want to share 40 markers equally. How many markers will each person have?

   40 markers shared equally by 5 persons is the unknown number of markers each person will have.
   40 ÷ 5 = ■

   Make 5 groups. Show how to share the 40 markers equally.

   Answer Each person will have __8__ markers.

☥ Think•Pair•Share

MP2 3. Twenty-seven students sat in 3 rows of 9 chairs to watch a science video. Draw a diagram to represent the situation. Then explain how the diagram represents the two equations 3 × 9 = 27 and 27 ÷ 9 = 3. Student diagrams should show 3 groups of 9. Possible explanation: The diagram shows 3 rows of 9 dots, so it shows 3 × 9 = 27. The diagram shows 27 dots in groups of 9 so it shows 27 ÷ 9 = 3.

Unit 1 ■ Focus on Operations and Algebraic Thinking **29**

Mathematical Practices

Mathematical Practice Standards underline the teaching and understanding of all concepts and skills presented. The emphasis of specific practices is noted throughout the guided and independent practice of this lesson.

MP2 **Reason abstractly and quantitatively.**

Item 3: Students use properties of operations and objects to relate multiplication and division.

Observational Assessment

Use page 29 to assess whether students are able to complete multiplication and division word problems. Look for correct use of diagrams as well as correct computation. If students have trouble deciding which operation to use, suggest that they make a list of what is known and what is unknown.

☥☥ Think•Pair•Share

Peer Collaboration Have one partner draw a number line and the other partner draw equal groups to represent the same situation. Have partners discuss how the two diagrams are the same and different. Ask questions such as:

- *How does each diagram illustrate the number of equal groups?*

- *How does each diagram illustrate the number of objects in each group?*

- *How does each diagram illustrate the total number of objects?*

To summarize, point out that both multiplication and division involve equal groups. There is more than one way to model and write an equation to represent a problem.

Return to the Essential Question

Reread the Lesson 3 Essential Question on page 26: *How can you use multiplication and division to solve problems involving equal groups?*

Ask volunteers to use what they learned in this lesson to answer this question. (Possible response: Multiplication can be used to join equal groups to find the total. Division can be used to separate a total number of objects into equal groups.)

Concept Application

Students may work independently on these pages in the classroom or at home. They may refer to the first four pages of the lesson to revisit the instruction or to see a worked-out example.

Common Errors and **Teaching Tips** may help you support student learning either in the classroom or as a follow-up for work done at home.

Teaching Tips

Items 1–2

Help students extend their thinking by asking how each model can be used to show the inverse operation.

Lesson 3   Problem Solving: **Multiplication/Division and Equal Groups**

Independent Practice

In exercises 1–3, use the drawing to represent the problem. Then write an equation and solve.

MP4   1. Sandy buys 7 bags of pears. Each bag holds 4 pears. How many pears does Sandy buy in all?

✏ **Show your work.**

$7 \times \underline{\ 4\ } = \underline{\ 28\ }$

Answer Sandy buys __28__ pears.

MP5   2. Joe is packing for a campout. He has 24 flashlight batteries. He puts 8 batteries each into some boxes. How many boxes does he use?

✏ **Show your work.**

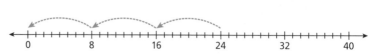

$24 \div \underline{\ 8\ } = \underline{\ 3\ }$

Answer Joe uses __3__ boxes.

Writing About Math

✏ **Write an Informative Text** Ask students to write a paragraph telling about a time they used multiplication or division to solve a real-world problem. Have students include a diagram to model the problem they solved. Students can share their real-world examples with the class.

Lesson 3

Independent Practice

MP4 3. Mrs. McGwin's students are planting flower seeds. If they plant 5 seeds in each of 8 flower pots, how many seeds do they plant in all?

Show your work.

$8 \times \underline{5} = 40$

Answer They plant $\underline{40}$ seeds in all.

MP1 4. The third grade class is selling baskets to raise money. The class has 15 baskets to sell.

a. If the class sells 3 baskets each day, how many days will it take to sell all 15 baskets?

$\blacksquare = 15 \div 3$

$\underline{5} = 15 \div 3$

Answer It will take $\underline{5}$ days to sell all 15 baskets.

Justify your answer using words or drawings.
Possible answer: 15 small squares in 5 groups of 3

b. If the class sells 5 baskets each day, how many days will it take to sell all 15 baskets?

$\bullet = 15 \div 5$

$\underline{3} = 15 \div 5$

Answer It will take $\underline{3}$ days to sell all 15 baskets.

Justify your answer using words or drawings.
Possible answer: 15 small squares in 3 groups of 5

Unit 1 ■ Focus on Operations and Algebraic Thinking **31**

Teaching Tips

Item 3
Remind students that objects can be represented by simple dot or line drawings. The model does not need to illustrate the actual object of the word problem.

Item 4
Have students explain how their drawings in parts a and b are alike and how they are different.

Mathematical Practices

MP1	**Make sense of problems and persevere in solving them.**

Item 4: Students analyze a problem and use pictures to justify their reasoning.

MP4	**Model with mathematics.**

Item 1: Students use concrete tools to explain operations.

Item 3: Students relate mathematics to everyday problems.

MP5	**Use appropriate tools strategically.**

Item 2: Students use a number line to model and complete a division word problem.

Independent Practice

Common Errors

Item 5

Students may misinterpret the problem as multiplication. Guide students to realize they are separating the total number of snack bars into equal groups and help them interpret the action as division.

Teaching Tips

Items 5–7

Remind students to first identify what information is known and what is unknown in each problem.

Item 7

Point out that this problem involves equal lengths rather than equal groups. Using a number line is a good way to represent equal lengths.

Independent Practice

Solve the problems.

MP2 **5.** A group of 10 hikers takes 30 snack bars on their hike. If they share the snack bars equally, how many will each hiker get?

· **Show your work.**
Possible answer: I can make a drawing to show 30 snack bars shared equally among 10 people. 30 ÷ 3 = 10.

Answer Each hiker gets 3 snack bars.

MP4 **6.** A group of campers is using 7 rowboats for fishing. Three campers are in each boat. How many campers are fishing?

· **Show your work.**
Possible answer: I can make a drawing to show 7 groups of 3 campers. 7 × 3 = 21.

Answer 21 campers are fishing.

MP5 **7.** A rubber band is 9 centimeters long. It is stretched to be 3 times as long. How long is the stretched rubber band?

· **Show your work.**
Possible answer: I can draw a number line to show 3 jumps of 9 centimeters each, 3 × 9 = 27.

Answer The stretched rubber band is 27 centimeters long.

32 Unit 1 ■ Focus on Operations and Algebraic Thinking

Mathematical Practices

MP2	**Reason abstractly and quantitatively.**
Item 5: Students pay attention to mathematical language to solve a real-world problem.	
MP4	**Model with mathematics.**
Item 6: Students relate mathematics to everyday problems.	
MP5	**Use appropriate tools strategically.**
Item 7: Students decide on an appropriate tool to use for the situation.	

MP6 **8.** Mr. Lee ran 35 miles this week. He runs every day from Monday through Friday but does not run on the weekend. This week he ran the same distance every day. How far did Mr. Lee run each day?

▶ **Show your work.**
Possible answer: I can divide 35 into 5 equal groups to get 7 or $35 \div 5 = 7$.

Answer Mr. Lee ran 7 miles each day.

MP3 **9.** Alexi drew this picture to show 3 bags with 4 oranges in each bag. What is wrong with Alexi's picture? Correct it.

Possible answer: Alexi did not show an equal number of oranges in each bag. All the bags should show 4 oranges.

MP4 **10.** Brie drew this number line to show 3 jumps of 5 inches each. What is wrong with Brie's picture? Correct it.

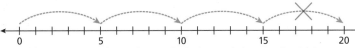

Possible answer: Brie drew 4 jumps of 5 inches each, but she should show only 3 jumps.

Common Errors

Item 8
Student may incorrectly divide 35 into 7 equal groups. Have children reread the problem to see that Mr. Lee ran 5 days each week, and therefore the equation is $35 \div 5 = 7$.

Teaching Tips

Items 9–10
Remind students to compare what is known and what is unknown in each problem with the given models.

Mathematical Practices	
MP6	**Attend to precision.**
Item 8: Students use measurement units appropriately.	
MP3	**Construct viable arguments and critique the reasoning of others.**
Item 9: Students construct arguments by using drawings.	
MP4	**Model with mathematics.**
Item 10: Students interpret the solution in the context of a situation.	

Common Core Focus:

3.OA.3 Use multiplication and division within 100 to solve word problems in situations involving equal groups, arrays, and measurement quantities.

OBJECTIVE

Use arrays to solve word problems involving multiplication and division.

ESSENTIAL QUESTION

Explain that an array is a drawing or arrangement of objects that can help students solve multiplication or division word problems. Point out that the use of arrays can help them further their understanding of multiplication and division.

FLUENCY PRACTICE

Fluency practice is available at **sadlierconnect.com**.

Concept Development

Understand: Using arrays to solve problems

■ It is important for students to have a variety of strategies to use for solving problems. This presentation focuses on the use of arrays as a visual representation. Arrays can help students visualize multiplication and division concepts to solve word problems.

■ You may wish to have students act out the marching band problem by arranging themselves in an array that matches the problem.

■ After students have added or counted to find the total number of dots in the array, explain how the equation matches the array.

▸ Ask students to explain how an array is similar to objects organized in equal groups. Point out that all rows of this array have 6 dots, and all columns have 3 dots. So, this array shows 3 groups of 6, or 6 groups of 3.

Lesson 4

Problem Solving: Multiplication/Division and Arrays

> **Essential Question:**
> How can you use an array to solve a word problem?
> 3.OA.3
>
> **Words to Know:**
> array

Guided Instruction

In this lesson you will learn how to solve word problems using arrays.

Understand: Using arrays to solve problems

> The trumpet players in the Youth Band march 6 in a row. When they march, they make 3 full rows. How many trumpet players are in the Youth Band?

To solve this problem, find 3 × 6.

One way to find 3 × 6 is to use an array. An array is an arrangement of objects or symbols in equal rows and equal columns.

Use a dot to represent a band member.

Draw 3 rows of 6 dots.

Then add or count to find the total.

There are 18 dots.

Another way to find 3 × 6 is to use an equation. The equals sign in an equation shows that the two sides of the equation are equal.

■ = 3 × 6 ◀— ■ represents the value of 3 × 6.

■ = 18 ◀— Multiply to find the value of ■.

▸ There are 18 trumpet players in the Youth Band.

> **Remember!**
> When you do not know the value of a number, use a ■ or other symbol to represent the number.

✏ Explain why you can use an array or an equation to solve the problem. Possible answer: The array shows the rows of trumpet players so I can find the answer by adding the number in each row or by counting the dots. The equation shows the numbers I can multiply to answer the question.

Words to Know

array: an arrangement of objects or symbols in equal rows and equal columns

Example:

There are 3 rows of 9 squares.
There are 27 squares.
3 × 9 = 27

Glossary can be found on pp. 347–350.

Guided Instruction

Understand: Representing problem situations with arrays

> Mrs. Stanton uses 28 floor tiles to cover her kitchen floor. If the floor tiles are in rows of 7 each, how many rows are there?

To find the unknown number of rows, find the number of groups of 7 in 28.

You can use an array to solve the problem.

Draw 28 squares to represent the tiles.
Put 7 squares in each row.
Count the number of rows.

You can also use division to find the unknown number of rows.

$28 \div 7 = $ ■
$28 \div 7 = 4$

➡ The floor tiles are in 4 equal rows.

✏ Explain why the array can also represent this multiplication.

$4 \times 7 = 28$
Possible explanation: The array shows 4 rows of 7 squares, so it shows that $4 \times 7 = 28$.

Unit 1 ■ Focus on Operations and Algebraic Thinking **35**

Understand: Representing problem situations with arrays

■ In this presentation, students know the total number of objects and the number of objects in each row. They will create an array to represent the arrangement of objects.

■ Students may count the number of rows to solve the problem.

■ Ask students how division can also be used to find the unknown number of rows. Explain to students that the number 28 represents the total number of floor tiles while the number 7 represents the number of tiles in each row.

■ Help students generate a complete sentence for the solution. For example, *the tiles on the floor are in 4 equal rows.* Explain to students that solutions to word problems must be answered with the proper unit used in the problem.

✏ After students have answered this question, ask a few volunteers to read their answers aloud. You may want to label the rows and columns of the array to show students the connection between the array and the multiplication equation. Help students realize that the quotient and the divisor of a division equation are the factors in a related multiplication equation.

Support English Language Learners

The term *array* is easier to understand with a visual example. Before class, make a poster of mathematical terms with pictures provided to illustrate the meaning of multiplication and division terms. Have students label the array on the poster with *row* and *column*. Explain that a row is positioned horizontally (side to side) and a column is positioned vertically (up and down).

Guided Instruction

Connect: What you know about representing and solving problems Use this page to help students understand how to use an array to solve a word problem involving division.

■ Help students understand the connection between the total number of objects in the array and the total number of students in the problem. Remind students that each row must have the same number of symbols because the students in the problem are being separated into 3 equal lines.

■ Review the meaning of row. Labeling the rows *lines,* and the columns *students per row* may be helpful.

■ When writing a division equation to represent the problem, explain to students that the number 27 represents the total number of students and the number 3 represents the number of lines.

✏ ▸ Have students explain how a multiplication equation can be formed using the array. Explain the connection between the numbers in both the division equation and the multiplication equation. Ask students to identify the *factors, product, dividend, divisor,* and *quotient* for the multiplication and division equations.

Guided Instruction

Connect: What you know about representing and solving problems

> Ms. Hardy's class has 27 students. Each time the students prepare to leave the classroom, they form 3 equal lines. How many students are in each line?

Step 1

Determine what is known and unknown.

Known: 27 students in all
Known: 3 equal lines of students
Unknown: number of students in each line

Step 2

Make an array to represent the problem.
Show 3 rows for the 3 lines.
Show a total of 27 symbols for the 27 students.

Remember!
Each row must have the same number of symbols.

Step 3

Count the symbols in each row.

There are __9__ symbols in each row.

You can also use division to represent and solve the problem.

$27 \div 3 =$ __9__

➡ There are __9__ students in each line.

✏ ▸ What multiplication is represented by the array? Explain your thinking. $3 \times 9 = 27$; Possible explanation: An array shows a total, so this array shows that 3 times 9 is equal to 27.

Math-to-Math Connection

Arranging Desks Desks are often arranged in arrays. Have students draw a diagram of a classroom with 36 desks arranged in an array. There are several possible arrays. Discuss which array works best and why. Label the rows and columns of the desk arrangement.

Extend the activity by informally discussing the Commutative Property. Tell students to rotate their diagrams so that the rows become the columns and the columns become the rows. Explain that arrays illustrate both factors in a multiplication equation. The number of rows and columns in the array can be interchanged without changing the total. So, the order of factors in a multiplication equation does not change the product.

Lesson 4

Guided Practice

Solve the problem. Use the array to help.

1. Jarrod has a collection of 21 sports cards. He wants to share them equally among his 3 brothers. How many sports cards will each brother receive?

   You can use division and an array to represent the problem.

   $21 \div 3 = \blacksquare$

   $21 \div 3 = \underline{7}$

   Each brother will receive __7__ sports cards.

2. Kayla has a collection of electronic games. She stores them in her game carrier in rows of 5 games each. If Kayla makes 4 rows, how many games are in her collection?

   You can use multiplication and an array to represent the problem.

   $4 \times 5 = \blacksquare$

   $4 \times 5 = \underline{20}$

   There are __20__ games in her collection.

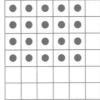

👣 Think•Pair•Share

MP4 3. Draw an array to represent 6×8. Then write a word problem that can be solved by finding 6×8.

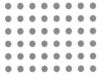

Possible answer: Fumi has 6 boxes of 8 crayons each. How many crayons does she have in all? Problems will vary but should be solved by using $6 \times 8 = 48$.

Unit 1 ▪ Focus on Operations and Algebraic Thinking **37**

Observational Assessment

Use page 37 to assess whether students are able to use arrays to complete multiplication and division equations to solve word problems.

👣 Think•Pair•Share

Peer Collaboration Ask pairs to present their work for class discussion. To ensure understanding, ask questions such as:

- *Does the number of rows and columns match the factors in the equation?*

- *How does your array help you find 6×8?*

- *What is the total number of objects that are in the array? Does this number match the product of 6×8?*

Return to the Essential Question

Reread the Lesson 4 Essential Question on page 34: *How can you use an array to solve a word problem?*

Ask volunteers to use what they learned in this lesson to answer this question. (Possible response: I can draw an array to represent the word problem. The array will show equal rows and equal columns. The total number of objects in the array might be the solution to the problem.)

Invite as many volunteers as possible to express ideas about using arrays to solve word problems.

Mathematical Practices

Mathematical Practice Standards underline the teaching and understanding of all concepts and skills presented. The emphasis of specific practices is noted throughout the guided and independent practice of this lesson.

MP4	**Model with mathematics.**

Item 3: Students draw an array to represent a multiplication equation and write a word problem that can be solved with the equation.

Concept Application

Students may work independently on these pages in the classroom or at home. They may refer to the first four pages of the lesson to revisit the instruction or to see a worked-out example.

Common Errors and **Teaching Tips** may help you support student learning either in the classroom or as a follow-up for work done at home.

Teaching Tips

Item 1

Remind students that part of the array is already provided. Point out that the first yellow dot must be counted as part of the first row and also part of the first column. Suggest that students check their work to make sure the array has an equal number of items in each row, and an equal number of items in each column.

Lesson 4   Problem Solving: **Multiplication/Division and Arrays**

Independent Practice

Use an array to represent the problem. Then solve.

MP4   1. You are setting up 56 chairs for the class play. If you arrange the chairs in 7 rows, how many chairs will be in each row?

$56 \div 7 = \blacksquare$

Draw dots to complete an array that represents the problem.

$56 \div 7 = \underline{\ 8\ }$

Answer $\underline{\ 8\ }$ chairs will be in each row.

MP1   2. The Ross High School band marches in 6 rows. There are 7 students in each row. How many students are in the band?

$6 \times 7 = \blacksquare$

Draw dots in this grid to make an array that represents the problem.

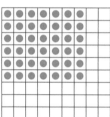

Arrays should show 6 rows of 7, but accept any that show 7 rows of 6.

$6 \times 7 = \underline{\ 42\ }$

Answer There are $\underline{\ 42\ }$ students in the band.

Mathematical Practices	
MP1	**Make sense of problems and persevere in solving them.**
Item 2: Students draw an array and complete the multiplication.	
MP2	**Reason abstractly and quantitatively.**
Item 5: Students understand the equations represented by an array.	
MP4	**Model with mathematics.**
Items 1, 4: Students complete an array to represent the word problem.	
MP7	**Look for and make use of structure.**
Item 3: Students use a grid to organize an array to solve a word problem.	

Lesson 4

Independent Practice

MP7 **3.** Lauren has 24 trading cards. She is putting them in an album with the same number of cards on each page. She uses 6 pages for the cards. How many cards are on each page?

$24 \div 6 = $

Use dots in this grid to show the array for this problem.

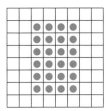

Accept arrays that show 6 rows of 4 or 4 rows of 6.

$24 \div 6 = \underline{\quad 4 \quad}$

Answer Each page of the album has $\underline{\quad 4 \quad}$ cards.

MP4 **4.** The school cafeteria buys eggs in cartons. If a carton has 6 rows of 6 eggs, how many eggs are in a carton?

$6 \times 6 = $

Answer There are $\underline{\quad 36 \quad}$ eggs in a carton.

MP2 **5.** Which multiplication or division is NOT shown by this array?

● ● ● ● ● ● ●
● ● ● ● ● ● ●
● ● ● ● ● ● ●

a. $3 \times 7 = 21$ b. $7 \times 3 = 21$

c. $21 \div 7 = 3$ (d.) $21 \times 3 = 7$

Unit 1 ■ Focus on Operations and Algebraic Thinking **39**

Teaching Tips

Item 5
Encourage students to write their own equations for the array before making a choice.

Writing About Math

▸ **Write an Informative Text** Ask students to write about the relationship between arrays and multiplication and between arrays and division. Students should use precise mathematical language in their writing. Illustrations should be included to show students' understanding of the concepts.

Independent Practice

Common Errors

Item 6
Some students may write $6 \div 3 = \blacksquare$ as the division equation. Ask students to identify what is known and what is unknown in the problem. Suggest that students make sure their arrays match the problem.

Teaching Tips

Items 7-8
Have students verbalize the steps in drawing an array when the total number of objects and the number of objects in each row is given. Then have them verbalize the steps when the total number of objects and the number of rows is given.

Independent Practice

Use an array and multiplication or division to solve problems 6–8.

MP4 **6.** Chad's mother made a quilt that is shaped like a rectangle. The quilt has 6 squares across and 3 squares down. How many squares are in the quilt?

▸ **Show your work.**
Possible answer: Students should draw a 6×3 rectangle with a total of 18 squares and multiply $6 \times 3 = 18$ or divide $\blacksquare \div 6 = 3$.

Answer There are 18 squares in the quilt.

MP1 **7.** The neighborhood garden has 56 plants. If there are 7 plants in each row, how many rows of plants are there?

▸ **Show your work.**
Possible answer: Students should draw an 8×7 array to show 56 and multiply $7 \times \blacksquare = 56$ or divide $56 \div 7 = 8$.

Answer The garden has 8 rows of plants.

MP5 **8.** There are 28 students in the choir. If they stand in 4 equal rows, how many students are in each row?

▸ **Show your work.**
Possible answer: Students should draw a 4×7 array to show 28 and multiply $4 \times \blacksquare = 28$ or divide $28 \div 4 = 7$

Answer There are 7 students in each row.

Mathematical Practices	
MP1	**Make sense of problems and persevere in solving them.**
Item 7: Students draw an array and provide either a multiplication or division equation to solve the word problem.	
MP4	**Model with mathematics.**
Item 6: Students draw a model and use their knowledge of arrays to solve a word problem.	
MP5	**Use appropriate tools strategically.**
Item 8: Students draw an array and provide either a multiplication or division equation to solve a word problem.	

MORE ONLINE) sadlierconnect.com

Lesson 4

Independent Practice

MP5 **9.** Write a problem that can be solved by using this array.

Possible answer:
My reading group has 12 students.
We sit in 4 rows.
How many students are in each row?

MP4 **10.** Draw as many arrays as you can to represent the product 16.
How many different arrays can you draw?
Possible arrays: 2×8, 8×2, 4×4. Some students may draw 1×16
and 16×1 arrays as well.

MP2 **11.** Stella drew this array to represent 6 groups of 2 students.
What is wrong with Stella's array? Correct it.

Possible answer: Stella's array shows 5 groups of 2 each instead of 6 groups
of 2 each.

Unit 1 ■ Focus on Operations and Algebraic Thinking **41**

Common Errors

Item 9
Some students may have trouble writing a word problem for an array. They may think the word problem needs to contain the words *rows* and *columns*. Explain that the word problem can be the same kind of problem they wrote for equal groups.

Teaching Tips

Item 10
Encourage students to draw as many arrays as they can to represent the product 16. Remind students that the number of items in each row must be equal, and the number of items in all the columns must be equal. If students need help getting started, provide a representation of a 2 × 8 array. Stress that each row has 8 objects, and each column has 2 objects. There are 16 objects in all.

Item 11
Encourage students to explain their thinking in writing about Stella's error.

Mathematical Practices	
MP2	**Construct viable arguments and critique the reasoning of others.**
Item 11: Students provide a drawing to correct the mistake and explain the mistake in writing.	
MP4	**Model with mathematics.**
Item 10: Students draw a variety of arrays to represent a given product.	
MP5	**Use appropriate tools strategically.**
Item 9: Students use an array to create a word problem.	

Guided Instruction

Common Core Focus:

3.OA.4 Determine the unknown whole number in a multiplication or division equation relating three whole numbers.

OBJECTIVE

Find an unknown number in a multiplication or division equation.

ESSENTIAL QUESTION

Emphasize that in this lesson students will use equations to find an unknown number. This skill will be critical in their understanding of how multiplication and division are related and how the operations can be used together to solve problems.

PREREQUISITE SKILLS

Use Item B on page 337 of the Foundational Skills Handbook to review related addition and subtraction equations before beginning the lesson.

FLUENCY PRACTICE

Fluency practice is available at **sadlierconnect.com**.

Concept Development

Understand: Finding unknown numbers in multiplication equations

■ Understanding the relationship between multiplication and division is essential for students to be successful in finding the unknown number in an equation. This presentation gives examples of the unknown quantity in every position of a multiplication equation.

■ By continuously showing the relationship between multiplication and division, students can gain a better understanding of how to interpret multiplication and division operations.

■ Have students explain what it means for an equation to be true. Student responses should include that both sides of the equation are equal.

Lesson 5

Find Unknown Numbers in Multiplication and Division Equations

Essential Question: How can you use multiplication and division equations to find an unknown number?
3.OA.4

Guided Instruction

In this lesson, you will learn how to find the value of an unknown number in a multiplication or division equation.

Understand: Finding unknown numbers in multiplication equations

> How can you find an unknown number in a multiplication equation?

The numbers in a multiplication equation are related. You can rewrite a multiplication equation as a division equation.

$$\text{factor} \times \text{factor} = \text{product} \qquad \text{product} \div \text{factor} = \text{factor}$$

When you find the value of the unknown number, you make the equation true because both sides are equal. There are two ways to find an unknown number in a multiplication equation.

Find an unknown first factor.   ■ × 4 = 12

1. Use a multiplication you know.
   What number times 4 equals 12?
   ■ × 4 = 12
   3 × 4 = 12
   ■ = 3

2. Divide the product by the known factor.
   12 ÷ 4 = ■
   12 ÷ 4 = 3
   ■ = 3

Find an unknown second factor.   3 × ■ = 12

1. Use a multiplication you know.
   3 times what number equals 12?
   3 × ■ = 12
   3 × 4 = 12
   ■ = 4

2. Divide the product by the known factor.
   12 ÷ 3 = ■
   12 ÷ 3 = 4
   ■ = 4

Find an unknown product.   3 × 4 = ■

1. Multiply the factors.
   3 × 4 = ■
   3 × 4 = 12
   ■ = 12

2. Use a division you know.
   ■ ÷ 4 = 3
   12 ÷ 4 = 3
   ■ = 12

➡ You can use multiplication or division to find an unknown number in a multiplication equation.

Support English Language Learners

To help students understand the concept of *unknown numbers,* have them look carefully at the word *unknown.* Explain that *un-* is a prefix that means "opposite of" or "not."

Ask students if they know any other words that use the prefix *un-*. Make a list together. Some examples are *common/uncommon, changed/unchanged, cooked/uncooked,* and *reliable/unreliable.*

Ask students what the word *unknown* means. Make sure that they understand that unknown means "something that is not known." Then have them explain what an unknown number would be. Point out that by following a certain process in math, they can make an *unknown* number *known.*

Understand: Finding unknown numbers in division equations

> How can you find the value of an unknown number in a division equation?

A division equation relates a dividend, a divisor, and a quotient. You can rewrite a division equation as a multiplication equation.

dividend ÷ divisor = quotient
quotient × divisor = product

There are two ways to find an unknown number in a division equation. You can use a letter instead of a ■ to represent an unknown number.

Find an unknown dividend. $n \div 4 = 3$

1. Use a division you know.
   What number divided by 4 equals 3?
   $n \div 4 = 3$
   $12 \div 4 = 3$
   $n = 12$

2. Multiply the quotient by the divisor.
   $3 \times 4 = n$
   $3 \times 4 = 12$
   $n = 12$

Find an unknown divisor. $12 \div n = 3$

1. Use a division you know.
   12 divided by what number equals 3?
   $12 \div n = 3$
   $12 \div 4 = 3$
   $n = 4$

2. Use a multiplication you know.
   $3 \times n = 12$
   $3 \times 4 = 12$
   $n = 4$

Find an unknown quotient. $12 \div 3 = n$

1. Divide.
   $12 \div 3 = n$
   $12 \div 3 = 4$
   $n = 4$

2. Use a multiplication you know.
   $n \times 3 = 12$
   $4 \times 3 = 12$
   $n = 4$

➡ You can use multiplication or division to find an unknown number in a division equation.

✏ Explain what it means to find the value of an unknown number in a division equation. Possible explanation: When you find the value of an unknown number, you make the equation true because both sides of the equation are equal.

Unit 1 ■ Focus on Operations and Algebraic Thinking   43

Understand: Finding unknown numbers in division equations

■ This presentation continues to build upon the understanding that a division equation can be rewritten as a multiplication equation. Students are familiar with inverse operations using addition and subtraction. Extend this understanding to multiplication and division.

■ Remind students that an unknown number can represent any part of an equation. Have students identify the unknown number in each equation using mathematical terms (factor, product quotient, divisor, dividend).

■ Make sure that students understand that any letter can replace the placeholder (square, circle, etc.). It is often helpful to use a letter that represents the unknown as in this case where *n* represents *number*.

✏ Ask for several students to share their answers. Be sure students can communicate their reasoning with others. Some students may understand a process, but have difficulty verbalizing their thought process.

Math-to-Geometry Connection

Squares and Triangles Provide students with 24 toothpicks. Challenge students to predict whether they can make more triangles or more squares with the toothpicks. Have students work in pairs, having each student build either the triangles or the squares. Guide the activity by asking:

Did the results match your prediction?
Why does it make sense that you can build more triangles than squares?

Students should understand that squares use more toothpicks because they have more sides.

Guided Instruction

Connect: What you know about multiplication and division equations to solve word problems Use this page to help students strengthen their understanding of multiplication and division as inverse operations, and how they can use this understanding to solve problems.

■ Throughout the school year, students will solve two-step word problems using two of the four operations. This experience will help students create a problem-solving plan to help them choose which operations to use.

■ Remind students to look for key words in word problems to strategize the best plan for finding a solution. Students will also need to identify the critical information. As the word problems become more complex, there may be additional, though unnecessary information added.

■ Direct students' attention to Step 1. Discuss the process of translating words to an equation using numbers and symbols. Some students may need help breaking apart the sentence into the corresponding parts of the equation.

 As students share their answers make a list of all the possible ways to find the unknown number.

Guided Instruction

Connect: What you know about multiplication and division equations to solve word problems

> At the craft fair, a large basket costs $28. This is 4 times as much as a small basket costs.
> How much does a small basket cost?

To solve the problem, find the number that 28 is 4 times as much as.

Step 1

Write an equation to represent the problem.

4 times the cost of a small basket equals $28

$$4 \times \quad s \quad = \quad 28$$

> **Remember!**
> You can use a ■ or a letter to represent an unknown number.

Step 2

Find the factor that makes the equation true. You can use multiplication or division.

Use a multiplication that you know.

$$4 \times s = 28$$
$$4 \times \underline{7} = 28$$

Or, divide.

$$s = 28 \div 4$$
$$\underline{7} = 28 \div 4$$

➡ A small basket costs $7.

 $a \times 5 = 40$
Describe two ways to find the unknown number.
Possible answer: Use multiplication. What number times 5 equals 40? Use division: $40 \div 5 = 8$.

Math-to-English Connection

Riddles Have students create a riddle to find an unknown number. Students should write clues for the unknown number and end the riddle with "What number am I?" Remind students that some equations use identical factors, such as $3 \times 3 = 9$. Encourage students to be creative with their clues and add extra clues, such as "the sum of the factors is 5."

Have students trade riddles with another classmate and solve. Ask volunteers to share their riddles and their solution with the class.

MORE ONLINE ▶ sadlierconnect.com   Lesson 5

Guided Practice

1. Each box of oranges at the supermarket has 7 rows of oranges with 7 oranges in each row. How many oranges are there altogether?

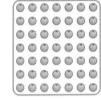

Write an equation to represent the problem. Then solve to find the unknown number of oranges.

How many oranges are in 7 rows of 7 oranges each?

$$o = \underline{7} \times \underline{7}$$
$$o = \underline{49}$$

There are $\underline{49}$ oranges altogether.

2. One bag has 36 dog treats. If the treats are shared equally among 9 dogs at the park, how many treats will each dog get?

How many treats times 9 dogs equals 36?
Write an equation to represent the problem. Find the unknown number that makes the equation true.

$$t \times \underline{9} = \underline{36}$$
$$\underline{4} \times \underline{9} = \underline{36}$$

Each dog will get $\underline{4}$ treats.

Use the same numbers to write a division equation that is true.

$$\underline{36} \div \underline{9} = \underline{4}$$

👑 Think•Pair•Share

MP2 3. What number makes the equation true?

$$18 \div 6 = \underline{3}$$

What multiplication could you use to check? Explain why you can use multiplication to check division?
Possible answers: 6 × 3 = 18 or 3 × 6 = 18. You can use multiplication to check division because the two operations are related. This is like using addition to check subtraction.

Unit 1 ■ Focus on Operations and Algebraic Thinking **45**

Observational Assessment

Use page 45 to assess whether students are able to find unknown numbers in multiplication and division equations.

👑 **Think•Pair•Share**

Peer Collaboration Ask students to share the multiplication they used to check their equations. Students may answer 6 × 3 = 18 or 3 × 6 = 18. Discuss why there is more than one multiplication equation that is related to the division equation.

- *How are the numbers in a multiplication and a division equation related?*

- *Does the order of the factors change the product or quotient?*

To summarize, represent multiplication as factor × factor = product and the related division as product ÷ factor = factor to reinforce the relationship between the two operations.

Return to the Essential Question

Reread the Lesson 5 Essential Question on page 42: *How can you use multiplication and division equations to find an unknown number?*

Ask volunteers to use what they learned in this lesson to answer this question. (Possible response: If you need to find an unknown factor, you can divide the product by the known factor. If you need to find an unknown product, use a division fact you know.)

Mathematical Practices

Mathematical Practice Standards underline the teaching and understanding of all concepts and skills presented. The emphasis of specific practices is noted throughout the guided and independent practice of this lesson.

MP2	Reason abstractly and quantitatively.

Item 3: Students explain how they can use multiplication to check division.

Independent Practice

Concept Application

Students may work independently on these pages in the classroom or at home. They may refer to the first four pages of the lesson to revisit the instruction or to see a worked-out example.

Common Errors and **Teaching Tips** may help you support student learning either in the classroom or as a follow-up for work done at home.

Common Errors

Items 7-12

Some students may not fully comprehend how to write a related division equation. It may help students to draw arrows between the product and the quotient in each item. Remind students that a division equation can be represented by *product ÷ factor = factor*. The factors can be in any order.

Teaching Tips

Items 1-6

If needed have students draw arrays to complete the equations. Remind students that in order to use multiplication, they must have equal groups.

Independent Practice

Write the unknown number to complete the equation.

1. $3 \times 5 = \underline{15}$

2. $6 \times 9 = \underline{54}$

3. $5 \times \underline{5} = 25$

4. $4 \times \underline{7} = 28$

5. $\underline{3} \times 3 = 9$

6. $\underline{8} \times 4 = 32$

Write a related division equation to find the unknown number. Then complete the division equation.

7. $2 \times \blacksquare = 12$ $\longrightarrow$ $12 \div \underline{2} = \blacksquare$
$12 \div \underline{2} = \underline{6}$

8. $7 \times \blacksquare = 70$ $\longrightarrow$ $\underline{70} \div \underline{7} = \blacksquare$
$\underline{70} \div \underline{7} = \underline{10}$

9. $\blacksquare \times 8 = 48$ $\longrightarrow$ $\underline{48} \div 8 = \blacksquare$
$\underline{48} \div 8 = \underline{6}$

10. $\blacksquare \times 4 = 24$ $\longrightarrow$ $\underline{24} \div \underline{4} = \blacksquare$
$\underline{24} \div \underline{4} = \underline{6}$

11. $5 \times t = 30$ $\longrightarrow$ $\underline{30} \div \underline{5} = t$
$\underline{30} \div \underline{5} = \underline{6}$

12. $c \times 9 = 81$ $\longrightarrow$ $\underline{81} \div \underline{9} = c$
$\underline{81} \div \underline{9} = \underline{9}$

Writing About Math

◗ **Write a Narrative** Have students create a narrative paragraph that explains the steps to take when finding an unknown number. The student should use dialogue and a description of the steps needed.

After students have written their paragraphs, have them share their work with a partner. Taking turns, one student reads his or her paragraph while the partner follows the steps he or she wrote to find the unknown number.

Discuss the paragraphs as a group. Ask if any students missed steps in their narrative. Discuss how important it is for the narrative to explain all the steps.

MORE ONLINE sadlierconnect.com

Lesson 5

Independent Practice

13. Which multiplication equation could you use to find the unknown number?

$$8 \times \blacksquare = 56$$

a. $7 \times 7 = 49$ (b.) $8 \times 7 = 56$

c. $8 \times 8 = 64$ d. $8 \times 9 = 72$

14. Which division equation could you use to find the unknown number?

$$3 \times n = 18$$

a. $18 \div 2 = 9$ b. $18 \div 9 = 2$

c. $18 \div 1 = 18$ (d.) $18 \div 3 = 6$

15. Which division equation could you use to find the unknown number?

$$63 = y \times 7$$

a. $70 \div 7 = 10$ b. $64 \div 8 = 8$

(c.) $63 \div 7 = 9$ d. $60 \div 6 = 10$

Find the unknown number.

16. $4 \times \blacksquare = 12$

▸ **Show your work.** $4 \times 3 = 12$ or $12 \div 4 = 3$

$\blacksquare = \underline{\ 3\ }$

17. $36 = \blacksquare \times 6$

▸ **Show your work.** $36 = 6 \times 6$ or $36 \div 6 = 6$

$\blacksquare = \underline{\ 6\ }$

Unit 1 ■ Focus on Operations and Algebraic Thinking **47**

Common Errors

Items 13–15

Students may incorrectly pick the first answer in each set of answer choices because the equation itself is true. Make sure students are reading the directions above each problem to know which equation they need to be looking for.

Digital Connection

Multiplication Flash Cards Use a search engine to find digital multiplication flash cards. Have students use these flash cards to write out the corresponding division equation. Students can also use these flash cards to create their own equations with an unknown number and then have a partner solve.

Teaching Tips

Items 18-19
Be sure students first understand what is being asked before forming a plan to find the unknown number.

Item 21
Offer support to students who struggle with writing an equation for word problems that do not use "equal group" terminology.

Independent Practice

MP6 **18.** Tell how you would find the unknown number that makes the equation true. Then solve.

$r \times 6 = 54$

Possible answers: I know $9 \times 6 = 54$; I can write a division equation and solve: $54 \div 6 = 9$.

$\underline{9} \times 6 = 54$

MP6 **19.** Tell how you would find the unknown number that makes the equation true. Then find the unknown number.

$72 \div \blacksquare = 8$

Possible answer: I can write a multiplication equation: $8 \times \blacksquare = 72$; $8 \times 9 = 72$.

$72 \div \underline{9} = 8$

Solve the problems.

MP4 **20.** Thirty-five nickels are shared equally among 5 friends. How many nickels does each friend get?

▭▶ Show your work.

Possible answers: I can write a multiplication equation to show the problem, then write the unknown number: $5 \times n = 35$; $5 \times 7 = 35$. Or, I can write a division equation: $35 \div 5 = n$; $n = 7$. Or I could draw an array to show 5 groups of 7 nickels each.

Answer Each friend gets 7 nickels.

MP1 **21.** At the toy store, a small plush animal costs $8. A large plush animal costs 2 times as much as a small one. How much does a large plush animal cost?

▭▶ Show your work.

Possible answer: I can write a multiplication equation: $8 \times 2 = n$; $8 \times 2 = 16$.

Answer A large plush animal costs $16.

Mathematical Practices	
MP1	**Make sense of problems and persevere in solving them.**
Item 21: Students solve a word problem.	
MP4	**Model with mathematics.**
Item 20: Students show the way they solved the word problem.	
MP6	**Attend to precision.**
Items 18-19: Students find the unknown number that makes the equation true.	

Lesson 5

Independent Practice

MP5 **22.** At the school concert, 64 singers stand in equal rows of 8. How many rows of singers are there? What equation can help you solve the problem?

▭ Show your work.
Possible answer: I can write a multiplication equation to show the problem, then find the missing factor: $s \times 8 = 64$; $8 \times 8 = 64$. Or I can write and solve a division equation: $64 \div 8 = s$; $s = 8$. I could also draw an array to show 8 rows of 8 singers each.

Answer There are 8 rows of singers.

MP2 **23.** Wei-Yin says that for the equation $30 = \blacksquare \times 3$, the unknown factor is 9. Is he correct?

Answer No. He is not correct.

▭ Justify your answer using words, drawings, or numbers.
Students should show an understanding that $30 = 10 \times 3$ and/or $30 \div 3 = 10$.

MP3 **24.** Maura says that for the equation $6 \times a = 48$, $a = 8$. Is she correct?

Answer Yes. She is correct

▭ Justify your answer using words, drawings, or numbers.
Students should show an understanding that $6 \times 8 = 48$ and/or $48 \div 6 = 8$.

Unit 1 ■ Focus on Operations and Algebraic Thinking **49**

Teaching Tips

Item 22
For students who have difficulty deciding how to answer the questions, suggest that they use manipulatives to show their work.

Item 24
Students may not be familiar with the representation $a = 8$. Although it may seem intuitive, explain to students that they need to replace a with 8 and determine if the equation is true.

Mathematical Practices	
MP2	**Reason abstractly and quantitatively.**
Item 23: Students justify their answer using words, drawings, or numbers.	
MP3	**Construct viable arguments and critique the reasoning of others.**
Item 24: Students justify their answer using words, drawings, or numbers.	
MP5	**Use appropriate tools strategically.**
Item 22: Students use an equation to help solve the problem.	

Common Core Focus:

3.OA.5 Apply properties of operations as strategies to multiply and divide.

OBJECTIVE

Use the Commutative and Associative Properties of Multiplication to find the product of two and three factors.

ESSENTIAL QUESTION

Remind students of the Commutative and Associative Properties of Addition. Then introduce and relate the multiplication properties. Explain that they can use the Commutative Property of Multiplication to multiply two factors in any order. They can use the Associative Property of Multiplication to change the grouping of factors. Point out that changing the order or grouping of addends or factors, can make computation easier.

FLUENCY PRACTICE

Fluency practice is available at **sadlierconnect.com**.

Concept Development

Understand: Two numbers can be multiplied in any order

■ This lesson will help students understand how and when to use the Commutative and Associative Properties of Multiplication.

■ Rectangular arrays help students see the Commutative Property of Multiplication. Reproducing and displaying the 4 by 6 array and demonstrating how rotating it produces a 6 by 4 array may help students understand that the product does not change.

✏ Have students model the Commutative Property by drawing rectangular arrays to solve 2 × 3 and 3 × 2, and use the arrays to justify their response.

Essential Question:
How can you use properties of multiplication?
3.OA.5

Words to Know:
property
Commutative Property of Multiplication
parentheses
Associative Property of Multiplication

Guided Instruction

In this lesson you will learn how to use two properties of multiplication.

Understand: Two numbers can be multiplied in any order

> The students in Ms. Ward's class sit in 4 rows of 6. The students in Mr. Rao's class sit in 6 rows of 4. Which class has more students?

To find which class has more students, multiply to find the number of students in each class. Then compare.

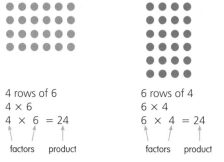

Ms. Ward's Class

4 rows of 6
4 × 6
4 × 6 = 24
↑ ↑   ↑
factors product

Mr. Rao's Class

6 rows of 4
6 × 4
6 × 4 = 24
↑ ↑   ↑
factors product

> Notice that both products are the same. If you know 4 × 6 = 24, then you also know 6 × 4 = 24.

➡ There are 24 students in each class.

When you multiply, the order of the factors does not matter. The product is the same. This is a property, or rule, of multiplication. It is called the Commutative Property of Multiplication. Some people call it the Order Property.

✏ How does the Commutative Property explain why 2 × 3 and 3 × 2 have the same product? Possible answer: You can multiply in any order and not change the result. Both 2 × 3 and 3 × 2 equal 6.

Words to Know

property: a mathematical rule

Commutative Property of Multiplication: changing the order of factors does not change the product

Example: 2 × 3 = 6   3 × 2 = 6

parentheses ( ): symbols used to show grouping within equations

Example: (2 × 3) × 2 = ▧

Associative Property of Multiplication: changing the grouping of factors does not change the product

Example: 2 × 3 × 2 = (2 × 3) × 2   2 × 3 × 2 = 2 × (3 × 2)

Glossary can be found on pp. 347–350.

Lesson 6

Guided Instruction

Understand: Three factors can be grouped in different ways

At a shirt factory, 2 shirts are put in each package. Three packages are put in each box. Two boxes of packages of shirts are delivered to Ms. Roman's store. How many shirts are in the delivery to Ms. Roman's store?

To find the number of shirts in all, multiply 2 × 3 × 2. Use an array to show 2 groups of 3 rows of 2.

← The array shows 2 groups of 3 rows of 2.

You can group three factors in two different ways to find the product. Put parentheses around the two factors you group together. This shows that you multiply them first.

$2 \times 3 \times 2 = $ ▦ $2 \times 3 \times 2 = $ ▦
$(2 \times 3) \times 2 = $ ▦ $2 \times (3 \times 2) = $ ▦

$\quad 6 \;\times\; 2 = $ ▦ $\quad 2 \;\times\; 6 \;= $ ▦
$\quad 6 \;\times\; 2 = 12$ $\quad 2 \;\times\; 6 \;= 12$

When you multiply three factors, you can group them in two different ways. The product is the same.

This is the Associative Property of Multiplication. Some people call it the Grouping Property.

➡ There are 12 shirts in the delivery to Ms. Roman's store.

When you use the Associative Property, you may not change the order of the factors. To do that, you must use the Commutative Property.

✏ Show how to group the factors 2 × 1 × 5 in two different ways to find their product. (2 × 1) × 5 and 2 × (1 × 5)

Understand: Three factors can be grouped in different ways

■ Students will use the Associative Property of Multiplication as a strategy and examine how to use parentheses to group factors. Students should group only two factors within parentheses.

■ Associate means to group together. When students use the Associative Property of Multiplication, they will associate, or group, factors using parentheses.

■ Help students realize that by starting with the multiplication fact in the parentheses, they are simplifying the multiplication from three factors to two factors.

■ Have students practice by presenting several different three-factor multiplications and asking volunteers to show two ways the factors in each multiplication can be grouped.

✏ The Associative Property doesn't change the order of factors. After students complete this problem on their own, have volunteers present their answers and discuss as a class why only parentheses should be moved when regrouping.

To extend the activity discuss how students could use the Commutative Property to group the factors another way.

Support English Language Learners

The terms *group* and *parentheses* may be familiar to some students in different contexts. These terms and their relationship to each other within mathematics may also be difficult for some students.

Demonstrate correct pronunciation of *parentheses* as you model writing and solving 2 × (3 × 2) and (2 × 3) × 2.

Have multilingual groups work together to write a multiplication expression using parentheses, and then demonstrate grouping real world objects to solve the problem.

If needed, explain that the term *group* can be used as both a noun and a verb in mathematics. For example, "An array shows 2 groups of 3." Or, "This can be grouped into 3 equal shares of 2."

Guided Instruction

Connect: Using the Commutative and Associative Properties Use this page to help students strengthen their understanding of how changing the order or grouping of factors does not change the product.

■ Be sure students understand that the Commutative Property of Multiplication reorders factors while the Associative Property of Multiplication regroups them.

■ Remind students that parentheses are used to group numbers and the operation in the parentheses must be done first.

■ For each property shown here, have students discuss their answers and use models or arrays to justify their reasoning.

✏ Have students use drawings similar to those shown on pages 50 and 51. Ask volunteers to share their answers and explain why they used the properties for each equation.

Lesson 6   Apply Commutative and Associative Properties to Multiply

Guided Instruction

Connect: Using the Commutative and Associative Properties

> You can use a property of multiplication to rewrite a multiplication. Tell what the property means and what it lets you do.

Use the Commutative Property to rewrite 3×4 and find the product.

You can rewrite 3×4 as $4 \times \underline{3}$.

$3 \times 4 = 12$ $4 \times 3 = 12$

The product is $\underline{12}$.

➡ The Commutative Property means that changing the order of the factors does not $\underline{change}$ the product.

The Commutative Property lets you change the order of the $\underline{factors}$ in a multiplication.

Use the Associative Property to rewrite $2 \times 2 \times 4$ and find the product.

You can rewrite $2 \times 2 \times 4$ as $(2 \times 2) \times 4$ or as $2 \times \underline{(2 \times 4)}$.

$(2 \times 2) \times 4 = 4 \times 4$ $2 \times (2 \times 4) = 2 \times 8$

$(2 \times 2) \times 4 = 16$ $2 \times (2 \times 4) = 16$

The product is $\underline{16}$.

➡ The Associative Property means that $\underline{changing}$ the grouping of the factors does not change the product. The Associative Property lets you choose which factors to $\underline{multiply}$ first.

✏ Complete the equations. Tell what property of multiplication you used.

$5 \times 9 = \underline{9} \times 5$ I used the Commutative Property.

$3 \times 2 \times 1 = (\underline{3} \times 2) \times 1$ I used the Associative Property.

52   Unit 1 ■ Focus on Operations and Algebraic Thinking

Math-to-Business Connection

Money Understanding the Commutative and Associative Properties of Multiplication is essential for many aspects of business, such as determining total cost or calculating total earnings.

For example, "Maria buys 3 notebooks for $2.00 each" can be represented as 3×2 or 2×3. Likewise, "Jose earns $8.00 per hour and works 10 hours each week for 2 weeks" can be represented as $(8 \times 10) \times 2$ or $8 \times (10 \times 2)$.

Providing a business context for multiplication may help students make real-world decisions.

Guided Practice

Draw lines to match the multiplications with the same product.

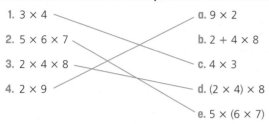

1. 3 × 4
2. 5 × 6 × 7
3. 2 × 4 × 8
4. 2 × 9

a. 9 × 2
b. 2 + 4 × 8
c. 4 × 3
d. (2 × 4) × 8
e. 5 × (6 × 7)

5. Use the Associative Property. Show two ways to find the product.

$3 \times 3 \times 2 = \blacksquare$
$(3 \times 3) \times 2 = \blacksquare$
↓   ↓
$\underline{9} \times 2 = \blacksquare$
$\underline{9} \times 2 = \underline{18}$

$3 \times 3 \times 2 = \blacksquare$
$3 \times (3 \times 2) = \blacksquare$
↓   ↓
$3 \times \underline{6} = \blacksquare$
$3 \times \underline{6} = \underline{18}$

Answer The product is $\underline{18}$.

✌ Think•Pair•Share

MP3 6. Max said he used only the Associative Property to group 3 × 5 × 2 in the three ways shown at the right. Is Max's work correct? Explain your answer.

> (3 × 5) × 2
> 3 × (5 × 2)
> (3 × 2) × 5

Possible answer: Max's work is not correct. For (3 × 2) × 5, he changed the order of the factors but he cannot change the order of the factors when he uses the Associative Property.

Mathematical Practices

Mathematical Practice Standards underline the teaching and understanding of all concepts and skills presented. The emphasis of specific practices is noted throughout the guided and independent practice of this lesson.

MP3 | **Construct viable arguments and critique the reasoning of others.**

Item 6: Students analyze a problem involving the Associative Property and justify their reasoning regarding the order of factors in the expression.

Observational Assessment

Use page 53 to assess whether students understand the Commutative and Associative Properties of Multiplication. Ensure that students can identify when each property is used or when it should be used. Check that students struggling with the matching exercise (exercises 1–4) understand the difference between ordering and grouping. These same students may use the two properties together to change the order of factors when working with the Associative Property.

✌ Think•Pair•Share

Peer Collaboration Divide students into pairs. Have volunteers share their work on the problem involving the factors 3, 5, and 2. Encourage them to explain why the order of the factors cannot change when using only the Associative Property. If some pairs are unsure or answer incorrectly, ask:

- *If Max had used only the Commutative Property, how would his answers have been different?*

- *How is the Associative Property different from the Commutative Property?*

To summarize for the class, remind students that grouping and ordering are different.

Return to the Essential Question

Reread the Lesson 6 Essential Question on page 50: *How can you use properties of multiplication?*

Ask volunteers to use what they learned in this lesson to answer this question. (Possible response: I can use the Commutative Property to change the order of factors. I can use the Associative Property to change the grouping of factors.)

Have volunteers show how to use the Commutative and Associative Properties of Multiplication.

Independent Practice

Concept Application

Students may work independently on these pages in the classroom or at home. They may refer to the first four pages of the lesson to revisit the instruction or to see a worked-out example.

Common Errors and **Teaching Tips** may help you support student learning either in the classroom or as a follow-up for work done at home.

Teaching Tips

Items 1-2

Help student distinguish the Commutative Property from the Associative Property. Remind students that the Commutative Property has to do with the order of factors and the Associative Property deals with grouping.

Item 9

Have students find the product of each multiplication and determine whether the products are the same and why. Discuss the differences between the Commutative and Associative Properties of Multiplication.

Independent Practice

Complete the equations. Circle the name of the property you used.

1. $5 \times 1 \times 9 = 5 \times (1 \times \underline{9})$

   Commutative Property   (Associative Property)

2. $9 \times 6 = \underline{6} \times 9$

   (Commutative Property)   Associative Property

For exercises 3–6, find each product.

3. $2 \times (2 \times 4) =$

   $2 \times \underline{8} = \underline{16}$

4. $(3 \times 2) \times 5 =$

   $\underline{6} \times 5 = \underline{30}$

5. $6 \times (2 \times 3) =$

   $6 \times \underline{6} = \underline{36}$

6. $(2 \times 2) \times 7 =$

   $\underline{4} \times 7 = \underline{28}$

For exercises 7 and 8, use the Commutative Property. Find each unknown product.

7. $1 \times 7 = 7$

   $7 \times 1 = \underline{7}$

8. $8 \times 5 = 40$

   $5 \times 8 = \underline{40}$

MP3   9. Stacy says that $(3 \times 5) \times 4 = 3 \times (5 \times 4)$. Is Stacy correct? What property helps you decide?

    ▶ Show your work.
    Possible answer: Yes; the Associative Property says that you can change the grouping of the factors and the product stays the same.

Mathematical Practices	
MP3	**Construct viable arguments and critique the reasoning of others.**
Item 9: Students can explain and use multiplication properties to assess the work of others and justify their reasoning.	

Find the product. You can use the Associative Property to group the factors. Accept any correct grouping of factors.

10. $5 \times 2 \times 3 = $ ▨

11. $3 \times 2 \times 3 = $ ▨

$5 \times 2 \times 3 = \underline{30}$

$3 \times 2 \times 3 = \underline{18}$

12. $6 \times 1 \times 2 = $ ▨

13. $2 \times 2 \times 3 = $ ▨

$6 \times 1 \times 2 = \underline{12}$

$2 \times 2 \times 3 = \underline{12}$

14. Which of the following is the same as 3×7?

    a. 3×3 **b.** 3×6

    (c.) 7×3 **d.** $7 \times 2 \times 3$

15. Which of the following is the same as $(4 \times 9) \times 3$?

    (a.) $4 \times (9 \times 3)$ **b.** $4 \times (9 \times 2)$

    c. $(4 \times 8) \times 3$ **d.** $(3 \times 9) \times 3$

Unit 1 ▪ Focus on Operations and Algebraic Thinking   **55**

Common Errors

Items 10-13

Students may change the order of the factors before placing parentheses. Point out that the Associative Property of Multiplication allows them to change the grouping, but not the order.

Writing About Math

▶ **Write a Narrative Text** Organize students into pairs. Have one partner write a narrative text that includes a character using the Commutative Property of Multiplication while the other partner writes a narrative that includes a character using the Associative Property of Multiplication.

Explain that students may use real or imagined experiences or events to establish a situation, introduce characters, and organize an event sequence. Have partners exchange their narratives and identify whether the Commutative Property or Associative Property was used and described correctly.

Teaching Tips

Item 18

Help students recognize that showing their work can be accomplished in several ways such as, using words, drawings, or numbers. Discuss as a class the different methods they can use.

Independent Practice

MP6 **16.** Explain why you can use the multiplication fact $7 \times 9 = 63$ to find the product of 9×7. Then find the product.

Possible answer: The Commutative Property states that the order of two factors does not matter. So, if $7 \times 9 = 63$, then I know that 9×7 also equals 63.

$9 \times 7 =$ 63

MP6 **17.** Explain how you could group $3 \times 2 \times 5$ to multiply. Then find the product.

Possible answer: I could group 3×2 and then multiply the product by 5; $(3 \times 2) \times 5$, or I could group 2×5 and then multiply the product by 3; $3 \times (2 \times 5)$.

$3 \times 2 \times 5 =$ 30

Solve the problems.

MP1 **18.** Six groups of 8 students are visiting the science museum. How many students are at the museum?

Show your work.

Students must find the product of 6×8. They can solve a related multiplication sentence, $8 \times 6 = 48$, or draw an array showing 6 groups of 8.

Answer 48 students

Mathematical Practices	
MP1	**Make sense of problems and persevere in solving them.**
Item 18: Students make sense of a real-world problem and may use words or drawings to solve the problem.	
MP6	**Attend to precision.**
Item 16: Students communicate their thought process to solve the problem using the Commutative Property. **Item 17:** Students communicate their thought process to solve the problem using the Associative Property.	

Independent Practice

MP4 **19.** **a.** There are 5 shelves on a bookshelf. Each shelf holds 9 books. How many books are there in all?

Answer There are 45 books in all.

b. There are 9 shelves on a bookshelf. Each shelf holds 5 books. How many books are there in all?

Answer There are 45 books in all.

c. Compare the answers to parts a and b. Explain your results.

Answer They are the same, because 5×9 is the same as 9×5.

MP8 **20.** Mr. Smith buys 3 cartons of eggs for his café. Each carton has 2 rows. There are 4 eggs in each row. How many eggs does Mr. Smith buy? Explain your thinking.

▶ **Show your work.**
Possible explanation: I wrote $3 \times 2 \times 4$ and then grouped it as $3 \times (2 \times 4)$ and multiplied to get 3×8, which I know is 24.

Answer Mr. Smith buys 24 eggs.

MP7 **21.** Jillian packs 6 gift mugs in each of 8 small boxes. Aaron packs 8 gift mugs in each of 6 large boxes. Compare the number of mugs they pack.

Answer They pack the same number of mugs.

▶ **Justify your answer using words, drawings, or numbers.**
Possible justification: The order you multiply two factors does not matter. So, $6 \times 8 = 8 \times 6$. Students might also show this with 6×8 and 8×6 arrays.

Unit 1 ■ Focus on Operations and Algebraic Thinking **57**

Teaching Tips

Item 19

Have students write or model the multiplication fact for parts a and b before finding the product of each. Help them notice that each part lists the number of shelves first, and the number of books on each shelf second. Remind them that their multiplication should mirror this left to right and first to last structure.

Item 20

If students are struggling with grouping the factors, help them recognize which grouping would be the most logical for the situation.

Mathematical Practices	
MP4	**Model with mathematics.**

Item 19: Students use the Commutative Property of Multiplication to determine the quantities in a situation and explain their rationale.

MP7	**Look for and make use of structure.**

Item 21: Students recognize and make use of the structure of the Commutative Property to compare quantities.

MP8	**Look for and express regularity in repeated reasoning.**

Item 20: Students recognize and express why the Associative Property of Multiplication can simplify multiplication.

Common Core Focus:
3.OA.5 Apply properties of operations as strategies to multiply and divide.

OBJECTIVE
Use the Distributive Property to rewrite a multiplication as the sum of two simpler multiplications.

ESSENTIAL QUESTION
Focus students on the lesson objective by reading the Essential Question. The Distributive Property is the last property of multiplication that students will learn about and use this year. Explain that they can use this property to help find a product when they cannot remember a multiplication fact.

FLUENCY PRACTICE
Fluency practice is available at **sadlierconnect.com**.

Concept Development

Understand: Breaking apart numbers to multiply

■ It is important for students to be able to use properties of operations to simplify computations. This presentation provides students with a conceptual picture of the Distributive Property. Students are asked to apply the Distributive Property to relatively simple multiplications, such as 7 × 6, in order to learn about and practice using this property.

■ Explain that 2 + 4 is only one way that 6 can be broken apart and that any of the other sums for 6 would also work. Because most students can multiply by 2 quite well, using 2 as one of the addends in breaking apart a factor means that students can use a known multiplication fact.

Lesson 7

Apply the Distributive Property to Multiply

Essential Question: How can you break apart numbers to rewrite multiplication problems? 3.OA.5
Words to Know: Distributive Property

Guided Instruction

In this lesson you will learn about another property of multiplication.

Understand: Breaking apart numbers to multiply

> Bart has 7 packages of pencils. Each package has 6 pencils. How many pencils does Bart have?

To find the total number of pencils, multiply 7 × 6.

One way to show 7 packages of 6 pencils each is to use an array.

The meaning of multiplication tells you that the number of groups times the number in each group is equal to the number in all.

Draw 7 groups of 6.

If you do not remember the product for 7 × 6, you can add 6 + 6 + 6 + 6 + 6 + 6 + 6.

Another way to find the product is to use multiplication facts you know. You can show one of the factors as a sum. Break apart the factor 6 into 2 + 4. Change the array to show 7 groups of 2 and 7 groups of 4.

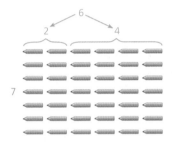

Multiply 7 × 2 and 7 × 4 and then add the products.

7 × 2 = 14   7 × 4 = 28
14 + 28 = 42

▷ Bart has 42 pencils in all.

Words to Know

Distributive Property: The product of a number and the sum of two numbers is equal to the sum of the two products. Multiplication can be distributed over addition.

Example: 7 × 9 = 7 × (5 + 4)
= (7 × 5) + (7 × 4)

Glossary can be found on pp. 347–350.

Lesson 7

Guided Instruction

Understand: Using parentheses with the Distributive Property

> Roger has 7 boxes of apples. Each box holds 9 apples.
> How many apples does Roger have in all?

To solve, find 7×9.

To find the product of 7×9, break apart the factor 9 into the sum of the addends $5 + 4$. Use parentheses to show the sum of the addends. Parentheses show numbers that belong together.

$7 \times 9 = 7 \times (5 + 4)$

Multiply each addend by 7 and then add the products. Now you use parentheses to show the factors that you will multiply.

$7 \times 9 = 7 \times (5 + 4)$

$= (7 \times 5) + (7 \times 4)$

$35 \quad + \quad 28$

63

> When you multiply a factor by a sum of two addends, you multiply the factor by each of the addends.

$7 \times 9 = 63$

Roger has 63 apples in all.

When you break apart a factor so that you can add two simpler multiplications to find a product, you are using the Distributive Property.

How could you use what you just learned about breaking apart one factor to find the product of 7×9 another way?

Possible answer: I could break apart the factor 7.

$(3 + 4) \times 9 = (3 \times 9) + (4 \times 9)$

$27 \quad + \quad 36$

$63 \qquad$ The product is the same.

Unit 1 ■ Focus on Operations and Algebraic Thinking   59

Support English Language Learners

The term *break apart* is used in this lesson to describe the decomposing of a factor into a sum of two addends.

To help students understand what the term *break apart* means, make a rod of connecting cubes (for example, 9 cubes). Then break it apart and explain that the two parts represent numbers that add to 9 (for example, 5 and 4). Students may count the cubes in each part to verify.

Write 9 on the board. Model describing how to break apart 9:

I can break apart 9 into 8 and 1. Have students continue using this statement to tell different ways to break apart 9 until all students have had a chance to verbalize the concept. It is fine if some students repeat addends. The goal is for students to use this term correctly.

Understand: Using parentheses with the Distributive Property

■ In this presentation, students see a shorter, more symbolic process for which drawing an array is not necessary, but may help those students who still need visual support.

■ To use the Distributive Property as a computation strategy, students need to know that either factor may be broken apart and that only one factor is broken apart. Deciding which factor to break apart and how to break it apart is a skill that will come with practice.

Help students realize that they can break a factor apart into numbers for which they know the multiplication facts. Choosing a 2 or a 5 as one of the break-apart numbers is a good strategy because many students know all those multiplication facts.

■ Students use parentheses in two ways as they apply the Distributive Property: to write the sum $(5 + 4)$ of the addends for the factor 9 that they break apart, and to show the two products (7×5) and (7×4). Help students to relate the two products to the array.

To find the product of 7×9, there are several other ways to break apart one of the factors using the Distributive Property. After students work through this exercise, you might make a class list of the ways that different students used. All the ways are listed below:

$7 \times (8 + 1)$ or $7 \times (1 + 8)$
$7 \times (7 + 2)$ or $7 \times (2 + 7)$
$7 \times (6 + 3)$ or $7 \times (3 + 6)$
$7 \times (4 + 5)$ or $7 \times (5 + 4)$
$9 \times (6 + 1)$ or $9 \times (1 + 6)$
$9 \times (5 + 2)$ or $9 \times (2 + 5)$
$9 \times (4 + 3)$ or $9 \times (3 + 4)$

Guided Instruction

Connect: Using the Distributive Property to find a product Use this page to help students strengthen their understanding of the Distributive Property and develop their ability to use it.

■ A key understanding is that there is not just one way to apply the Distributive Property to find a product, but there may be several, depending on how many ways a factor can be broken apart.

■ For each way shown here, ask students to explain how the Distributive Property is used. Ask them to justify their answer using a model.

✏️ ▸ Ask students to share the ways they used the Distributive Property as they worked on this problem. During the discussion, you might list the ways that students present. All the ways are listed below:

$9 \times (3 + 1)$ or $9 \times (1 + 3)$
$9 \times (2 + 2)$
$4 \times (8 + 1)$ or $4 \times (1 + 8)$
$4 \times (7 + 2)$ or $4 \times (2 + 7)$
$4 \times (6 + 3)$ or $4 \times (3 + 6)$
$4 \times (5 + 4)$ or $4 \times (4 + 5)$

Emphasize that regardless of how students choose to use the Distributive Property for this problem, the product will always be 36.

Guided Instruction

Connect: Using the Distributive Property to find a product

> Katya has 9 playlists on her phone. Each playlist has 4 country songs. How many country songs does Katya have in all?

To find the number of country songs Katya has, multiply 9×4. You can use the Distributive Property to rewrite 9×4 as two simpler multiplications. To do this, break apart the factor 9 or the factor 4.

One way to break apart the factor 4 is into $2 + 2$.

$9 \times 4 = 9 \times (2 + 2)$

$= (9 \times 2) + (9 \times 2)$

$18 \quad + \quad 18$

36

One way to break apart the factor 9 is into 3 and 6.

$9 \times 4 = (3 + 6) \times 4$

$= (3 \times 4) + (6 \times 4)$

$12 \quad + \quad 24$

36

Whichever factor you break apart, the final product is the same. $9 \times 4 = 36$

▷ Katya has 36 country songs in all.

You can use the Distributive Property to rewrite a multiplication as two simpler multiplications.

✏️ · You can break apart the factors of 9×4 in other ways. Use the Distributive Property to show two or more other ways.
Possible ways:
$(5 + 4) \times 4 \qquad 9 \times (1 + 3) \qquad (1 + 8) \times 4$

60   Unit 1 ■ Focus on Operations and Algebraic Thinking

Math-to-Math Connection

Arithmetic and Algebra A sound understanding of the Commutative, Associative, and Distributive Properties is essential for later work in algebra. The work students are doing now with the Distributive Property relies heavily on arithmetic and is an early introduction to working with equations. However, in later work with algebra, this property will be used when students generalize from working with numbers to working with variables as they use these properties to simplify expressions.

It is not critical that third-grade students know the names of these properties. It is important that they know how they can use these properties (or rules) to do computation.

Lesson 7

Guided Practice

1. Use the array to find the product of 4 × 7. Break apart the factor 7.

$4 \times 7 = 4 \times (5 + \blacksquare)$

$4 \times (5 + 2) = (4 \times 5) + (4 \times 2)$

$4 \times 5 = \underline{20}$ $4 \times 2 = \underline{8}$

$\underline{20} + \underline{8} = \underline{28}$

$4 \times 7 = \underline{28}$

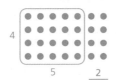

4   5   2

2. Use the Distributive Property to find the product of 7 × 5. The array may help.

$7 \times 5 = (\blacksquare + 4) \times 5$

$(3 + 4) \times 5 = (3 \times 5) + (4 \times 5)$

$3 \times 5 = \underline{15}$ $4 \times 5 = \underline{20}$

$\underline{15} + \underline{20} = \underline{35}$

$7 \times 5 = \underline{35}$

3. Use the Distributive Property to find 8 × 6. Draw an array if it helps.

Possible answer shown

$8 \times 6 = (\underline{6} + \underline{2}) \times 6$

$8 \times 6 = (\underline{6} \times 6) + (\underline{2} \times 6)$

$8 \times 6 = \underline{36} + \underline{12}$

$8 \times 6 = \underline{48}$

Think•Pair•Share

MP7   4. Show two ways you could use the Distributive Property to find 5 × 9. Explain why the products are the same for each way.

Possible answer:

$5 \times 9 = (3 + 2) \times 9$ $5 \times 9 = 5 \times (2 + 7)$
     $(3 \times 9) + (2 \times 9)$ $(5 \times 2) + (5 \times 7)$
       $27 + 18$ $10 + 35$
        45   45
$5 \times 9 = 45$ $5 \times 9 = 45$

Mathematical Practices

Mathematical Practice Standards underline the teaching and understanding of all concepts and skills presented. The emphasis of specific practices is noted throughout the guided and independent practice of this lesson.

MP7   **Look for and make use of structure.**

Item 4: Students recognize that the Distributive Property can be applied in different ways to the same problem.

Observational Assessment

Use page 61 to assess whether students have a grasp of the Distributive Property. As the amount of scaffolding in the problems drops off, note those students who need to use an array to break apart a factor and check whether they need extra practice with breaking apart a number into two addends.

Think•Pair•Share

Peer Collaboration Ask pairs to present their work for class discussion. For each pair of presenters, ask questions such as:

- *Why did you choose to break apart the 9 (or the 5)?*
- *What is the next step after you break apart the 9 (or the 5)?*
- *Why might the Distributive Property be helpful if you do not remember a multiplication fact?*

To summarize, point out that even though different ways were used, the product of 5 × 9 is always 45.

Return to the Essential Question

Reread the Lesson 7 Essential Question on page 58: *How can you break apart numbers to rewrite multiplication problems?*

Ask volunteers to use what they learned in this lesson to answer this question. (Possible response: One way to find a product of two factors is to write a sum for one factor, then multiply each addend by the other factor, and finally add those two products. That gives the same product as multiplying the first two factors.)

Invite as many volunteers as possible to express ideas about the Distributive Property in their own words.

Concept Application

Students may work independently on these pages in the classroom or at home. They may refer to the first four pages of the lesson to revisit the instruction or to see a worked-out example.

Common Errors and **Teaching Tips** may help you support student learning either in the classroom or as a follow-up for work done at home.

Teaching Tips

Items 4–5

Point out to students that there is more than one answer for each question.

Independent Practice

In exercises 1 and 2, break apart the array. Then show how to use the Distributive Property to find the product.

1. $6 \times 9 = $ ▨

Possible answer:
$6 \times (6 + 3)$
$(6 \times 6) + (6 \times 3)$
$36 + 18 = 54$

$6 \times 9 = \underline{\quad 54 \quad}$

2. $7 \times 7 = $ ▨

Possible answer:
$7 \times (5 + 2)$
$(7 \times 5) + (7 \times 2)$
$35 + 14 = 49$

$7 \times 7 = \underline{\quad 49 \quad}$

3. Which of the following is the same as 12×6?

   a. $(9 \times 4) + (3 \times 2)$ **(b.)** $(8 \times 6) + (4 \times 6)$

   c. $(3 \times 4) + (3 \times 2)$ **d.** $6 \times (3 + 4)$

4. Choose all of the following that are the same as $(4 \times 3) + (4 \times 5)$.

   a. 8×8 **(b.)** $4 \times (3 + 5)$

   (c.) 4×8 **d.** $4 \times (3 \times 5)$

5. Choose all of the following that have the same total as $(3 \times 5) + (3 \times 6)$.

   (a.) $3 \times (7 + 4)$ **b.** 6×11

   (c.) $3 \times (10 + 1)$ **(d.)** 3×11

Writing About Math

▸ **Write Explanatory Text** Ask students to write an explanation of how to use the Distributive Property to find the product of 8×9. Have students choose their audience and purpose for writing and describe them at the beginning of the explanatory text.

You might describe an example for them: Miguel wants to write an explanation for his friend Kim who was at home with a bad cold when the class studied the Distributive Property.

When the papers are completed, you might distribute them to the class so that no one gets his or her own paper. Then ask students to read the papers, follow the instructions, and decide whether the explanation works.

Independent Practice

Draw lines to match.

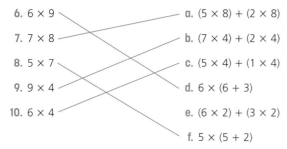

6. 6 × 9   a. (5 × 8) + (2 × 8)

7. 7 × 8   b. (7 × 4) + (2 × 4)

8. 5 × 7   c. (5 × 4) + (1 × 4)

9. 9 × 4   d. 6 × (6 + 3)

10. 6 × 4   e. (6 × 2) + (3 × 2)

                  f. 5 × (5 + 2)

Teaching Tips

Items 6–10
Students may try to match all the choices in the right column to items in the left column. If necessary, point out that there is one more choice in the right column than there are items in the left column so that there will be one unmatched choice when they complete all the items.

Find each product.

11. $7 \times 5 = 7 \times (3 + 2)$

$= (7 \times 3) + (7 \times \underline{2})$

$\underline{21} + \underline{14} = \underline{35}$

$7 \times 5 = \underline{35}$

12. $6 \times 6 = (6 \times 3) + (6 \times \underline{3})$

$\underline{18} + \underline{18} = \underline{36}$

$6 \times 6 = \underline{36}$

13. $8 \times 3 = (2 \times 3) + (\underline{6} \times 3)$

$\underline{6} + \underline{18} = \underline{24}$

$8 \times 3 = \underline{24}$

14. $9 \times 8 = (9 \times 5) + (9 \times \underline{3})$

$\underline{45} + \underline{27} = \underline{72}$

$9 \times 8 = \underline{72}$

Unit 1 ■ Focus on Operations and Algebraic Thinking **63**

Digital Connection

Internet Resources Use a search engine to locate videos that focus on the Distributive Property at the third-grade level. Students may benefit from the interactive approach used in some of these videos. You might make a list of videos for students to use after you have reviewed them.

Independent Practice

Common Errors

Item 15

Students may make errors as they work through the Distributive Property because they do not place parentheses correctly around the numbers they need to group. You might point out that the parentheses are like two arms that are holding the numbers together.

Teaching Tips

Item 16

Students may have difficulty solving the problem because they do not draw the array correctly. Provide grid paper for those who have difficulty aligning rows and columns.

Independent Practice

15. Write two ways to find the product of 5×8.
Use the Distributive Property.
Possible answers:

$5 \times (6 + 2)$ $(4 + 1) \times 8$
$(5 \times 6) + (5 \times 2)$ $(4 \times 8) + (1 \times 8)$
$30 + 10$ $32 + 8$
40 40

$5 \times 8 = \underline{\quad 40 \quad}$

Solve the problems.

MP4 16. Vera bought 8 cans of tennis balls.
Each can has 3 tennis balls.
How many tennis balls did Vera buy?

> **Draw an array to justify your answer.**

Possible justification:

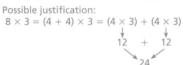

Answer Vera bought 24 tennis balls.

MP4 17. Bill planted 3 rows of pepper plants in his vegetable garden. He planted 7 plants in each row. How many pepper plants did Bill plant? Draw an array to model the pepper plants in Bill's garden.

> **Show your work.** Possible answer:
$3 \times 7 = 21$

Answer Bill planted 21 pepper plants.

MP6 18. Jason buys 8 cartons of oranges. Each carton has 6 oranges in it. How many oranges does Jason buy altogether?

> **Show your work.** Possible answer:
$8 \times 6 = 8 \times (5 + 1)$
$8 \times 6 = (8 \times 5) + (8 \times 1)$
$8 \times 6 = 40 + 8$
$8 \times 6 = 48$

Answer Jason buys 48 oranges altogether.

Mathematical Practices		
MP4	**Model with mathematics.**	
Item 16: Students apply the mathematics to everyday situations.		
Item 17: Students are able to identify quantities in an everyday situation and use them to solve problems.		
MP6	**Attend to precision.**	
Item 18: Students calculate accurately and efficiently by applying the Distributive Property to solve.		

Lesson 7

Independent Practice

MP7 **19.** Evan thinks that 9×8 is the same as $(9 \times 4) + (9 \times 4)$.
Is he correct?

Answer Yes, Evan is correct.

▸ **Justify your answer using words, drawings, or numbers.**
Possible justification:
$9 \times 8 = 9 \times (4 + 4) = (9 \times 4) + (9 \times 4)$
$\qquad\qquad\qquad\quad\; 36 \;\;+\;\; 36$
$\qquad\qquad\qquad\qquad\quad 72$

MP3 **20.** Show how to use the Distributive Property to find 6×11.
Possible answer:
$6 \times 11 = 6 \times (10 + 1)$
$\qquad\qquad\; (6 \times 10) + (6 \times 1)$
$\qquad\qquad\quad 60 \;\;+\;\; 6 \;\; = 66$

MP7 **21.** Lauren says that $(4 \times 3) + (2 \times 3)$ is the same as 6×6.
Is she correct?

Answer No, Lauren is not correct.

▸ **Justify your answer using words, drawings, or numbers.**
Possible justification:
$(4 \times 3) + (2 \times 3) = (4 + 2) \times 3$
$\qquad\qquad\qquad\qquad\; 6 \;\;\times 3$
$\qquad\qquad\qquad\qquad\; 6 \;\;\times 3 = 18$
It is 6×3, not 6×6.

Common Errors

Item 19

Students may make errors by breaking apart the 8 into factors instead of addends when they check Evan's work. Suggest that they look at the plus sign to remind them that they are looking for addends.

Teaching Tips

Item 21

Students may not think of working backward from the sum of the two products to find Lauren's error. Suggest that they do, but if they still have problems, ask them to find a correct way to use the Distributive Property to write a sum of products for 6×6. Then have students compare their answers to Lauren's answer.

Mathematical Practices

MP3	Construct viable arguments and critique the reasoning of others.

Item 20: Students can use objects or drawings to explain how to use the Distributive Property to find 6×11.

MP7	Look for and make use of structure.

Item 19: Students study the structure of a multiplication rewritten using the Distributive Property.

Item 21: Students evaluate the structure of the problem to determine if two expressions are equivalent by applying the Distributive Property.

Guided Instruction

Common Core Focus:

3.OA.6 Understand division as an unknown-factor problem.

OBJECTIVE

Understand how to use a related multiplication fact to find a quotient.

ESSENTIAL QUESTION

In Lesson 5, students learned how to use related equations to find an unknown number when multiplying or dividing. In this lesson, students will use related equations to rewrite a division equation as a multiplication equation with an unknown factor. It is important for students to understand that in multiplication they find an unknown product and that in division they find an unknown factor.

FLUENCY PRACTICE

Fluency practice is available at **sadlierconnect.com**.

Concept Development

Understand: Multiplication and division fact families

■ This lesson extends students' knowledge of relating multiplication and division equations. Students will learn to find a quotient by writing a related multiplication fact with an unknown factor.

■ Be sure students understand how to rewrite a division equation as a multiplication equation. Discuss why a division equation, dividend ÷ divisor = quotient, can be rewritten as a multiplication equation, quotient × divisor = dividend.

■ Once students have rewritten a division as a multiplication, they must be able to recall the multiplication fact that includes the two known numbers.

■ Be sure students understand why this division can be rewritten as a multiplication, and that division and multiplication are inverse operations.

Lesson 8 — Divide by Finding an Unknown Factor

Essential Question: How can you use what you know about how multiplication and division are related to divide? 3.OA.6

Words to Know: fact family

Guided Instruction

In this lesson you will divide using a related multiplication to find an unknown factor.

Understand: Multiplication and division fact families

Three students are making a large poster. Ms. Peters gives them 21 markers to share equally. How many markers does each student get?

To find how many markers each student gets, divide 21 ÷ 3.

One way to find 21 ÷ 3 is to use an array.

Draw 21 dots in 3 equal rows.

Count to see that there are 7 dots in each row.

Another way to find 21 ÷ 3 is to find the value of an unknown factor.

You can use a fact family to find the value of an unknown factor. A fact family shows related multiplication and division facts.

3 times what number is equal to 21? ← Think of a multiplication fact with 21 and 3.

3 × ■ = 21 ← ■ is an unknown factor.

3 × 7 = 21 ← 7 is the unknown factor.

21 ÷ 3 = 7 ← Use the unknown factor to divide.

Fact Family for 3, 7, and 21:
3 × 7 = 21   7 × 3 = 21
21 ÷ 3 = 7   21 ÷ 7 = 3

➡ Each student gets 7 markers.

✏ What fact family can you use to find an unknown factor to divide 72 ÷ 8? I can use the fact family for 8, 9, and 72.

66 Unit 1 ■ Focus on Operations and Algebraic Thinking

Words to Know

fact family: a set of equations that shows related addition and subtraction facts or related multiplication and division facts

Example: Fact family for 6, 7, and 42:
6 × 7 = 42   7 × 6 = 42
42 ÷ 6 = 7   42 ÷ 7 = 6

Glossary can be found on pp. 347–350.

Copyright © by William H. Sadlier, Inc. All rights reserved.

66 Unit 1 ■ Focus on Operations and Algebraic Thinking

Understand: Using a fact family to find an unknown factor

> Sixteen students are on a field trip. The teacher groups them into pairs. How many pairs of students are there?

To find how many pairs, you can divide 16 by 2.

You can use related multiplication facts to solve division problems.

Remember!
A pair is equal to 2.

16 ÷ 2 = ▪
↑ number in all
↑ number in each group
↑ number of groups

Think: What number times 2 makes 16?

▪ × 2 = 16
↑ number of groups
↑ number in each group
↑ number in all

You can use the fact family for 2, 8, and 16 to help solve the problem.

$2 \times 8 = 16$ $8 \times 2 = 16$
$16 \div 2 = 8$ $16 \div 8 = 2$

Find the unknown factor in the multiplication.

▪ × 2 = 16

Use the unknown factor to complete the related division.

$16 \div 2 = 8$

➡ There are 8 pairs of students.

✏ Why does finding an unknown factor help you divide?
Possible answer: The divisor and the quotient are the factors of a related multiplication fact.

Understand: Using a fact family to find an unknown factor

■ Students learn to use related multiplication facts to divide. To explain this strategy, have students start by writing the division equation that represents the problem. It is conceptually difficult for third-graders to write the unknown-factor multiplication equation based on the word problem. They need to write an equation that describes the division situation before they can go on to solve an unknown-factor multiplication equation to find the quotient.

■ Discuss how the equations are related. Help students notice that the quotient is the product and the divisor is one factor of the related multiplication. Emphasize that knowing the complete multiplication fact that includes the two factors is the easiest way that students can find the unknown factor.

✏ After students have answered this question, ask a few volunteers to read their answers aloud. Have students discuss when and why they would use the "finding an unknown factor" strategy over drawing equal groups or making an array. Encourage students to compare the different strategies by discussing when they would use each strategy.

Support English Language Learners

The word *family* in English has similar pronunciations in other languages. For example, *familia* is the word for family in Spanish. Ask students to say the word for *family* in their native language. Discuss that all the people in a family are related.

Explain that there are *fact families* for addition and subtraction and for multiplication and division. These are called fact families because they are made up of related parts, similar to how a family is made up of related people. Write a fact family on the board and show how the parts are related. Have students retell in their own words how the parts of the fact family are related.

Guided Instruction

Connect: Division equations and finding an unknown factor

Use this page to help students strengthen their understanding of how dividing and finding an unknown factor are related.

■ Remind students that a letter is sometimes used to represent an unknown number. In this case, the letter *a* is used. Guide students to see that the letter stands for "what number" and that using a letter makes it easier to represent the situation with an equation. Explain that students may have used question marks or boxes in earlier lessons to represent an unknown number, but that they now can also use letters. Point out that any letter can be used to represent an unknown.

■ In Step 1, have students explain why 4 is used as the divisor and 36 is used as the dividend. Discuss how to decide which is the factor and which is the product when writing the related multiplication in Step 2.

■ In Step 3, ask volunteers to tell how they can find the value of the unknown factor. Some students will simply know that 9 × 4 = 36 while others may need to count by 4s until they reach 36 or recite the multiplication facts for 4 until they find one with a product of 36.

■ Have students share the fact families they have written. During the discussion, make a list of various fact families to display in the classroom.

Connect: Division equations and finding an unknown factor

Lana wants to store 36 trading cards in plastic sleeves. Each plastic sleeve can hold 4 trading cards. How many plastic sleeves will Lana need?

Step 1

Write a division equation to represent the problem.

$36 \div 4 = a$

Remember!
You can use a letter to represent an unknown number.

Step 2

Think: What number times 4 is equal to 36?

Write the related multiplication.

$a \times 4 = 36$

Step 3

Find the value of the unknown factor in the multiplication.

$\underline{9} \times 4 = 36$

Then complete the related division.

$36 \div 4 = \underline{9}$

▶ Lana needs 9 plastic sleeves.

 · Choose a multiplication fact you know. Write the other related multiplication and divisions in the fact family. Explain why they are related. Possible answer: 7 × 8 = 56; 8 × 7 = 56, 56 ÷ 7 = 8, 56 ÷ 8 = 7. They are related because the same numbers are used in all four facts and because multiplication and division are related.

Math-to-Math Connection

Arithmetic and Algebra Algebra has been described as a way to generalize the rules of arithmetic. To do this, it is necessary to show that a rule holds for all situations. Instead of attempting to prove something for every possible numerical case, algebra uses letters as variables to show that something is true regardless of what numbers are used. In this lesson, students use a letter to represent a specific unknown number—a first step on the way to using a variable to represent any number.

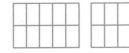
Guided Practice

Complete each fact family.

1. $3 \times 7 = 21$ $21 \div 7 = \underline{3}$ 2. $\underline{3} \times 5 = 15$ $15 \div 5 = \underline{3}$

   $\underline{7} \times 3 = 21$ $21 \div 3 = \underline{7}$ $\underline{5} \times 3 = 15$ $15 \div 3 = \underline{5}$

3. $7 \times \underline{8} = 56$ $56 \div 8 = \underline{7}$ 4. $\underline{8} \times \underline{8} = 64$ $64 \div 8 = \underline{8}$

   $8 \times \underline{7} = 56$ $56 \div 7 = \underline{8}$

Solve the problem.

5. The soccer team orders two pizzas with a total of 20 slices. There are 10 players on the team. How many slices will each player get?

This division equation represents the problem.

$20 \div 10 = s$

Write a related multiplication equation.

$\underline{10} \times s = \underline{20}$

Find the unknown factor.

$10 \times \underline{2} = 20$

Then complete the related division.

$20 \div 10 = \underline{2}$

Complete the fact family for 2, 10, and 20.

$\underline{2} \times 10 = 20$ $20 \div 10 = \underline{2}$

$\underline{10} \times 2 = 20$ $20 \div 2 = \underline{10}$

Answer Each player will get $\underline{2}$ slices.

☆♔☆ Think•Pair•Share

MP7   6. Amy makes triangles to show multiplication and division fact families. Complete the fact family triangle for 4, 9, and 36. How can you use the triangle to help you multiply and divide? Possible answer: The factors are in the squares and the product is in the circle, so I can use the triangle to write or think of all the related facts.

Unit 1 ■ Focus on Operations and Algebraic Thinking   **69**

Observational Assessment

Use page 69 to assess whether students are able to divide by using related facts and completing fact families. Students having difficulty may benefit from using models or arrays. Encourage these students to explain how they used these tools to identify unknown factors.

☆♔☆ Think•Pair•Share

Peer Collaboration Have volunteers present their work. Discuss how the fact family triangle shows the relationships among the three numbers (4, 9, and 36), and why a fact family triangle can help students multiply and divide.

Then have students choose one of the fact families in items 1–4 and draw the fact family triangle. Again let volunteers present their work.

- *How did you decide where in the triangle to place each number?*

- *Which fact family has only two facts?*

- *How did you draw the triangle for that fact family?*

Return to the Essential Question

Reread the Lesson 8 Essential Question on page 66: *How can you use what you know about how multiplication and division are related to divide?*

Ask volunteers to use what they learned in this lesson to answer this question. (Possible response: I can divide by writing a related multiplication equation with an unknown factor. The unknown factor is the answer to the division.)

Invite as many volunteers as possible to express their ideas about using multiplication facts to help them divide.

Mathematical Practices

Mathematical Practice Standards underline the teaching and understanding of all concepts and skills presented. The emphasis of specific practices is noted throughout the guided and independent practice of this lesson.

MP7   **Look for and make use of structure.**

Item 6: Students see how the structure of the fact family triangle can help them recall all facts within the fact family.

Unit 1 ■ Focus on Operations and Algebraic Thinking   **69**

Concept Application

Students may work independently on these pages in the classroom or at home. They may refer to the first four pages of the lesson to revisit the instruction or to see a worked-out example.

Common Errors and **Teaching Tips** may help you support student learning either in the classroom or as a follow-up for work done at home.

Teaching Tips

Items 1–4

If students are struggling, then guide them to see how they can use the given division equations to determine the factors of the related multiplication equations.

Independent Practice

Complete each fact family.

1. $\underline{6} \times \underline{7} = 42$
   $\underline{7} \times \underline{6} = 42$
   $42 \div 7 = \underline{6}$
   $42 \div 6 = \underline{7}$

2. $\underline{3} \times \underline{9} = 27$
   $\underline{9} \times \underline{3} = 27$
   $27 \div 9 = \underline{3}$
   $27 \div 3 = \underline{9}$

3. $\underline{5} \times \underline{8} = 40$
   $\underline{8} \times \underline{5} = 40$
   $40 \div 8 = \underline{5}$
   $40 \div 5 = \underline{8}$

4. $\underline{7} \times \underline{9} = 63$
   $\underline{9} \times \underline{7} = 63$
   $63 \div 9 = \underline{7}$
   $63 \div 7 = \underline{9}$

To divide, find the unknown factor.

5. $42 \div 7 = \blacksquare$ ⟶ What number times 7 equals 42?
   $\underline{6} \times 7 = 42$
   $42 \div 7 = \underline{6}$

6. $64 \div 8 = \blacksquare$ ⟶ What number times 8 equals 64?
   $\underline{8} \times 8 = 64$
   $64 \div 8 = \underline{8}$

7. $63 \div 7 = \blacksquare$ ⟶ What number times 7 equals 63?
   $\underline{9} \times 7 = 63$
   $63 \div 7 = \underline{9}$

8. $50 \div 10 = \blacksquare$ ⟶ What number times 10 equals 50?
   $\underline{5} \times 10 = 50$
   $50 \div 10 = \underline{5}$

Writing About Math

▸ Write an Opinion Text Ask students to write a paragraph giving their opinion on which division strategy is helpful to them. Have students provide reasons that support their opinion and use linking words such as *because, since,* and *for example* when writing their paragraph.

Ask volunteers to read their paragraphs aloud. Remind students that these are opinion paragraphs, so there is no right or wrong way to write the paragraph. Some students may explain that a strategy is helpful for some problems, such as $63 \div 7 = \blacksquare$, and not as helpful for others, such as $64 \div 8 = \blacksquare$.

Independent Practice

9. Which multiplication fact could you use to find the unknown number?

   $36 \div 9 = \blacksquare$

   a. $4 \times 8 = 32$

   b. $5 \times 7 = 35$

   c. $4 \times 9 = 36$

   d. $5 \times 9 = 45$

10. Which multiplication fact could you use to find n?

    $24 \div 3 = n$

    a. $7 \times 3 = 21$

    b. $8 \times 3 = 24$

    c. $9 \times 3 = 27$

    d. $10 \times 3 = 30$

For exercises 11 and 12, find the unknown number.

11. $63 \div 7 = m$

    Show your work. $9 \times 7 = 63; 63 \div 7 = 9$

    Answer $63 \div 7 = \underline{9}$

12. $48 \div 8 = m$

    Show your work. $6 \times 8 = 48; 48 \div 8 = 6$

    Answer $48 \div 8 = \underline{6}$

Unit 1 ■ Focus on Operations and Algebraic Thinking   **71**

Teaching Tips

Items 11-12

If students are struggling, ask them to rewrite the division as a related multiplication equation with an unknown factor. After students rewrite the equation, for example, in item 12, guide them to think: what number times 8 equals 48?

Digital Connection

Random Number Generator Use a search engine to find a website with a random number generator. Assign parameters for the random number generator to select two numbers between 1 and 10. Pair students and assign each pair two randomly selected numbers as factors. Encourage pairs to create their own fact family triangles. Some students may notice that certain numbers can be used in two different fact families. For example, 2 and 6 can be used in the fact family for 2, 3, and 6 or they can be used in the fact family for 2, 6, and 12. In some instances, the random number generator may select the same number twice. Use it to point out that some fact families have only two facts.

Common Errors

Item 13

If students have difficulty due to the placement of the equal sign, explain that an unknown factor can be written on either side of the equal sign. Remind them that the dividend becomes the product in a related multiplication equation.

Teaching Tips

Item 15

Some students may benefit by drawing a diagram to represent the problem.

Independent Practice

MP6 **13.** Tell how you would find a. Then solve.

$a = 49 \div 7$

Possible answer: I know that $7 \times 7 = 49$, so I can use that fact to find that $49 \div 7 = 7$.

Answer __7__ $= 49 \div 7$

MP8 **14.** Ethan knows that $6 \times 9 = 54$. How can he use that fact to solve the following equation?

$54 \div 9 = d$

Possible answer: Ethan can write an unknown factor problem to find the unknown number; for example, what number times 9 equals 54 or $d \times 9 = 54$? Then he can use the multiplication fact $6 \times 9 = 54$ to find the unknown factor, 6, which is the answer to the division problem.

Answer $54 \div 9 =$ __6__

Solve the problems.

MP2 **15.** Zoey has flower plants to sell at the spring fair. She has 72 plants and 9 boxes. How many plants can she put in each box?

▓▓▓▓ **Show your work.**

Students' work might include the following steps in words or pictures: writing $72 \div 9 = \blacksquare$; finding the unknown factor, $8 \times 9 = 72$, and using it to answer the division problem; $72 \div 9 = 8$.

Answer Zoey can put 8 flower plants in each box.

Mathematical Practices	
MP2	**Reason abstractly and quantitatively.**
Item 15: Students decontextualize a word problem to identify the unknown factor as they divide to solve the problem.	
MP6	**Attend to precision.**
Item 13: Students must choose the appropriate multiplication to solve the equation.	
MP8	**Look for and express regularity in repeated reasoning.**
Item 14: Students explain the logic used to solve a division equation.	

Lesson 8

Independent Practice

MP5 **16.** Six tacos from the Lunch Place cost $18. How much does 1 taco cost?

▸ **Show your work.**
Students' work might include the following steps in words or pictures: writing the equations $18 \div 6 = \blacksquare$; $\blacksquare \times 6 = 18$; finding the unknown factor in $3 \times 6 = 18$; using it in the division problem; $18 \div 6 = 3$.

Answer $3

MP3 **17.** C.J. does not know the answer to $54 \div 9$. Can C.J. correctly find the answer in each of the following ways? Explain why or why not for each way.

▸ **Justify your answer using words, drawings, or numbers.**

a. He can make an array to show that 6 rows of 9 makes 54. So 54 divided by 9 is 6.
Possible justification: This works; C.J. can use an array or another drawing (such as one showing equal groups) to find the answer.

b. He knows that $6 \times 9 = 54$, so 54 divided by 9 must be 6.
Possible justification: This works; C.J. can use a multiplication fact in the same fact family to find the answer.

Answer Yes. He can use either way to find the answer.

Teaching Tips

Item 17
Have students draw the array as described in part **a**. Ask students to identify the dividend, divisor, and quotient in the model.

Return to the

Remind students to return to the Progress Check self-assessment, page 7, to check off additional items they have mastered during the unit.

Mathematical Practices

MP3	**Construct viable arguments and critique the reasoning of others.**

Item 17: Students analyze two different strategies to decide whether none, one, or both methods result in the correct answer.

MP5	**Use appropriate tools strategically.**

Item 16: Students can use equations and/or models to solve the problem.

The Common Core Review covers all the standards presented in the unit. Use it to assess your students' mastery of the unit's concepts and skills.

Depth of Knowledge

The depth of knowledge is a ranking of the content complexity of assessment items based on Webb's Depth of Knowledge (DOK) levels. The levels increase in complexity as shown below.

Level 1: Recall and Reproduction
Level 2: Basic Skills and Concepts
Level 3: Strategic Reasoning and Thinking
Level 4: Extended Thinking

Item	Standard	DOK
1	3.OA.1	1
2	3.OA.1	1
3	3.OA.2	2
4	3.OA.2	2
5	3.OA.4	1
6	3.OA.6	1
7	3.OA.5	2
8	3.OA.5	2
9	3.OA.5	2
10	3.OA.5	2
11	3.OA.5	2
12	3.OA.5	2
13	3.OA.6	1
14	3.OA.6	1
15	3.OA.4	2
16	3.OA.4	2
17	3.OA.3	3
18	3.OA.3	3
19	3.OA.3	4
20	3.OA.3	4

 **Common Core Review**

For exercises 1 and 2, find the product. You can use the drawing.

1. $4 \times 4 =$ ▨

2. $5 \times 6 =$ ▨

$4 \times 4 = \underline{16}$

$5 \times 6 = \underline{30}$

For exercises 3 and 4, find the quotient. Make a drawing to justify your answer. Check drawings.

3. $15 \div 3 = \underline{5}$

4. $32 \div 4 = \underline{8}$

5. Which multiplication equation could you use to find the unknown number?
$$7 \times \blacksquare = 35$$

(a.) $7 \times 5 = 35$

b. $7 \times 6 = 42$

c. $7 \times 7 = 49$

d. $7 \times 8 = 56$

6. Which division equation could you use to find the unknown number?
$$4 \times n = 20$$

a. $20 \div 10 = 2$

(b.) $20 \div 5 = 4$

c. $20 \div 2 = 10$

d. $20 \div 1 = 20$

For exercises 7 and 8, find the unknown product.

7. $3 \times 6 = 18$
   $6 \times 3 = \underline{18}$

8. $9 \times 6 = 54$
   $6 \times 9 = \underline{54}$

UNIT 1 Common Core Review

For exercises 9 and 10, use the Associative Property to group the factors. Find the unknown product. Show your work.

9. $2 \times 5 \times 4 = $ ▨

10. $4 \times 2 \times 3 = $ ▨

$2 \times 5 \times 4 = \underline{40}$

$4 \times 2 \times 3 = \underline{24}$

11. Which of the following is the same as 12×7?

a. $(9 \times 4) + (3 \times 3)$

b. $(6 \times 6) + (3 \times 4)$

c. $(4 \times 8) + (7 \times 1)$

d. $(8 \times 7) + (4 \times 7)$

12. Choose all the following that are the same as $(3 \times 4) + (3 \times 4)$.

a. 6×4

b. 6×8

c. $(6 \times 2) + (6 \times 2)$

d. $(2 \times 2) + (4 \times 4)$

For exercises 13 and 14, complete the fact family.

13. $\underline{4} \times 7 = 28$ $28 \div 7 = \underline{4}$

   $\underline{7} \times 4 = \underline{28}$ $\underline{28} \div 4 = \underline{7}$

14. $\underline{3} \times 9 = 27$ $27 \div 9 = \underline{3}$

   $\underline{9} \times 3 = \underline{27}$ $\underline{27} \div 3 = \underline{9}$

For exercises 15 and 16, find the unknown number. Show your work.

15. $64 \div 8 = n$

$8 \times 8 = 64; 64 \div 8 = 8$

16. $42 \div 6 = m$

$7 \times 6 = 42; 42 \div 6 = 7$

Unit 1 ■ Focus on Operations and Algebraic Thinking **75**

This chart correlates the Common Core Review items with the lessons in which the concepts and skills are presented.

Item	Lesson
1	1
2	1
3	2
4	2
5	5
6	8
7	6
8	6
9	6
10	6
11	7
12	7
13	8
14	8
15	5
16	5
17	3
18	4
19	4
20	4

Writing About Math

✏️ Direct students to respond to the Unit 1 Essential Question. (This can also be found on student page 9.)

Essential Question:
How are multiplication and division related?

Possible responses:
- Division is the inverse of multiplication.
- Multiplication is the inverse of division.
- You can use multiplication to check the answer of a division problem.

Unit Assessment

- Unit 1 Common Core Review, *pp. 74–76*
- Unit 1 Performance Task (ONLINE)

Additional Assessment Options

Optional Purchase:
- iProgress Monitor (ONLINE)
- Progress Monitor Student Benchmark Assessment Booklet

UNIT **1** **Common Core Review**

Solve the problems.

MP1 **17.** A group of 8 people take 16 water bottles on their hike. If they share the water bottles equally, how many water bottles will each person get?

✏️ **Show your work.**
Possible answers: I can draw a picture to show 16 water bottles shared equally among 8 people; ■ × 8 = 16; 2 × 8 = 16; or I can solve a related division equation: 16 ÷ 8 = ■; 16 ÷ 8 = 2.

Answer Each person will get 2 water bottles.

MP1 **18.** There are 48 people in a marching band. If they stand in 6 equal rows, how many people will stand in each row?

✏️ **Show your work.**
Possible answer: I can draw a 6 × 8 array to show 48; 6 × ■ = 48; 6 × 8 = 48; or I can solve a related division equation: 48 ÷ ■ = 6; 48 ÷ 8 = 6.

Answer 8 people will stand in each row.

MP3 **19.** Tamara drew this array to represent 4 rows of 5 marbles. What is wrong with Tamara's array? Correct it.
Possible answer: Tamara's array shows 3 rows of 5 each instead of 4 rows of 5 each.

MP7 **20.** Mr. Kent has 28 students in his gym class. He wants the students to sit in rows with the same number of students in each row. What are two ways Mr. Kent can arrange the 28 students?

Answer Mr. Kent can arrange the students into 4 rows of 7 students each or 7 rows of 4 students each.

✏️ **Justify your answer using words, drawings, or numbers.**
Possible justification: I know that the order of the factors does not matter. So, I can find two factors that when multiplied together make 28: 4 × 7 = 28 and 7 × 4 = 28. I can use these factors to arrange the students into rows in two different ways: 4 rows of 7 students each or 7 rows of 4 students each. Students can also show this with 4 × 7 and 7 × 4 arrays.

Mathematical Practices

MP1	**Make sense of problems and persevere in solving them.**
Item 17: Students analyze a problem and plan a solution.	
Item 18: Students analyze relationships and explain their reasoning.	
MP3	**Construct viable arguments and critique the reasoning of others.**
Items 19: Students explain an approach to a problem.	
MP7	**Look for and make sure use of structure.**
Item 20: Students use multiplication patterns to solve a problem.	

Progress Check

Look at how the Common Core standards you have learned and will learn connect.

It is very important for you to understand the standards from the prior grade level so that you will be able to develop an understanding of operations and algebraic thinking / number and operations in base ten in this unit and be prepared for next year. To practice your skills, go to sadlierconnect.com.

GRADE 2			GRADE 3			GRADE 4
I Can...	Before Unit 2		**Can I ?**	After Unit 2		**I Will...**
		☐	**3.OA.7** Fluently multiply and divide within 100	☐		**4.NBT.5** Multiply multi-digit whole numbers by one-digit whole numbers
2. OA.1 Solve one- and two-step word problems by adding and subtracting within 100 Use drawings and equations to represent word problems		☐	**3.OA.8** Solve two-step problems using the four operations	☐		**4.OA.3** Solve multistep word problems using the four operations
		☐	Check reasonableness of answers to problems using mental math and estimation	☐		Represent multistep word problems using equations
		☐	Represent two-step word problems using equations			
		☐	**3.OA.9** Identify arithmetic patterns	☐		**4.OA.5** Generate and analyze patterns
2.NBT.1 Understand place value in two-digit and three-digit numbers		☐	**3.NBT.1** Round whole numbers to the nearest 10 or 100	☐		**4.NBT.3** Round multi-digit whole numbers to any place
2.NBT.5 Fluently add and subtract within 100		☐	**3.NBT.2** Fluently add and subtract within 1000	☐		**4.NBT.4** Fluently add and subtract multi-digit whole numbers
2.NBT.6 Add up to four two-digit numbers						
2.NBT.7 Add and subtract within 1000						
		☐	**3.NBT.3** Multiply one-digit numbers by multiples of 10	☐		**4.NBT.5** Multiply multi-digit whole numbers by one-digit whole numbers Multiply two two-digit numbers

Unit 2 ■ Focus on Operations and Algebraic Thinking / Number and Operations in Base Ten

Student Page 77

Progress Check

Progress Check is a self-assessment tool that students can use to gauge their own progress. Research shows that when students take accountability for their learning, motivation increases.

Before students begin work in Unit 2, have them check any items they know they can do well. Explain that it is fine if they don't check any of the boxes; they will have the opportunity to learn and practice all the standards through the course of the unit.

Let them know that at the end of the unit they will review their checklists to check their progress. After students have completed the last lesson of the unit, before they begin Common Core Review, you will be prompted to have students revisit this page.

HOME ◆ CONNECT...

In third grade, your child will solve word problems using addition, subtraction, multiplication, and division. Support your child by using the following problem-solving model:

- **Read** Read the problem with your child. Focus on the facts and the questions. Ask: *What facts do you know? What do you need to find out?*

- **Plan** Outline a plan with your child. Plan how to solve the problem. Ask: *What operation (addition, subtraction, multiplication, or division) will you use? Do you need to use 1 step or 2 steps? Will you draw a picture? How have you solved similar problems?*

- **Solve** Follow the plan to solve the problem with your child. Ask: *Did you answer the question? Did you label your answer?*

- **Check** Test that the solution is reasonable. Ask: *How can you solve the problem a different way? Is the answer the same? How can you estimate to check your answer?*

Conversation Starters: Estimation is another strategy your child will use in third grade. Talk about situations in which you need to use estimation. For example: planning a family celebration for twenty people. Ask questions such as: *How many people can sit at a table? About how many tables would we need? How many people would eat hamburgers? About how many packages of hamburgers would we need?*

In this unit your child will:

- Fluently multiply and divide.
- Solve two-step problems.
- Check answers for reasonableness.
- Represent two-step word problems using equations.
- Identify arithmetic patterns.
- Round whole numbers to the nearest 10 or 100.
- Fluently add or subtract numbers within 1,000.
- Multiply one-digit numbers by multiples of 10.

NOTE: All of these learning goals for your child are based on the Grade 3 Common Core State Standards for Mathematics.

Ways to Help Your Child

Your child will likely have daily homework assignments. Establishing a homework routine can help promote good study habits. Schedule a consistent time for doing homework. The homework routine should also include a homework space that is quiet and comfortable, free from distractions. You may want to use a kitchen or dining room table so that you can easily monitor your child and provide assistance as needed.

ONLINE
For more Home Connect activities, continue online at sadlierconnect.com

78   Unit 2 ■ Focus on Operations and Algebraic Thinking/Number and Operations in Base Ten

Student Page 78

HOME ◆ CONNECT...

The Home Connect feature is a way to keep parents or other adult family members apprised of what their children are learning. The key learning objectives are listed, and some ideas for related activities and discussions are included.

Explain to students that they can share the Home Connect page at home with their families. Let students know there is an activity connected to their classroom learning that they can do with their families.

Encourage students and their parents to share their experiences using the suggestions on the Home Connect. You may wish to invite students to share this work with the class.

UNIT PLANNER

Lesson		Standard(s)	Objective
9	Multiply and Divide Fluently within 100	3.OA.7	Use properties of operations and the relationship between multiplication and division to multiply and divide one-digit numbers.
10	Problem Solving: Two-Step Problems	3.OA.8	Use the four operations to solve two-step word problems.
11	Problem Solving: Use Equations	3.OA.8	Write an equation to solve a two-step word problem.
12	Identify and Explain Arithmetic Patterns	3.OA.9	Identify and use arithmetic patterns in multiplication and addition tables.
13	Round Whole Numbers to the Nearest 10 or 100	3.NBT.1	Use rounding to the nearest 10 or 100 to estimate.
14	Add and Subtract Fluently within 1,000	3.NBT.2	Use strategies to add and subtract within 1,000.
15	Multiply One-Digit Whole Numbers by Multiples of 10	3.NBT.3	Multiply one-digit numbers by multiples of 10.

Essential Question: How does understanding place value help you add, subtract, and multiply?

UNIT 2

Essential Question	Words to Know
What strategies can you use to multiply and divide with one-digit numbers?	strategy, Zero Property, Identity Property of Multiplication
How can you use two steps to solve a problem?	operations, estimation, compatible numbers
How can you use an equation to solve a problem?	
How can you identify and explain arithmetic patterns?	pattern, odd, even, rule
How can you round whole numbers?	round
How can you add and subtract within 1,000?	Associative Property of Addition, Commutative Property of Addition
How can you multiply a number by a multiple of 10?	multiple

Unit Assessment

- Unit 2 Common Core Review, *pp. 136–138*
- Unit 2 Performance Task ONLINE

Additional Assessment Options

Optional Purchase:
- iProgress Monitor ONLINE
- Progress Monitor Student Benchmark Assessment Booklet

ONLINE Digital Resources

- Home Connect Activities
- Unit Performance Tasks
- Additional Practice
- Fluency Practice
- Teacher Resources
- iProgress Monitor (optional purchase)

Go to SadlierConnect.com to access your Digital Resources.

For more detailed instructions see page T3.

LEARNING PROGRESSIONS

This page provides more in-depth detail on the development of the standards across the grade levels. See also the unit Progress Check page in the Student Edition for a roadmap of the Learning Progressions.

Grade 2

- Students represent and solve one- and two-step word problems involving addition and subtraction within 100 for situations involving adding to/taking from, putting together/taking apart, and comparing, using drawings and equations as representations. (2.OA.1)
- Students extend their understanding of place value to hundreds, viewing a hundred as a new unit composed of 10 tens. (2.NBT.1)
- Students fluently add and subtract within 100. (2.NBT.5)
- Students add up to four two-digit numbers and add and subtract within 1,000. (2.NBT.6, 2.NBT.7)

Grade 3

- Mastery of multiplication and division facts with understanding is crucial to students' future work with multi-digit numbers and decimals. (3.OA.7)
- Students solve two-step word problems using combinations of the four operations. (3.OA.8)
- Students assess the reasonableness of answers to word problems using mental math or estimation strategies, including rounding. (3.OA.8)
- Students use a letter to stand for the unknown when representing a problem situation with an equation. (3.OA.8)
- Students identify arithmetic patterns and relate them to properties of operations. (3.OA.9)
- Students round whole numbers to the nearest 10 or 100 and use rounding as an estimation strategy. (3.OA.8, 3.NBT.1)
- Students apply strategies and algorithms based on place value and properties of operations to fluently add and subtract within 1,000. (3.NBT.2)
- Concepts of place value and properties of operations are also applied to multiply one-digit whole numbers by multiples of 10. (3.NBT.3)

Grade 4

- Students solve multi-step word problems and check the reasonableness of their answers. They represent these problems with equations. (4.OA.3)
- Students generate and analyze patterns that follow a given rule. (4.OA.5)
- Rounding whole numbers is extended to rounding to any given place. (4.NBT.3)
- Students apply the standard algorithms to fluently add and subtract multi-digit whole numbers. (4.NBT.4)
- Students use strategies based on place value and properties of operations to multiply multi-digit whole numbers by one-digit whole numbers and to multiply two two-digit numbers. (4.NBT.5)

Focus on Operations and Algebraic Thinking / Number and Operations in Base Ten

UNIT **2**

Essential Question: How does understanding place value help you add, subtract, and multiply?

Activity

Materials: grid paper

Tell students that the parking lot is laid out in a specific way. Ask students to sketch the entire parking lot if each of the ten rows in the lot has 20 parking spaces.

Ask students to determine how many cars will fit in the parking lot if it is full. Explain that there are many ways to find the number of cars it will hold. Ask them to look for patterns in their calculations.

Discuss why the organization of the parking lot is important. Elicit ideas about the predictable layout and how it helps you better understand quantities related to the parking lot.

Essential Question:
How does understanding place value help you add, subtract, and multiply?

As students become involved with the Essential Question they will use place value and the value of digits to explore arithmetic patterns, to round numbers, to fluently add and subtract within 1,000, and to multiply by multiples of 10.

Conversation Starters

Have students discuss the photograph. Ask questions such as: *What are you looking at in the photo? What kind of cars do you see? What size cars are there?*

Have the students look at the parking spaces. *Look at the white lines that define the spaces. How is the lot organized? How are these spaces arranged?* (Each of the spaces is the same size and parallel.)

Have the students look at the cars. *How are the cars parked? What rule do you think there is for parking?* (There are two cars in each spot. The rule is that no more than two cars can be parked in any spot.) *Why do you think they have this rule?* (The spots are not large enough for more than two cars, and this way they can get either car out of the spot without having to move another car.)

Let students work in pairs to discuss how to count the number of cars in the lot and to determine the number of spaces that are available. Lead them to develop a multi-step plan for solving this problem using addition or multiplication and subtraction.

Common Core Focus:

3.OA.7 Fluently multiply and divide within 100, using strategies such as the relationship between multiplication and division or properties of operations. By the end of Grade 3, know from memory all products of two one-digit numbers.

OBJECTIVE

Use properties of operations and the relationship between multiplication and division to multiply and divide one-digit numbers.

ESSENTIAL QUESTION

Students have already learned how to use the Commutative, Associative, and Distributive Properties. Tell students they will learn two more strategies that they can use to multiply and divide: the Zero Property and the Identity Property of Multiplication. Using strategies will help them multiply and divide fluently.

FLUENCY PRACTICE

Fluency practice is available at **sadlierconnect.com**.

Concept Development

Understand: How multiplication and division are related

■ Students will be expected to use different strategies to multiply and divide, emphasizing a deep understanding of numbers and their properties. The focus is not to memorize, but to make use of number properties and understand how to use related facts to multiply and divide fluently.

■ Students should observe that arrays can be used to represent multiplications and their related divisions. After working through this page with students, you might ask them to use strategies and the Commutative Property to find three related facts for 36 ÷ 4 = 9.

Lesson 9 — Multiply and Divide Fluently within 100

Guided Instruction

Essential Question:
What strategies can you use to multiply and divide with one-digit numbers?
3.OA.7

Words to Know:
strategy
Zero Property
Identity Property of Multiplication

In this lesson you will learn to use different strategies to multiply and divide.

Understand: How multiplication and division are related

> You have used an array to show equal groups. What does an array tell you about multiplication and division?

This array shows 4 equal groups of 5.
You can write 4 × 5 = 20.

Turn the array to show 5 equal groups of 4.
You can write 5 × 4 = 20.

You can also write 4 × 5 as

$$\begin{array}{r} 4 \\ \times\, 5 \\ \hline 20 \end{array}$$

You can also write 20 ÷ 4 as

$$4\overline{)20}^{\,5}$$

The array shows that 20 can be divided into 4 equal groups of 5. You can write 20 ÷ 4 = 5.

The turned array shows that 20 can be divided into 5 equal groups of 4. You can write 20 ÷ 5 = 4.

▶ The arrays show that multiplication and division are related, because they undo each other.

The relationship between multiplication and division is a strategy or method you can use when you multiply or divide. When you know 4 × 5 = 20, you also know that 20 ÷ 4 = 5.

The Commutative Property is another strategy you can use to multiply. This tells you that when you know 4 × 5 = 20, you also know that 5 × 4 = 20.

You can use the relationship between multiplication and division again to undo 5 × 4 = 20 to find 20 ÷ 5 = 4.

Remember!
The Commutative Property says that changing the order of factors does not change the product.

Words to Know

strategy: a plan or method for solving a problem

Zero Property: the product of any number and 0 is 0

Example: 5 × 0 = 0

Identity Property of Multiplication: the product of any number and 1 is that number

Example: 5 × 1 = 5

Glossary can be found on pp. 347–350.

Lesson 9

Guided Instruction

Understand: How to use properties of multiplication to learn facts

The multiplication table shows all 100 products of two 1-digit numbers. You need to learn all of these facts this year. How can using a property of multiplication help?

The left column and the top row show factors. To find a product of two factors, move across a row and down a column until you reach a box where the row and the column meet. The number in that box is the product of those two factors.

The red row and column show that $7 \times 3 = 21$.

The Commutative Property helps you learn two facts at the same time.

Notice that the green row and column show that $3 \times 7 = 21$. For every multiplication fact with two different factors, there is another fact with the order of the factors changed.

The Zero Property says that if you multiply any number by 0, the product is 0.

The purple row and column use the Zero Property. The product for all facts that have 0 as a factor is 0.

The Identity Property of Multiplication says that if you multiply any number by 1, the product is that number.

The orange row and column use the Identity Property. The product for all facts with 1 as a factor is the other factor itself.

➡ Using a property is a strategy that helps save time and work while you learn all the multiplication facts.

×	0	1	2	3	4	5	6	7	8	9
0	0	0	0	0	0	0	0	0	0	0
1	0	1	2	3	4	5	6	7	8	9
2	0	2	4	6	8	10	12	14	16	18
3	0	3	6	9	12	15	18	21	24	27
4	0	4	8	12	16	20	24	28	32	36
5	0	5	10	15	20	25	30	35	40	45
6	0	6	12	18	24	30	36	42	48	54
7	0	7	14	21	28	35	42	49	56	63
8	0	8	16	24	32	40	48	56	64	72
9	0	9	18	27	36	45	54	63	72	81

×	0	1	2	3	4	5	6	7	8	9
0	0	0	0	0	0	0	0	0	0	0
1	0	1	2	3	4	5	6	7	8	9
2	0	2	4	6	8	10	12	14	16	18
3	0	3	6	9	12	15	18	21	24	27
4	0	4	8	12	16	20	24	28	32	36
5	0	5	10	15	20	25	30	35	40	45
6	0	6	12	18	24	30	36	42	48	54
7	0	7	14	21	28	35	42	49	56	63
8	0	8	16	24	32	40	48	56	64	72
9	0	9	18	27	36	45	54	63	72	81

×	0	1	2	3	4	5	6	7	8	9
0	0	0	0	0	0	0	0	0	0	0
1	0	1	2	3	4	5	6	7	8	9
2	0	2	4	6	8	10	12	14	16	18
3	0	3	6	9	12	15	18	21	24	27
4	0	4	8	12	16	20	24	28	32	36
5	0	5	10	15	20	25	30	35	40	45
6	0	6	12	18	24	30	36	42	48	54
7	0	7	14	21	28	35	42	49	56	63
8	0	8	16	24	32	40	48	56	64	72
9	0	9	18	27	36	45	54	63	72	81

×	0	1	2	3	4	5	6	7	8	9
0	0	0	0	0	0	0	0	0	0	0
1	0	1	2	3	4	5	6	7	8	9
2	0	2	4	6	8	10	12	14	16	18
3	0	3	6	9	12	15	18	21	24	27
4	0	4	8	12	16	20	24	28	32	36
5	0	5	10	15	20	25	30	35	40	45
6	0	6	12	18	24	30	36	42	48	54
7	0	7	14	21	28	35	42	49	56	63
8	0	8	16	24	32	40	48	56	64	72
9	0	9	18	27	36	45	54	63	72	81

Unit 2 ▪ Focus on Operations and Algebraic Thinking/Number and Operations in Base Ten **81**

Understand: How to use the properties of multiplication to learn facts

■ Make sure students can use the multiplication table correctly. If students struggle following straight lines to find the product, suggest they use two pencils or two rulers as guides to help them mark the row and column.

■ You may wish to provide students with four larger copies of the multiplication table and have them color the tables to match those in the book as you go through the directions for finding products.

■ Ask students how the Commutative Property helps them learn two facts at the same time. Explain that once students have learned that $4 \times 8 = 32$, they also know that $8 \times 4 = 32$.

■ Write an example of the Zero Property and an example of the Identity Property of Multiplication on the board. Have volunteers write additional examples. Seeing many examples helps student understand the general rules.

■ Point out that any number multiplied by one is that number. When a number is multiplied by zero the product is 0.

Support English Language Learners

Help students understand that the term *undo* means "to reverse." When multiplication *undoes* division and vice versa, the operation and arrangement of an array's parts will change, but the array stays the same.

To give students practice in using words to express mathematical ideas, use the arrays on page 80 to have students practice explaining the relationship between the related facts. For example, "I can undo $4 \times 5 = 20$ to find $20 \div 4 = 5$." Students will tell different ways that these three numbers can *undo* each other. The goal is to use the term correctly and also visually understand what it means to *undo* multiplication and division.

Connect: Using what you know to multiply and divide within 100

Use this page to help students strengthen their understanding of multiplication properties and the inverse relationship between multiplication and division. Building this understanding will help students develop their ability to choose appropriate strategies to multiply and divide fluently.

■ A key understanding in this presentation is that there are many strategies, such as skip counting, relating multiplication and division, and using the Distributive Property, that students can use to multiply and divide. Learning different strategies helps students build fluency with multiplication and division facts.

■ Some strategies may work for some students, while others may not. Students should choose strategies that they are comfortable with, and that are appropriate for the situation.

■ Have students explain how they can use the multiplication table to find factors, products, dividends, divisors, and quotients. Being familiar with the multiplication table will help prepare students for finding factors and multiples of whole numbers in Grade 4.

✏ Have students explain the strategy they used for the chosen fact. Have them identify any additional strategies they could have used. This will emphasize that there is more than one way to effectively solve a problem.

Lesson 9 Multiply and Divide Fluently within 100

Guided Instruction

Connect: Using what you know to multiply and divide within 100

> What are some other strategies you can use for multiplying and dividing within 100?

You can skip count by 2s or by 5s, so you can multiply by 2 or 5.

Look at the red and blue rows and columns. The numbers you see in the red column and row are the numbers you would use to count by 2s: 2, 4, 6, 8, 10, 12, 14, 16, and 18. The numbers you see in the blue column and row are the numbers you would use to count by 5s: 5, 10, 15, 20, 25, 30, 35, 40, and 45.

You know that division undoes multiplication. You can use a multiplication table to find quotients. First find the divisor in the top row of factors. Next move down the column until you find the dividend. Then move left to the column of factors. The factor you find is the quotient.

To find $42 \div 7$, go to the 7 in the top row of factors. Move down until you find 42. Then move left to the column of factors where you find 6. $42 \div 7 = 6$

You know how to use the Distributive Property to find a product. To find 6×8, start by breaking apart 8.

$6 \times 8 = 6 \times (5 + 3)$ ← Break 8 apart into $5 + 3$.
$= (6 \times 5) + (6 \times 3)$ ← Multiply both addends by 6.
$= 30 + 18$ ← Add the two products.
$= 48$ ← The product of 6×8.

Using 5 as one of the addends means you will use a 5s fact.

➤ Some strategies for multiplying and dividing are skip counting, undoing multiplication, and using the Distributive Property.

✏ Choose a fact that you are not sure of. Explain a strategy that you can use to learn it. **Possible answer:** 8×7 is a fact I am not sure of. I will use the Distributive Property to find it. $8 \times 7 = 8 \times (5 + 2)$; $8 \times (5 + 2) = (8 \times 5) + (8 \times 2)$; $(8 \times 5) + (8 \times 2) = 40 + 16$; $40 + 16 = 56$.

82 Unit 2 ■ Focus on Operations and Algebraic Thinking/Number and Operations in Base Ten

---

Math-to-Math Connection

Arithmetic and Algebra Creating a strong foundation for inverse operations and using a symbol for an unknown helps students to informally understand the process of solving algebraic equations. A deep understanding of multiplications, their related divisions, and strategies will allow students to complete more difficult problems in the future.

Give students the problem 3×6. Have 18 students in the class stand up and create an array with their bodies. While they are creating an array, have the other students sit and independently work out the problem using a strategy of their choosing. Then, as a class, compare and contrast the various strategies used.

Lesson 9

Guided Practice

Multiply. Use the Zero Property and the Identity Property.

1. $5 \times 0 = \underline{0}$ 2. $1 \times 9 = \underline{9}$ 3. $1 \times \underline{0} = 0$

Multiply. Skip count by 2s or 5s to help.

4. $5 \times 7 = \underline{35}$ 5. $7 \times 2 = \underline{14}$ 6. $2 \times \underline{9} = 18$

Divide. Write the related multiplication.

7. $28 \div 7 = \underline{4}$ The related multiplication is $\underline{7 \times 4 = 28}$.

8. $36 \div 4 = \underline{9}$ The related multiplication is $\underline{4 \times 9 = 36}$.

9. $56 \div 8 = \underline{7}$ The related multiplication is $\underline{8 \times 7 = 56}$.

10. $81 \div 9 = \underline{9}$ The related multiplication is $\underline{9 \times 9 = 81}$.

Multiply or divide. Use any strategy you like.

11. $1 \times 5 = \underline{5}$ 12. $3 \times 5 = \underline{15}$ 13. $5 \times \underline{5} = 25$

14. $\begin{array}{r} 6 \\ \times\ 2 \\ \hline 12 \end{array}$ 15. $\begin{array}{r} 6 \\ \times\ 0 \\ \hline 0 \end{array}$ 16. $\begin{array}{r} 6 \\ \times\ 3 \\ \hline 18 \end{array}$

17. $10 \div 2 = \underline{5}$ 18. $15 \div 3 = \underline{5}$ 19. $12 \div 3 = \underline{4}$

20. $2\overline{)14}$ ^{7} 21. $2\overline{)12}$ ^{6} 22. $2\overline{)16}$ ^{8}

♔ Think•Pair•Share

MP1 23. Explain two strategies you can use to find $42 \div 7$.
What is the quotient?
Possible explanations: To find $42 \div 7$, I can use a related multiplication to find
the number that equals 42 when multiplied by 7; $6 \times 7 = 42$, so $42 \div 7 = 6$; to
find $42 \div 7$, I can make an array with rows of 7 until I make 6 rows to show
42, so $42 \div 7 = 6$. The quotient is 6.

Unit 2 ■ Focus on Operations and Algebraic Thinking/Number and Operations in Base Ten   **83**

Mathematical Practices

Mathematical Practice Standards underline the teaching and understanding of all concepts and skills presented. The emphasis of specific practices is noted throughout the guided and independent practice of this lesson.

MP1   Make sense of problems and persevere in solving them.

Item 23: Students understand how multiplication and division can be solved using different strategies. Using two different strategies will allow students to analyze and plan strategies.

Observational Assessment

Use page 83 to assess whether students understand multiplication and division relationships and properties, and appropriately use them to multiply and divide fluently. Practicing different specific strategies first (exercises 1–10) will provide experience, which will help students to choose strategies they find appropriate and effective later (exercises 11–23). Check that students understand each strategy and then are able to apply it successfully.

♔ Think•Pair•Share

Peer Collaboration Ask pairs to share their strategies with each other, and then share with the class. While they are in pairs circulate and ask these questions:

- *Which strategy did you use?*

- *What strategy did your partner use?*

- *Why did you pick the strategy you used to find the quotient?*

Asking these same questions when students are presenting in front of the class will give all students an opportunity to share effectively.

Return to the Essential Question

Reread the Lesson 9 Essential Question on page 80: *What strategies can you use multiply and divide with one-digit numbers?*

Ask volunteers to use what they learned in this lesson to answer this question. (Possible response: When multiplying and dividing, I can use many different strategies, such as skip counting, undoing multiplication, making an array, or using the Distributive Property. I pick the one that is easy for me to use and is appropriate for the problem.)

Invite as many volunteers as possible to express ideas about using different strategies. Ask for specific examples or have students solve problems in different ways and discuss results.

Independent Practice

Concept Application

Students may work independently on these pages in the classroom or at home. They may refer to the first four pages of the lesson to revisit the instruction or to see a worked-out example.

Common Errors and **Teaching Tips** may help you support student learning either in the classroom or as follow-up for work done at home.

Teaching Tips

Item 1

Remind students that multiplication and division are related by the equations *factor × factor = product* and *product ÷ factor = factor*.

Items 4–11

Since all these exercises involve multiplying by 9, suggest to students that they use the Distributive Property for those exercises where it would be helpful.

Independent Practice

1. Use the array. Write four related multiplications and divisions.

$$\underline{4} \times \underline{9} = \underline{36}$$
$$\underline{9} \times \underline{4} = \underline{36}$$
$$\underline{36} \div \underline{4} = \underline{9}$$
$$\underline{36} \div \underline{9} = \underline{4}$$

2. Which property says that $8 \times 0 = 0$?
   a. Associative Property
   b. Commutative Property
   c. Distributive Property
   d. Zero Property *(circled)*

3. Which property says that $8 \times 9 = 9 \times 8$?
   a. Associative Property
   b. Commutative Property *(circled)*
   c. Distributive Property
   d. Zero Property

Find the product.

4. $1 \times 9 = \underline{9}$

5. $9 \times 2 = \underline{18}$

6. $3 \times 9 = \underline{27}$

7. $5 \times 9 = \underline{45}$

8. $9 \times 8 = \underline{72}$

9. $0 \times 9 = \underline{0}$

10. $9 \times 6 = \underline{54}$

11. $9 \times 9 = \underline{81}$

12. Which multiplication could you use to find *n*?
    $$24 \div 3 = n$$
    a. $8 \times 3 = 24$ *(circled)*
    b. $6 \times 4 = 24$
    c. $4 \times 6 = 24$
    d. $1 \times 24 = 24$

13. Which division could you use to find *n*?
    $$3 \times n = 12$$
    a. $12 \div 1 = 12$
    b. $12 \div 2 = 6$
    c. $12 \div 3 = 4$ *(circled)*
    d. $12 \div 6 = 2$

Writing About Math

▸ **Write a Narrative Text** Tell students that they will write a story about a new student in the class who has not learned multiplication and division strategies. The new student thinks that 3×5 and 5×3 are different problems so they cannot have the same product. Have students write a paragraph responding to the new student's misconception. Make sure students include strategies they would share with the new student.

When students are finished, ask for student volunteers to share their stories with the class.

Independent Practice

Divide. Write the related multiplication.

14. $18 \div 3 = \underline{6}$ The related multiplication is $\underline{3 \times 6 = 18}$.

15. $45 \div 5 = \underline{9}$ The related multiplication is $\underline{5 \times 9 = 45}$.

16. $64 \div 8 = \underline{8}$ The related multiplication is $\underline{8 \times 8 = 64}$.

17. $72 \div 9 = \underline{8}$ The related multiplication is $\underline{9 \times 8 = 72}$.

Find the product.

18. $8 \times 0 = \underline{0}$

19. $5 \times 1 = \underline{5}$

20. $8 \times 6 = \underline{48}$

21. $6 \times 3 = \underline{18}$

22. $9 \times 5 = \underline{45}$

23. $7 \times 6 = \underline{42}$

24.
$$\begin{array}{r} 4 \\ \times\ 2 \\ \hline 8 \end{array}$$

25.
$$\begin{array}{r} 0 \\ \times\ 6 \\ \hline 0 \end{array}$$

26.
$$\begin{array}{r} 4 \\ \times\ 4 \\ \hline 16 \end{array}$$

27.
$$\begin{array}{r} 8 \\ \times\ 7 \\ \hline 56 \end{array}$$

28.
$$\begin{array}{r} 7 \\ \times\ 1 \\ \hline 7 \end{array}$$

29.
$$\begin{array}{r} 2 \\ \times\ 5 \\ \hline 10 \end{array}$$

Find the quotient.

30. $24 \div 6 = \underline{4}$

31. $35 \div 7 = \underline{5}$

32. $42 \div 6 = \underline{7}$

33. $63 \div 7 = \underline{9}$

34. $45 \div 9 = \underline{5}$

35. $48 \div 8 = \underline{6}$

36. $3\overline{)12}$ quotient 4

37. $2\overline{)8}$ quotient 4

38. $1\overline{)9}$ quotient 9

39. $3\overline{)21}$ quotient 7

40. $6\overline{)54}$ quotient 9

41. $8\overline{)56}$ quotient 7

Unit 2 ■ Focus on Operations and Algebraic Thinking/Number and Operations in Base Ten   **85**

Teaching Tips

Items 14-17
Suggest that students use the multiplication table for these items to provide additional practice using different tools.

Items 18-41
It is important to present multiplication and division both vertically and horizontally. Watch for students who struggle when different formats are presented.

Digital Connection

Music Videos Use a search engine to find music videos or songs about multiplication or division strategies or the Commutative and Distributive Properties of Multiplication. Provide lyrics for the songs, if possible, and have students sing along. Have students watch these videos and then vote on which one they liked best.

Independent Practice

Common Errors

Item 43

When using the Distributive Property, some students may reverse the multiplication and addition symbols, such as $4 \times 7 = (2 + 7) \times (2 + 7)$. Remind students about the general structure of the Distributive Property. Have students identify that they have made an error by asking them if their answer is reasonable.

Teaching Tips

Items 42–45

For each item, have students explain their reasons for using specific strategies. Ask them to validate using models or have students discuss which strategy works best and why.

Independent Practice

MP6 **42.** Tell how you would find m. Then solve.

$m = 7 \times 9$

Possible answers: I can use the Commutative Property since I know that $9 \times 7 = 63$; I can use the Distributive Property because $7 \times (6 + 3) = (7 \times 6) + (7 \times 3)$, which equals $42 + 21$, or 63; I can draw a 7×9 array and count the squares or objects.

Answer $\underline{63} = 7 \times 9$

MP7 **43.** Marcus knows that $2 \times 7 = 14$. How can he use that fact to find the answer to 4×7?

Possible answer: Marcus can use the Distributive Property because $4 \times 7 = (2 + 2) \times 7$ and that equals $(2 \times 7) + (2 \times 7)$. He knows that $2 \times 7 = 14$, so $4 \times 7 = 14 + 14$, or 28.

Answer $4 \times 7 = \underline{28}$

MP8 **44.** Simone knows that 8 groups of 6 make 48. How can she find $48 \div 6$?

Possible answer: If 8 groups of 6 equals 48, then 48 divided by 6 equals 8. Simone can also write the multiplication fact $8 \times 6 = 48$ and use it to find the quotient.

Answer $48 \div 6 = \underline{8}$

Solve the problems.

MP2 **45.** The school band has 9 rows, with 9 students in each row. How many students are in the band?

▭▬· **Show your work.**

Students should use any strategy to find that $9 \times 9 = 81$.

Answer There are 81 students in the band.

Mathematical Practices

MP2	**Reason abstractly and quantitatively.**
Item 45: Students use different strategies to multiply.	
MP6	**Attend to precision.**
Item 42: Students communicate their multiplication process and strategy.	
MP7	**Look for and make use of structure.**
Item 43: Students evaluate the structure of the problem.	
MP8	**Look for and express regularity in repeated reasoning.**
Item 44: Students generalize by relating multiplication and division.	

MORE ONLINE sadlierconnect.com

Independent Practice

MP1 **46.** For a long camping trip, the Rubio family packed 42 apples. Mr. and Mrs. Rubio and their four children will each eat one apple a day. How many days will it take the Rubio family to eat all the apples?

✏️ **Show your work.**
Students should use any strategy to find that $42 \div 6 = 7$.

Answer It will take 7 days for the Rubio family to eat all the apples.

MP7 **47.** Rey says that for the equation $472 = ? \times 472$, the unknown is 1. Is he correct?

Answer Yes; $472 = 1 \times 472$

✏️ **Justify your answer using words, drawings, or numbers.**
Possible justification: I know Rey is correct because the product of any number times 1 equals that number.

MP3 **48.** Chiyo knows that $2 \times 8 = 16$. She uses this fact to find that $16 = 8 \div 2$. Is her answer correct? Explain your thinking.

Answer No, Chiyo's answer is not correct; $8 \div 2 = 4$.

✏️ **Justify your answer using words, drawings, or numbers.**
Students' work should show an understanding that Chiyo tried to undo the multiplication, but she mixed up the division sign and the equals sign.

Unit 2 ■ Focus on Operations and Algebraic Thinking/Number and Operations in Base Ten **87**

Common Errors

Item 46

Some students may use the numbers they see in the problem and try to divide 42 by 4. Point out that the Rubio family includes Mr. and Mrs. Rubio and four children.

Teaching Tips

Item 47

Remind students that according to the Identity Property, the product of any number and 1 is that number. After students correctly answer the question, challenge them to think of other equations to illustrate the Identity Property where one factor is a 3-digit number.

Mathematical Practices	
MP1	**Make sense of problems and persevere in solving them.**
Item 46: Students analyze a real world problem and plan a solution.	
MP3	**Construct viable arguments and critique the reasoning of others.**
Item 48: Students explain a plan to solve a problem using words, drawings, or numbers.	
MP7	**Look for and make use of structure.**
Item 47: Students use the pattern of multiplying by 1 to determine an unknown factor.	

Guided Instruction

Common Core Focus:

3.OA.8 Solve two-step word problems using the four operations. Represent these problems using equations with a letter standing for the unknown quantity. Assess the reasonableness of answers using mental computation and estimation strategies including rounding.

OBJECTIVE

Use the four operations to solve two-step word problems.

ESSENTIAL QUESTION

Students have previously used the four operations to solve word problems with one step. This lesson builds on this knowledge to include the use of two steps. Students will also use their knowledge of equations and solving for the unknown number to solve problems.

FLUENCY PRACTICE

Fluency practice is available at **sadlierconnect.com**.

Concept Development

Understand: Solving a two-step word problem

■ For success in this problem-solving lesson, students should be comfortable performing operations in the conventional order (left to right), and also applying the Commutative and Associative Properties of Addition and Multiplication to simplify operations.

■ Students will build upon previous problem-solving knowledge to solve two-step problems. Making the transition from one step to two steps can be daunting for some students. It is important that students be presented with multiple problem-solving strategies.

■ Ask students to explain how the use of parentheses was helpful in checking the answer to the problem.

Lesson 10 — Problem Solving: Two-Step Problems

Guided Instruction

Essential Question:
How can you use two steps to solve a problem?
3.OA.8

Words to Know:
operations
estimation
compatible numbers

In this lesson you will learn how to solve word problems with two steps.

Understand: Solving a two-step word problem

> The Maroni family bought 3 lunches for $5 each and 1 lunch for $7. How much did the lunches cost in all?

Read to find the information and the question.

> 3 lunches cost $5 each and 1 lunch cost $7.
> What is the cost of all the lunches?

Plan how to find the answer.

Draw a diagram to represent the problem.

Total cost of the lunches			
$5	$5	$5	$7

You can use the diagram and two operations to find the total cost.

> First find the cost of the three $5 lunches. Multiply. ← $3 \times \$5$
> Then add the cost of the $7 lunch. ← $+ \$7$

Solve the problem.

> $3 \times \$5 = \$15$
> $\$15 + \$7 = \$22$

> You use two steps to find the answer, so this is a two-step word problem.

➡ The lunches cost $22 in all.

Check your work. Make sure your solution answers the question in the problem.

You can work backward to check whether the answer is reasonable.

Start at the end and work back to the beginning.

> $\$22 - (\$7 + \$5 + \$5 + \$5)$ should equal 0.
> $\$22 - \$22 = 0$

The check shows that the answer is reasonable.

Words to Know

operations: mathematical processes, such as addition, subtraction, multiplication, and division

estimation: a strategy used to determine an approximate answer

compatible numbers: numbers that can be easily added, subtracted, multiplied, or divided

Glossary can be found on pp. 347–350.

Lesson 10

Guided Instruction

Understand: Checking that an answer is reasonable

> Greenmount School has 627 students. One day, 48 students are absent. Another 103 students are on a field trip. How many students are at the school that day?

First read to find the information you will need to solve the problem. Ask the question in your own words.

> The school has 627 students. 48 are absent. 103 are on a field trip. How many students are at the school?

Next plan what you will do and how you will find the answer.

Use a diagram to represent the problem.

Find the number of students that are not at the school. Add. ← 48 + 103

Then subtract the sum from 627. ← 627 − (48 + 103)

627 students		
48 absent	103 on trip	?

Write an equation. Let ■ be the number of students at the school. Solve to find the answer.

$$■ = 627 − (48 + 103)$$
$$■ = 627 − \underline{151}$$
$$■ = 476$$

➡ There are __476__ students at the school that day.

Check your work. Use estimation with compatible numbers, to see whether the answer makes sense. Compatible numbers are numbers that are easy to add and subtract.

Estimate: 627 − (48 + 103) should be close to

$$600 − (50 + 100) = 600 − 150 = 450$$

> 627 is close to 600.
> 48 is close to 50.
> 103 is close to 100.

Compare the answer and the estimate.

476 is close to 450, so the answer __makes__ sense.

Understand: Checking that an answer is reasonable

■ As students move through the problem-solving process, they are asked to use a symbol to represent an unknown number. In a previous lesson, students used a symbol or letter to represent the unknown number. As students progress, the use of a letter to represent the unknown number will occur with more regularity.

■ Using parentheses can be a stumbling block for some students. These same students may only subtract the first number in the parentheses and add the second number. Remind students that the operation within the parentheses must be performed first in this equation.

■ Using estimation allows students to quickly gauge the reasonableness of their answers. This is the first lesson where they use estimation with compatible numbers. Some students may recognize that rounding to the nearest ten would produce the same estimate, but rounding to the nearest 100 would be less accurate.

■ If students are struggling with estimation with compatible numbers, take some time to practice. Give students examples of pairs of numbers and discuss which compatible numbers could be used. Encourage students to share why they chose the compatible numbers they did.

Support English Language Learners

Word problems can be challenging for English language learners. Students have to understand both the mathematical operations involved, as well as the language to make sense of the problem.

If necessary, read aloud problems and help students identify necessary key words from each word problem before they start. Tell them to look for words and phrases such as *in all, fewer than, total,* or *left,* explaining that these are clues to which operations to use. Encourage students to create a list of these words and their corresponding operation. Have them add to this list as they encounter new key words and phrases in the word problems.

Guided Instruction

Connect: Why checking your answer is important when solving a problem Use this page to help reinforce the importance of checking the reasonableness of an answer.

■ Presenting a wide range of word problems helps students build an understanding of which operation to use in a given situation. Developing a problem-solving plan, like the one presented here, can be used for any operation or sequence of operations.

■ Remind students that there are several different ways to check their answers, such as drawing a model or working backward. As a group, come up with a list of different ways to check the answer of a problem. You may wish to post this list for students to use as a reference for future problem-solving activities.

■ Guide students through what a reasonable answer is and what an unreasonable answer is by giving examples of both. Explain to students that *reasonable* does not mean the answer is correct, but it may help students identify if they made an error. Encourage students to create a definition for reasonable as it relates to mathematical problem solving.

■ Have students explain why Step 4 is important. Students should explain that by checking the answer, they can determine if they made an error and, if necessary, correct the answer.

Guided Instruction

Connect: Why checking your answer is important when solving a problem

> Kimi made 20 popcorn balls for a party. She ate 2 popcorn balls and put the rest in bags of 3 each. How many bags of popcorn balls does Kimi have?

Step 1

Read to find what the problem is asking. Then find the information you need.

Kimi made __20__ popcorn balls.

Kimi ate __2__ popcorn balls.

Kimi put the rest in bags of __3__ each.

How many ___bags of popcorn balls___ does she have?

Step 2

Plan how to use two steps to find the answer.

First find the number of popcorn balls Kimi put into bags of 3 each. Draw a diagram.

Then find the number of bags.

20 popcorn balls	
ate 2	? left to put in bags of 3

Step 3

Solve the problem.

$20 - 2 = $ __18__

$18 \div 3 = $ __6__

 Kimi has __6__ bags of popcorn balls.

Step 4

Explain how to check your answer. Possible explanations: I know that 20 − 2 is 18 so I could draw an array to see if I can make 6 equal groups of 3. I could work backward and multiply 6 × 3 to get 18 and then add 2 to get 20, which is the number of popcorn balls Kimi made.

90   Unit 2 ■ Focus on Operations and Algebraic Thinking/Number and Operations in Base Ten

---

Math-to-English Connection

Using Precise Words It is very important when writing to use precise language. When solving word problems, it is important to know whether the problem is asking for an exact or an estimated answer.

Words such as *about, approximately,* and *almost* are used to indicate an estimate. Have students use a thesaurus to make a list of 10 synonyms for the word *approximately.* Then, have them choose three of those synonyms and use each word in a sentence.

Guided Practice

1. Riley has 9 crayons. Terrell has twice as many crayons as Riley. How many crayons do they have in all?

    a. Read to understand. What is the question?

    How many crayons do Riley and Terrell have in all?

    b. Explain how you plan to solve the problem. Possible answer:

    I can draw a diagram to see what operations to use. The diagram shows

    that I need to add 9 and 2×9.

Total number of crayons	
Riley: 9	Terrell: 2×9

    c. Then solve to find the answer.
    Possible answer: $\blacksquare = 9 + (2 \times 9)$
    $= 9 + 18$
    $= 27$

    Riley and Terrell have __27__ crayons in all.

    d. Check to show that your answer makes sense. Explain your reasoning.
    Possible answer:

    | | | | | | | | | | | | | | | | | | | | | | | | | | |

    The 27 lines show the crayons. I can make 1 group of 9 and 2 groups of 9 and there are none left over. So the answer makes sense.

Think•Pair•Share

MP1 2. Write a two-step word problem. Then find the answer. Check that your answer is reasonable. Possible answer: There are 14 girls and 12 boys in our class. Two students are absent today. How many students are here? $14 + 12 = 26$; $26 - 2 = 24$; 24 students are here. Check: I can work backward to see if I get 0. $24 + 2 = 26$; $26 - 12 = 14$; $14 - 14 = 0$.

Unit 2 ■ Focus on Operations and Algebraic Thinking/Number and Operations in Base Ten **91**

Mathematical Practices

Mathematical Practice Standards underline the teaching and understanding of all concepts and skills presented. The emphasis of specific practices is noted throughout the guided and independent practice of this lesson.

MP1 **Make sense of problems and persevere in solving them.**

Item 2: Students create their own problems, solve them, and then check their answers for reasonableness.

Observational Assessment

Use page 91 to assess whether students are able to solve two-step word problems and to check that their answers are reasonable. There are many steps involved in this process, so it is critical to determine the point where a student is having difficulty. Some students will struggle from determining what information they need to solve the problem, while other students may struggle to check their work.

Think•Pair•Share

Peer Collaboration Ask each pair of students to trade their two-step word problems and solve each other's problem. If a student gets an incorrect answer, have the student identify the mistake and correct it. Have the student explain how the error was made. After pairs have completed their solutions and checks, have them share their work with the class. As students present their problems, ask:

- *What steps and operations were used in the problem?*

- *How did you solve the problem? Did you use a model? An equation?*

- *How did you check that your answer was reasonable?*

Remind students that there may be more than one way to solve a two-step problem. There may also be more than one way to check an answer.

Return to the Essential Question

Reread the Lesson 10 Essential Question on page 88: *How can you use two steps to solve a problem?*

Ask volunteers to use what they learned in this lesson to answer this question. (Possible response: I can break the problem apart into two steps and solve one step at a time.)

Have students share their responses. Discuss with students the steps involved in developing a plan to solve word problems.

Independent Practice

Concept Application

Students may work independently on these pages in the classroom or at home. They may refer to the first four pages of the lesson to revisit the instruction or to see a worked-out example.

Common Errors and **Teaching Tips** may help you support student learning either in the classroom or as a follow-up for work done at home.

Teaching Tips

Items 1-2

Students will use various strategies to solve the problems. Some students may require some guidance on choosing an appropriate strategy. Continuously remind students of the importance of checking the reasonableness of their answers.

Lesson 10 Problem Solving: Two-Step Problems

Independent Practice

Follow the steps to solve the problems.

MP4 1. On a vacation, the Jones family travels 722 miles in three days. They travel 328 miles the first day and 115 miles the second day. How many miles do they travel on the third day?

a. Read. What information is in the problem?
The family travels 328 miles the first day, 115 miles the second day, and 722 miles in three days.

b. Plan. What will you do? Possible answer: I can draw a diagram to see what operations to use. The diagram shows that I need to add 328 and 115 and subtract the sum from 722.

722		
328	115	?

Remember to label your answer.

c. Solve. What is your answer?
Possible answer: 328 + 115 = 443
722 − 443 = 279

Answer The family traveled __279 miles__ on the third day.

d. Check. Explain why your answer is reasonable.
Possible answer: I can estimate. 722 is about 700 miles; 328 is about 300 miles; 115 miles is about 100 miles; 700 − (300 + 100) = 700 − 400, or 300; 300 miles and 279 miles are close, so the answer is reasonable.

MP1 2. Taylor has 4 packages of stickers. Each package has 10 stickers in it. Leah has 14 fewer stickers than Taylor. How many stickers does Leah have?

a. Read. Underline the information you need. See possible answer above.

b. Plan. What will you do? Possible answer: I need to find the number of stickers Taylor has. Then I need to subtract 14 to find the number of stickers Leah has.

c. Solve. What is your answer?
Possible answer: 4 × 10 = 40
40 − 14 = 26

Answer Leah has __26__ stickers.

d. Check. Explain why your answer is reasonable.
Possible explanation: I can estimate. 4 × 10 is 40; 14 is close to 10; 40 − 10 = 30; 26 and 30 are close, so 26 stickers is a reasonable answer.

92 Unit 2 ■ Focus on Operations and Algebraic Thinking/Number and Operations in Base Ten

Copyright © by William H. Sadlier, Inc. All rights reserved.

Mathematical Practices

MP1	**Make sense of problems and persevere in solving them.**

Items 2 and 4: Students plan how to solve the problem and then check their work after solving.

MP2	**Reason abstractly and quantitatively.**

Item 3: Students use reasoning to solve the word problem.

MP4	**Model with mathematics.**

Item 1: Students may draw a diagram as a step toward solving a word problem.

Lesson 10

Independent Practice

MP2 **3.** At a basketball tournament, each of the 8 teams has 9 players and a coach. There are 100 bottles of water. How many bottles of water are left over after each player and coach get 1 bottle?

    a. Read to find the information in the problem.
There are 8 teams. Each team has 9 players and 1 coach. There are 100 bottles of water.

    b. Plan what you will do.
Possible answer: I need to find the number of players and coaches. Then I need to subtract that number from 100.

    c. Solve to find the answer.
Possible answer: $8 \times (9 + 1) = 8 \times 10$, or 80
$100 - 80 = 20$

> What label will you use for your answer?

    Answer There will be __20 bottles__ of water left over.

    d. Explain why your answer makes sense.
Possible answer: $8 \times 9 = 72$ players. $8 \times 1 = 8$ coaches. $72 + 8 = 80$ people who got a bottle of water; $100 - 20 = 80$ bottles of water used. $80 = 80$, so the answer makes sense.

MP1 **4.** Mikhail has 48 stamps. His uncle gives him 15 more. The pages in his small stamp book have spaces for 9 stamps. How many pages can he fill with the stamps he has now?

    a. As you read, underline the information you need. See possible answer above.

    b. What is your plan? Possible answer: I need to add $48 + 15$ to find the total number of stamps. Then I need to divide that number by 9 to find the number of pages Mikhail can fill.

    c. Solve to answer the question.
Possible answer: $48 + 15 = 63$
$63 \div 9 = 7$

    Answer Mikhail can fill __7 pages__ with his stamps.

    d. Explain why your answer is reasonable.
Possible explanation: I can estimate. 48 is close to 50; 15 is close to 20; $50 + 20 = 70$; 9 is close to 10; $70 \div 10 = 7$. The answer and the estimate are the same, so 7 pages is a reasonable answer.

Unit 2 ■ Focus on Operations and Algebraic Thinking/Number and Operations in Base Ten **93**

Common Errors

Item 3
Students may scan the problem, looking only for numbers, and may overlook the fact that each team also has a coach. Remind students to add the coach to each team's count.

Teaching Tips

Item 4
This problem asks students to underline the information they need. This is a good problem-solving skill for struggling students. If needed, have students use this strategy while solving other word problems.

Writing About Math

▸ **Write an Explanatory Text** Ask students to write a two-step word problem and step-by-step instructions on how to solve the problem. Students may want to follow a structure similar to the presentations in this book, as if they were the authors. Encourage students to include illustrations to aid comprehension.

Ask volunteers to share their word problems and their solutions.

Independent Practice

Common Errors

Item 5

Because it does not specifically ask to calculate how many marbles Trane keeps, some students may not take that into account when solving this problem. Make sure students determine the number of marbles Trane keeps before comparing all the numbers.

Teaching Tips

Items 6-7

Some students may struggle with how to get started with solving these word problems. Have these students underline the information they need. Make sure students show their work for each problem.

Independent Practice

MP2 **5.** Trane has 145 marbles. He gives 20 to Katie, 52 to Gwen, and 31 to Yusef. He keeps the rest. Who has the most marbles?

    a. Trane

    b. Katie

    (**c.**) Gwen

    d. Yusef

Solve the problems. Check that your answer is reasonable.

MP4 **6.** Erica planted 9 zinnias each in 2 big pots. She planted another 49 zinnias, one in each small pot. How many zinnias did she plant in all?

▬▬▶ **Show your work.**

Possible answer: $9 \times 2 = 18$; $18 + 49 = 67$

Answer Erica planted 67 zinnias in all.

MP6 **7.** For the school play, most of the chairs are in rows of 10 each, with one row of 8 chairs. If there are 78 chairs altogether, how many rows are there?

▬▬▶ **Show your work.**

Possible answer: $78 - 8 = 70$; $70 \div 10 = 7$ or $7 \times 10 = 70$. There is 1 row of 8 chairs and 7 rows of 10 chairs each for a total of 8 rows.

Answer There are 8 rows of chairs.

Mathematical Practices

MP2	**Reason abstractly and quantitatively.**
Item 5: Students solve the problem by reasoning quantitatively.	
MP4	**Model with mathematics.**
Item 6: Students show how they solved the word problem.	
MP6	**Attend to precision.**
Item 7: Students solve the word problem then check their answer for reasonableness.	

MORE ONLINE sadlierconnect.com   Lesson 10

Independent Practice

MP3   **8.** Mr. Cook bakes 6 pans of fruit bars for a bake sale. He cuts each pan into 9 bars. He eats one bar and wraps 5 to go in his freezer. He puts the rest in a box to take to the bake sale. How many fruit bars does Mr. Cook take to the bake sale?

▬▶ **Show your work.**
Possible answer: $6 \times 9 = 54$
               $54 - (1 + 5) = 54 - 6$, or 48

Answer _Mr. Cook takes 48 fruit bars to the bake sale._

MP1   **9.** When Sean adds $202 + 124 + 192$, he finds that the sum is 518. To check his work, he estimates that the sum is about 600. He sees that his estimate does not agree with his answer. Which is correct, Sean's answer or his estimate?

Answer _Sean's answer is correct, but his estimate is not._

▬▶ **Justify your answer using words, drawings, or numbers.**
Possible justification: The estimate is not correct because 202 is close to 200, 124 is close to 100, and 192 is close to 200. Adding $200 + 100 + 200$ gives 500. So, the sum is about 500, not 600. Since 500 is close to 518, 518 is a reasonable answer.

MP3   **10.** Farah and her aunt are making 3 batches of jam. Each batch makes 7 jars of jam. To be sure there are enough jars, Farah's aunt wants to have 2 extra jars ready for each batch. How many jars does Farah need to get ready for the 3 batches?

▬▶ **Show your work.**
Possible answer: $3 \times 7 = 21$
               $3 \times 2 = 6$
               $21 + 6 = 27$

Answer _Farah needs to get 27 jam jars ready._

Unit 2 ■ Focus on Operations and Algebraic Thinking/Number and Operations in Base Ten   **95**

Teaching Tips

Items 8 and 10
In each of these problems, students are presented with a lot of information at one time. Make sure students take the time to plan how to use each piece of information. Some students will read the first sentence and begin solving without reading the whole problem. Remind students to read the problem in its entirety, first.

Item 9
In this problem, Sean estimated incorrectly. Use this as an opportunity to review compatible numbers and how important it is to use the best numbers when estimating.

Mathematical Practices	
MP1	**Make sense of problems and persevere in solving them.**

Item 9: Students decide whether an answer or an estimate is correct and then justify why the estimate is wrong.

MP3	**Construct viable arguments and critique the reasoning of others.**

Items 8 and 10: Students decide on the best way to solve the problems.

Common Core Focus:

3.OA.8 Solve two-step word problems using the four operations. Represent these problems using equations with a letter standing for the unknown quantity. Assess the reasonableness of answers using mental computation and estimation strategies including rounding.

OBJECTIVE

Write an equation to solve a two-step word problem.

ESSENTIAL QUESTION

This lesson continues to expand students' knowledge of solving two-step problems. Students continue to progress using algebraic language by using a letter for an unknown quantity. Determining information, planning to solve the two-step word problem, and checking the reasonableness of an answer are reinforced from the previous lesson.

FLUENCY PRACTICE

Fluency practice is available at **sadlierconnect.com**.

Concept Development

Understand: Writing an equation for a two-step word problem

■ Students continue to develop an understanding that an equation can be used to solve a two-step word problem. Students must be able to decipher the information provided in the word problem. Provide students with opportunities to read the problem and determine which information is essential in solving the problem.

■ Model highlighting or underlining information from the problem as in the previous lesson. Ask students to share the important information in the problem.

Lesson 11 — Problem Solving: Use Equations

Essential Question: How can you use an equation to solve a problem? 3.OA.8

Guided Instruction

In this lesson you will learn how to write an equation to represent a word problem.

Understand: Writing an equation for a two-step word problem

> Reid buys a box of crayons for 75¢ and 3 stickers for 8¢ each. What is the total cost of these items?

Read to find the information and the question.

The crayons cost 75¢ and the stickers each cost 8¢.
What is the total cost of the items?

Plan how to find the answer. Write an equation.

total cost of items = cost of crayons + cost of stickers ← Start with words.
t = 75¢ + (3 × 8¢) ← Represent the words.

Solve the equation to find the total cost.

$t = 75¢ + (3 × 8¢)$
$t = 75¢ + 24¢$ ← Multiply 3 × 8.
$t = 99¢$ ← Add 75 + 24.

▶ The total cost of the items is 99¢.

Estimate to check your answer.

75¢ is close to 80¢.
8¢ + 8¢ + 8¢ is 24¢, which is close to 20¢.
80¢ + 20¢ = 100¢.

Comparing 100¢ and 99¢ shows that the estimate and the answer are very close to each other.

This means that 99¢ is a reasonable answer.

Support English Language Learners

Take this opportunity to reinforce language that is key to word problems, but is challenging for English language learners. Students must understand both the mathematical operations to be performed in a word problem, and also the language to comprehend what the word problem is asking.

For this particular lesson, review the word *unknown*. Ask students to define *unknown* in their own words. Next, write a word problem on the board and ask students to determine what is unknown in the problem.

Guided Instruction

Understand: Using diagrams in solving two-step word problems

> Sabrena bikes 3 miles a day. Her goal is to bike 25 miles. After 6 days, how many more miles must Sabrena bike to meet her goal?

After you read, describe the problem in words.

> number of miles more
> equals 25 miles minus 6 days times 3 miles a day

Use the words to write an equation.

Represent the words with numbers and symbols.

$m = 25 - (6 \times 3)$ ← Use m to represent the number of miles more

Solve the equation to find the answer.

$m = 25 - (6 \times 3)$

$m = 25 - 18$ ← Multiply 6×3.

$m = 7$ ← Subtract: $25 - 18$.

➡ Sabrena must bike __7__ more miles to meet her goal.

Draw a number line to check your answer.

6 times 3 equals 18, and 18 plus 7 equals 25.

▬▬· Look at the problem. Find another way to solve it.
Possible answer: I could draw a diagram to see what operations to use to solve the problem.

Unit 2 ▪ Focus on Operations and Algebraic Thinking/Number and Operations in Base Ten **97**

Math-to-Social Studies Connection

Maps Students study maps and routes traveled in social studies. Discuss that people not only use maps for ways to travel, but maps are also a resource for determining distances between two locations. Generally in the U.S., miles is the unit of measurement for longer distances, such as the distance between cities. In several of the problems provided in this lesson, students are asked to find distance in miles. Use a city or county map and have students write their own word problems using the distance between two locations.

Understand: Using diagrams in solving two-step word problems

■ In this presentation, students are offered another problem-solving strategy to solve a two-step word problem. Here, students start by describing the problem in their own words in order to better understand the information provided. As the process continues, these words are converted to numbers, mathematical operations, and a letter for an unknown quantity.

■ Guide students through the steps of the problem. Remind students what m represents in this problem. Ask students why 6×3 is grouped together in the equation. Then ask students why 18 is subtracted from 25 to find the unknown quantity.

■ Help students understand that a number line can be an effective model to check the reasonableness of an answer. The steps in the problem can be used in sequence and labeled on the number line.

■ Model and encourage students to use different colors on the number line to illustrate the multiple steps used to solve the word problem.

✏▬· After students have answered this question, ask volunteers to read their answers aloud. Remind students that there are multiple strategies for solving word problems. As students share examples of strategies they used, create a poster of effective problem-solving strategies, focusing on the use of diagrams.

Guided Instruction

Connect: Using a diagram and writing an equation Use this page to help students strengthen their understanding of how the use of diagrams and written equations can help solve a two-step word problem.

■ The lesson reinforces the problem-solving strategy of underlining key information in a word problem. In this lesson, this strategy is used in conjunction with drawing a diagram to organize the information. Remind students that there are multiple ways to solve problems, and it is appropriate to use multiple strategies to organize information.

■ Guide students to connect the information from the diagram to each part of the equation. Be sure students notice that each part of the equation is the same color as the corresponding numbers and labels in the diagram. This color-coordination can be used as a strategy to keep information organized.

■ Ask students to explain why 32 is subtracted from 68 to find the unknown quantity *r*. Students should explain that 32 is the total number of rocks in the small boxes. Subtracting this amount from 68 will indicate how many rocks are in the fifth box.

■ Have students discuss or explain why an answer to a problem involves not only a number, but also a label. Explain that there can be more than one kind of item in a problem, like the rocks and boxes in this presentation. Students need to determine which label goes with the solution to the problem. Labels can also help guide students to a solution by understanding what information they need to find.

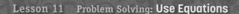

Lesson 11   Problem Solving: **Use Equations**

Guided Instruction

Connect: Using a diagram and writing an equation

> The 68 rocks in John's rock collection are stored in 5 boxes. Four small boxes hold 8 rocks each. The fifth box is larger and holds the rest of the rocks. How many rocks are in the fifth box?

Step 1

Read the problem again and underline the information you need.

Step 2

Draw a diagram to help plan your work.

The diagram shows how you can write an equation.

number of rocks in larger box = number of rocks in all − 4 boxes of 8 rocks

r = 68 − (4 × 8)

Step 3

Solve the equation to find the answer.

$r = 68 − (4 × 8)$

$r = 68 − \underline{32}$

$r = \underline{36}$

➡ There are ___36 rocks___ in the fifth box.

> What label should you use for your answer?

Step 4

Check that your answer is reasonable.

Estimate.   68 is close to _70_. 8 is close to 10, and 4 × 10 = _40_.

70 − 40 = _30_
Compare 30 and 36.
36 is close to 30, so 36 is a _reasonable_ answer.

98   Unit 2 ■ Focus on Operations and Algebraic Thinking/Number and Operations in Base Ten

Reading About Math

Interpret Information Ask students to recall the difference between statements and questions. In a word problem, information is provided through the use of both statements and questions. The beginning sentences are often statements that provide necessary information needed to solve the problem. The word problem usually ends with a question that helps the reader determine how to answer the problem.

Have students identify the statements and questions in the presentations on the first four pages of the lesson. Then have them write their own word problems using the format of two to three statements with numerical information followed by a question.

Lesson 11

Guided Practice

1. The Durands are driving 900 miles to visit their cousins. The first day they drive 385 miles. The second day they drive 319 miles. How many miles do they have left to drive?

   a. Read the problem again. Underline information and the question.

   b. Explain how you plan to solve the problem.
   Possible answer: I can write an equation. $d = 900 - (385 + 319)$

   c. Solve to find the answer.
   Possible answer: $d = 900 - (385 + 319)$
   $= 900 - 704$
   $= 196$

   d. Explain how you can check to show that your answer makes sense.
   Possible explanation: I used mental math. 385 is close to 400 and 319 is close to 300. $400 + 300 = 700$. $900 - 700 = 200$. 196 is close to 200, so 196 miles makes sense.

   Answer The Durands have ___196 miles___ left to drive.

   ### ☙ Think•Pair•Share

   MP7 2. One way to solve a two-step problem is to find and solve the two one-step problems that are inside the two-step problem. Look at problem 1. Explain what the two one-step problems are and solve them. Compare your answer with your answer to problem 1.
   Possible answer: One problem is to find how far they drive on the first two days, which is 704 miles. The second problem is to find how far they have left to drive. This is the difference between 704 and 900 miles, which is 196 miles. The answers are the same.

Unit 2 ■ Focus on Operations and Algebraic Thinking/Number and Operations in Base Ten **99**

Mathematical Practices

Mathematical Practice Standards underline the teaching and understanding of all concepts and skills presented. The emphasis of specific practices is noted throughout the guided and independent practice of this lesson.

| MP7 | **Look for and make use of structure.** |

Item 2: Students decompose a two-step problem into two one-step problems.

Observational Assessment

Use page 99 to assess whether students are able to write an equation to solve a two-step word problem given the information provided. Take notice to which students fail to underline key information in the word problem.

☙ Think•Pair•Share

Peer Collaboration Break the class into pairs. Ask each student pair to find the two one-step problems that are inside the two-step problem. Have students share the problems they find with their partners. Ask students the following questions.

- *What are the two one-step problems found within the two-step problem?*

- *Which problem needs to be solved first? Why?*

- *How did the strategy of determining two one-step problems help you solve Problem 1?*

Return to the Essential Question

Reread the Lesson 11 Essential Question on page 96: *How can you use an equation to solve a problem?*

Ask volunteers to use what they learned in this lesson to answer the question. (Possible response: I can use an equation to help me plan how to solve the problem. I can use words to explain the problem and replace the words with numbers, symbols, and a variable for the unknown number. I can also make a diagram to help me write an equation.)

Independent Practice

Concept Application

Students may work independently on these pages in the classroom or at home. They may refer to the first four pages of the lesson to revisit the instruction or to see a worked-out example.

Common Errors and **Teaching Tips** may help you support student learning either in the classroom or as a follow-up for work done at home.

Common Errors

Items 1–3

The equations provided in the answer choices for each problem have minor differences. Students might be slightly inaccurate in their choice. Encourage students to re-write the problem in words or make a diagram to write the appropriate equation.

Independent Practice

Circle the letter of the correct answer.

1. Xavier shoots 75 baskets on Monday and 110 baskets on Tuesday. His goal is to shoot a total of 500 baskets by the end of the week. How many baskets does he have left to shoot?

   Which equation could you use to solve this problem?

   a. $75 + 110 = b + 500$

   b. $110 - 75 + b = 500$

   c. $75 + 100 - b = 500$

   d. $75 + 110 + b = 500$

2. In Natalie's class, August has 3 times as many birthdays as February. September has 2 fewer birthdays than August. There are 4 birthdays in February. How many birthdays are in September?

   Which equation could you use to solve this problem?

   a. $3 \times 4 = s$

   b. $(3 \times 4) - 2 = s$

   c. $(3 \times 4) + 2 = s$

   d. $3 \times 4 \times 2 = s$

3. Taren bikes 2 miles to school each day, and 2 miles back home. How many miles does Taren bike in 5 days?

   Which equation could you use to solve this problem?

   a. $5 \times (2 + 2) = t$

   b. $5 \times (2 - 2) = t$

   c. $2 + (2 \times t) = 5$

   d. $2 + 5 + t = 10$

Digital Connection

Equation Videos Use a search engine to locate how-to videos on solving two-step equations for Grade 3. Students can watch the various videos at home to reinforce the concept. Provide a list of links to these videos or post on your classroom website for students and family to access.

Independent Practice

As you read each problem, underline information you need. Follow the steps to solve. Show your work.

MP2 **4.** Jia-li needs 32 trading cards to fill her album. Each of 4 friends gives her 6 cards. How many more cards does Jia-li need?

    a. What information helps you write an equation?
        Possible answer: 4 × 6 cards plus how many cards equals 32 cards?

    b. Write and solve an equation.
        Possible answer: $4 \times 6 + c = 32$; $24 + c = 32$; $c = 32 - 24$; $c = 8$

    c. Check your answer. Does it make sense? Explain.
        Answers will vary. Students might draw a number line to show that 4 groups of 6 cards each equal 24. They can then use the number line to find the difference between 24 and 32 to get the answer, 8.

    Answer Jia-li needs __8__ more cards.

MP1 **5.** Five hundred seventy-nine students are at school today. Three hundred fifteen students rode the bus, ninety-four rode to school in a car, and the rest walked to school. How many students walked to school today?

    a. What information can you use to write an equation?
        Possible answer: number of students who walked equals 579 minus the sum of 315 and 94.

    b. Write and solve an equation to find the answer.
        Possible answer: $w = 579 - (315 + 94)$
                $= 579 - 409$
                $= 170$

    c. Check to show that your answer is reasonable.
        Possible answer: 579 is close to 600
                     315 is close to 300,
                     94 is close to 100
                     $300 + 100 = 400$
                     $600 - 400 = 200$
        200 is close to 170, so the answer is reasonable.

    Answer Today, __170__ students walked to school.

Common Errors
Item 4
Some students may misinterpret or omit information, and incorrectly record the equation as $c + 6 = 32$. Point out that "each of 4 friends gives her 6 cards" means *4 × 6 cards*. So, the equation can be written as $4 \times 6 + c = 32$, or $c = 32 - (4 \times 6)$.

Teaching Tips
Items 4 and 5
Remind students that following the provided steps will allow them to better understand and solve the word problem. Recommend that students follow the order of these steps for other problems.

Mathematical Practices	
MP1	**Make sense of problems and persevere in solving them.**

Item 5: Students identify useful information, write an equation to solve the problem, and check the reasonableness of their answers.

MP2	**Reason abstractly and quantitatively.**

Item 4: Students solve an equation and explain the reasonableness of their answers.

Common Errors

Items 6 and 7

Students may be confused about which mathematical operations to perform for each problem, since there are multiple steps. Remind students to look for keywords within each problem and to show their work.

Teaching Tips

Items 6 and 7

Drawing a visual model can help a student solve a word problem. Encourage students to draw a visual model to illustrate the problem.

Independent Practice

Write an equation to solve. Tell how you checked your answer.

MP4 **6.** A delivery truck was carrying 136 packages. At the next stop, 25 packages were dropped off and 13 packages were picked up. How many packages did the truck carry then?

Show your work.

Possible answer: $136 - 25 + 13 = p$; $111 + 13 = p$; $124 = p$.
I checked the answer by estimating. 136 is about 140, 25 is about 30, 13 is about 10. $140 - 30 + 10 = 120$. 120 is close to 124, so 124 is a reasonable answer.

Answer The truck carried __124 packages__ after the stop.

MP6 **7.** Ana filled 9 baskets with blueberries at the farm. Jeremiah filled three times as many baskets as Ana. How many baskets of blueberries did they fill together?

Show your work.

Possible answer: $9 + (3 \times 9) = b$; $9 + 27 = b$; $36 = b$.
I checked the answer by estimating. 9 is about 10, $10 + (3 \times 10) = 10 + 30$, or 40. 40 is close to 36, so 36 is a reasonable answer.

Answer Jeremiah and Ana together filled __36 baskets__ with blueberries.

Mathematical Practices	
MP4	**Model with mathematics.**
Item 6: Students provide a written equation to solve a word problem and to check their solutions.	
MP6	**Attend to precision.**
Item 7: Students check the accuracy of their calculations to solve the word problem.	

Lesson 11

Independent Practice

MP5 **8.** For a food drive, Jack collected 3 cans of food from each of 8 neighbors. His goal is 30 cans of food. How many more cans does he need?

▸ **Show your work.**

Possible answer: $8 \times 3 + c = 30$; $24 + c = 30$; $c = 30 - 24$; $c = 6$
I checked the answer by making a drawing to show 30 cans of food, then crossing out 8 groups of 3 cans each. There are 6 cans left, which is the answer I got when I solved the equation.

Answer Jack needs __6__ more cans of food.

MP7 **9.** Lillian is shopping for a bicycle. The red bike costs $79 more than the blue bike. The blue bike costs $18 less than the yellow bike. The yellow bike costs $125. How much does the red bike cost?

▸ **Show your work.**

Possible answer: $79 + b =$ cost of red bike; $b = \$125 - \$18 = \$107$, so the cost of the red bike is $79 + \$107 = \$186$.
To check the answer, I estimated with numbers that are easy to add and subtract. The red bike costs about $80 more than the blue bike. The blue bike costs about $20 less than the yellow bike. The yellow bike costs about $130, so the blue bike costs about $110 and the red bike costs about $190. The estimate is close to $186, so my answer is reasonable.

Answer The red bike costs __$186__.

Unit 2 ■ Focus on Operations and Algebraic Thinking/Number and Operations in Base Ten **103**

Teaching Tips

Items 8 and 9

Some students may struggle with how to show their work. Encourage them to explain each step they used in writing as if they were explaining it to a friend.

Mathematical Practices
MP5 Use appropriate tools strategically.
Item 8: Students can make a drawing to explain how they organized information in a word problem and solved it.
MP7 Look for and make use of structure.
Item 9: Students may write an equation using a variable for the unknown information in the word problem.

Common Core Focus:

3.OA.9 Identify arithmetic patterns (including patterns in the addition table or multiplication table), and explain them using properties of operations.

OBJECTIVE
Identify and use arithmetic patterns in multiplication and addition tables.

ESSENTIAL QUESTION
In this lesson students will identify patterns in multiplication and addition tables. Have students review how to use the multiplication table to find the product of two numbers. Remind students that they used multiplication tables in Lesson 9 to learn about the properties of multiplication.

FLUENCY PRACTICE
Fluency practice is available at **sadlierconnect.com**.

Concept Development

Understand: Patterns in the multiplication table

■ This presentation helps students identify patterns in the rows and columns of a multiplication table. Students should see that arithmetic patterns in the table increase by adding the same number.

■ Students should explain patterns using properties of operations. Review that the 0 row and 0 column show the Zero Property of Multiplication and the 1 row and 1 column show the Identity Property of Multiplication.

✏ Students should be able to explain why their patterns make sense mathematically. For example, the products in the 8-column are two times the products in the 4-column because the factor 8 is two times greater than the factor 4.

Lesson

12 Identify and Explain Arithmetic Patterns

Essential Question:
How can you identify and explain arithmetic patterns?
3.OA.9

Words to Know:
pattern
odd
even
rule

Guided Instruction

In this lesson you will work with arithmetic patterns, including patterns in the multiplication and addition tables.

Understand: Patterns in the multiplication table

> Look at the multiplication table. What patterns do you see?

×	0	1	2	3	4	5	6	7	8	9
0	0	0	0	0	0	0	0	0	0	0
1	0	1	2	3	4	5	6	7	8	9
2	0	2	4	6	8	10	12	14	16	18
3	0	3	6	9	12	15	18	21	24	27
4	0	4	8	12	16	20	24	28	32	36
5	0	5	10	15	20	25	30	35	40	45
6	0	6	12	18	24	30	36	42	48	54
7	0	7	14	21	28	35	42	49	56	63
8	0	8	16	24	32	40	48	56	64	72
9	0	9	18	27	36	45	54	63	72	81

Remember that the numbers in the blue boxes at the top and the left are factors. Use them to identify a row or a column.

Look at the 1 column and the 1 row. The numbers are the same. Every column has a matching row with the same numbers. This is just one pattern that you can see in the multiplication table.

Look at the 3 row. The difference between 2 numbers next to each other in that row is 3. Notice that 3 is the factor for that row. This kind of pattern is true for all rows.

Look at the 6 column. The difference between 2 numbers above and below each other in that column is 6. Notice that 6 is the factor for that column. This kind of pattern is true for all columns.

Look at the 7 row. Start with the 1 column. The product 7 × 1 is odd. An odd number always has one left over when broken into equal addends. Look at the 2 column. The product 7 × 2 is even. An even number can be broken down into two equal addends. This pattern continues across the row.

➡ There are many number patterns in the multiplication table.

✏ Find another pattern in the multiplication table.
Possible answers: The numbers in the 8 row are equal to 2 times the numbers in the 4 row. All the numbers in the rows or columns with even factors are even.

Words to Know

pattern: a predictable sequence

Example: 1 2 3 1 2 3 1 2 3

odd: any number that when divided by 2 has a remainder of 1

even: any number that when divided by 2 has no remainder

rule: tells the number to start with and how to find the next number in an arithmetic pattern

Glossary can be found on pp. 347–350.

Understand: Patterns in the addition table

> Look at the addition table.
> What patterns do you see?

+	0	1	2	3	4	5	6	7	8	9
0	0	1	2	3	4	5	6	7	8	9
1	1	2	3	4	5	6	7	8	9	10
2	2	3	4	5	6	7	8	9	10	11
3	3	4	5	6	7	8	9	10	11	12
4	4	5	6	7	8	9	10	11	12	13
5	5	6	7	8	9	10	11	12	13	14
6	6	7	8	9	10	11	12	13	14	15
7	7	8	9	10	11	12	13	14	15	16
8	8	9	10	11	12	13	14	15	16	17
9	9	10	11	12	13	14	15	16	17	18

The numbers in the green boxes at the top and the left are addends. Use them to identify a row or a column.

Look at the 1 column and the 1 row. The numbers are the same. Every column has a matching row.

Look at the 3 row. Each number is __1__ greater than the one before it. This pattern is true for all rows and columns.

Look at the 6 column. Each number is 1 ___less___ than the one after it. This pattern is true for all rows and columns.

Look at the 7 row. The first number is ___odd___, the next one is ___even___, and this pattern continues across the row. You can find this pattern in any row or column with an odd addend.

➡ There are many number patterns in the addition table.

✏ Find another pattern in the addition table.
Possible answers: The numbers in the columns with even addends have an even-odd pattern. From right to left in a row, each number is 1 less than the one before it.

Understand: Rules for patterns

> Look at the 6 row. What pattern do you see? Describe its rule.

A rule for a pattern tells what number to start with and how to find the next number in the pattern.

> The pattern in the 6 row shows that the row starts with 6, and each number is 1 more than the one before it.

➡ The pattern rule is: Start with 6. Add 1.

Unit 2 ■ Focus on Operations and Algebraic Thinking/Number and Operations in Base Ten   **105**

Understand: Patterns in the addition table

■ Have students look for number patterns in each row, column, and diagonal.

■ Display an addition table with some of the numbers missing. Have students explain how they can use patterns to find the missing numbers.

■ Show students how to make generalizations using the addition table. For example, the sum of two even numbers is even, the sum of two odd numbers is even, and the sum of an even and odd number is odd. Knowing this, students can predict whether the sum of any two addends will be even or odd.

✏ Challenge students to make a generalization about the sum of three addends and explain the pattern. A sum of two even numbers and an odd number is always odd because even + even = even, and even + odd = odd. Have students work through other examples of three addends and use numbers to demonstrate that the generalization holds true.

Understand: Rules for patterns

■ Emphasize that a rule has two parts: the starting number and how to find the next number in the pattern. Use the addition table to show students that as you go across rows or down columns, the sums increase by 1. The starting number of the rule is the addend for the row or column. The way to find the next number in the pattern is the same: add 1.

■ Ask students to write a rule for a pattern in the 5 column of the addition table. Students should give their answers in the form: Start with 5. Add 1.

Support English Language Learners

Review the terms *odd* and *even*. Tell students that both words have several different meanings and uses outside of mathematics. Two definitions for each word are listed below. Have students choose the definition that is more closely related to the mathematical definition.

Odd: 1. strange, unusual; for example, odd habits
2. left over after others are paired or grouped; for example, an odd shoe

Even: 1. having a level surface; for example, even ground
2. equal or balanced; for example, an even score

Students should choose the second definition for each word. Explanations may include that an odd number has 1 *left over* when broken into equal addends and an even number can be broken into *equal* addends.

Connect: Patterns and multiplying by 9 Use this page to help students strengthen their understanding of patterns in multiplication.

■ As students complete the table, ask if they can use patterns to complete the last two columns without knowing the product. Students should recognize an increasing pattern in the third column (the tens place of the product increases by 1), and a decreasing pattern in the fourth column (the ones place of the product decreases by 1).

■ Ask students to explain how to check that they multiplied by 9 correctly. Students can use the pattern in the second column to check that the sum of the digits of the product is always 9.

🖉 After students have explained their answers, work through other multiplications by 9. Instead of asking for the product, ask for the tens digit of the product, and then ask for the ones digit of the product. Asking for the product in this way will strengthen students' understanding of how to use the patterns effectively.

Additional Answer

Possible answer: I know that the tens digit of the product is 1 less than 7, so it is 6. I know that the sum of the digits is 9, so the ones digit has to be 3 because 6 + 3 = 9. This means that 9 × 7 = 63.

Connect: Patterns and multiplying by 9

> Some students think that learning the facts for the 9s multiplications is difficult. How can using patterns make it easier to learn the 9s facts?

Complete this table to look for patterns in the 9s multiplications.

9s fact	Sum of the digits in the product	Digit in tens place in the product	Digit in ones place in the product
9 × 1 = 09	0 + 9 = 9	0	9
9 × 2 = 18	1 + 8 = 9	1	8
9 × 3 = 27	2 + 7 = __9__	2	7
9 × 4 = 36	3 + 6 = __9__	3	6
9 × 5 = 45	4 + 5 = __9__	4	5
9 × 6 = 54	5 + 4 = 9	5	4
9 × 7 = 63	6 + 3 = 9	6	3
9 × 8 = 72	7 + 2 = 9	7	2
9 × 9 = 81	8 + 1 = 9	8	1

The sum of the digits in the products for all the 9s facts is __9__.

The pattern of the digits in the tens place for the 9s facts is that the digits increase by __1__ for each multiplication.

The pattern of the digits in the ones place for the 9s is that the digits are 1 __less__ for each multiplication.

For any 9s fact, the digit in the __tens__ place is 1 less than the factor you multiply by 9.

➡ The patterns in the 9s multiplications show relationships that make them easier to remember.

🖉 Explain how you can use these patterns to find 9 × 7. See Additional Answers.

Math-to-Math Connection

Pascal's Triangle Pascal's Triangle is named after a French mathematician, Blaise Pascal. It has many important uses in higher mathematics. Display rows 1–6 of Pascal's Triangle as shown. Have students identify any patterns that they see. For example, each element is the sum of the two numbers above it. Have students find the sum of the elements in each row to see that the sum of each row is twice the sum of the row above it. Challenge students to use patterns to write the next row in the triangle. They should verify that the patterns listed above still hold true for the row they created.

```
            1
          1   1
        1   2   1
      1   3   3   1
    1   4   6   4   1
  1   5  10  10   5   1
1   6  15  20  15   6   1
```

Lesson 12

Guided Practice

Use the addition table for exercises 1–4.

1. Complete the addition table.

+	0	1	2	3	4	5	6	7	8	9
0	0	1	2	3	4	5	6	7	8	9
1	1	2	3	4	5	6	7	8	9	10
2	2	3	4	5	6	7	8	9	10	11
3	3	4	5	6	7	8	9	10	11	12
4	4	5	6	7	8	9	10	11	12	13
5	5	6	7	8	9	10	11	12	13	14
6	6	7	8	9	10	11	12	13	14	15
7	7	8	9	10	11	12	13	14	15	16
8	8	9	10	11	12	13	14	15	16	17
9	9	10	11	12	13	14	15	16	17	18

2. Possible answer: As you move across a row, each number is 1 more than the one before. As you move up a column, each number is 1 less than the one before.

3. Possible answer: Find the row for 5 and go across until you reach the column for 9 with the sum, 14; go down the column for 5 until you reach the row for 9 with the same sum, 14.

4. Possible answer: The sum of any number and 0 is that number. For example, $0 + 0 = 0$, $0 + 1 = 1$, $0 + 2 = 2$.

2. Describe two patterns you see in the addition table.

3. How can you use the addition table to find the sum of $5 + 9$ two different ways?

4. Look at the row and column for 0. What can you say about the sum of any number and 0? Explain.

☝ Think·Pair·Share

MP7 5. The house numbers on the south side of East Street form a pattern. Write the next three house numbers. Explain how you decided on the next three house numbers. Possible explanation: The pattern rule is: Start with 4. Add 4. So, to find the next three numbers, I can add 4 to the number to the left or skip-count by 4s.

4	8	12	16	20	24	28

Unit 2 ■ Focus on Operations and Algebraic Thinking/Number and Operations in Base Ten **107**

Mathematical Practices

Mathematical Practice Standards underline the teaching and understanding of all concepts and skills presented. The emphasis of specific practices is noted throughout the guided and independent practice of this lesson.

MP7	**Look for and make use of structure.**

Item 5: Students analyze a pattern and generate three consecutive terms.

Observational Assessment

Use page 107 to assess whether students are able to identify patterns in the addition table. Remind students to look for patterns in rows, columns, and diagonals. Encourage students to look for patterns in rows from right-to-left and in columns from bottom-to-top.

You may wish to point out that the 0 row and the 0 column show that the sum of any number and 0 is that number, which is the Identity Property of Addition. This is similar to the Identity Property of Multiplication where any number multiplied by 1 is the number itself.

☝ Think·Pair·Share

Peer Collaboration Have students work on the problem individually, and then with a partner to compare explanations. Encourage pairs to share their answers with the class. Ask students questions such as:

- *Did you and your partner use the same rule or different rules?*

- *How did you determine a rule for the pattern?*

- *Are the numbers in the pattern even or odd?*

- *Could you use the multiplication table to find the missing terms?*

Keep a list of the patterns that students use. To summarize, tell students that there is often more than one way to describe a pattern.

Return to the Essential Question

Reread the Lesson 12 Essential Question on page 104: *How can you identify and explain arithmetic patterns?*

Ask volunteers to use what they learned in this lesson to answer this question. (Possible responses: I can look for patterns in rows and columns in the addition table and in the multiplication table. I can use those patterns to make general rules for other patterns.)

Concept Application

Students may work independently on these pages in the classroom or at home. They may refer to the first four pages of the lesson to revisit the instruction or to see a worked-out example.

Common Errors and **Teaching Tips** may help you support student learning either in the classroom or as a follow-up for work done at home.

Teaching Tips

Item 1

Remind students that as you go across rows or down columns, the numbers follow the same pattern as skip counting by that factor.

---

1. Complete the multiplication table for factors to 10.

×	0	1	2	3	4	5	6	7	8	9	10
0	0	0	0	0	0	0	0	0	0	0	0
1	0	1	2	3	4	5	6	7	8	9	10
2	0	2	4	6	8	10	12	14	16	18	20
3	0	3	6	9	12	15	18	21	24	27	30
4	0	4	8	12	16	20	24	28	32	36	40
5	0	5	10	15	20	25	30	35	40	45	50
6	0	6	12	18	24	30	36	42	48	54	60
7	0	7	14	21	28	35	42	49	56	63	70
8	0	8	16	24	32	40	48	56	64	72	80
9	0	9	18	27	36	45	54	63	72	81	90
10	0	10	20	30	40	50	60	70	80	90	100

MP7 **2.** What pattern do you see in the 10 row and the 10 column? Describe the pattern. Then name the pattern rule.

Possible answers: each product is 10 more than the product before it; you can skip-count by 10s; there is always a 0 in the ones place; all the products are even.

Rule: _____ Start with 0. Add 10. _____

Multiply. Then draw lines to match each pair of products.

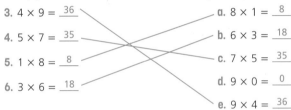

3. 4 × 9 = __36__

4. 5 × 7 = __35__

5. 1 × 8 = __8__

6. 3 × 6 = __18__

a. 8 × 1 = __8__

b. 6 × 3 = __18__

c. 7 × 5 = __35__

d. 9 × 0 = __0__

e. 9 × 4 = __36__

MP8 **7.** Use exercises 3–6. What do you notice about each pair of products? What property of multiplication does this show?
Possible answer: When you multiply two factors, the order of the factors does not matter. This is the Commutative Property of Multiplication.

Mathematical Practices

MP7	**Look for and make use of structure.**

Item 2: Students look for a pattern in a multiplication table and then determine a rule to describe the pattern.

Item 10: Students look for a pattern in a multiplication table and describe the pattern in different ways.

MP8	**Look for and express regularity in repeated reasoning.**

Item 7: Students use patterns in the multiplication table to identify the Commutative Property of Multiplication.

Item 11: Students look for and describe a pattern in the multiplication table.

Lesson 12

Independent Practice

Teaching Tips

Items 8–11
Provide a ruler or straight edge to help students focus on a particular row or column.

Item 9
Some students may make errors because they lose their place when working with the multiplication table. Have students use the edges of two pieces of paper to help them follow the lines from each factor to the product.

Use the multiplication table for exercises 8–11.

8. Complete the multiplication table for the factors 3 and 9.

×	0	1	2	3	4	5	6	7	8	9
0	0	0	0	0	0	0	0	0	0	0
1	0	1	2	3	4	5	6	7	8	9
2	0	2	4	6	8	10	12	14	16	18
3	0	3	6	9	12	15	18	21	24	27
4	0	4	8	12	16	20	24	28	32	36
5	0	5	10	15	20	25	30	35	40	45
6	0	6	12	18	24	30	36	42	48	54
7	0	7	14	21	28	35	42	49	56	63
8	0	8	16	24	32	40	48	56	64	72
9	0	9	18	27	36	45	54	63	72	81

9. Use the multiplication table or skip-counting to find each product.

$0 \times 3 = 0$ $6 \times 3 = 18$ $0 \times 9 = 0$ $6 \times 9 = 54$

$1 \times 3 = 3$ $7 \times 3 = 21$ $1 \times 9 = 9$ $7 \times 9 = 63$

$2 \times 3 = 6$ $8 \times 3 = 24$ $2 \times 9 = 18$ $8 \times 9 = 72$

$3 \times 3 = 9$ $9 \times 3 = 27$ $3 \times 9 = 27$ $9 \times 9 = 81$

$4 \times 3 = 12$ $10 \times 3 = 30$ $4 \times 9 = 36$ $10 \times 9 = 90$

$5 \times 3 = 15$ $5 \times 9 = 45$

MP7 **10.** What patterns do you see for the products of 3 and the factors 0–9?
Possible answers: Each product is 3 more than the product before it; you can skip-count by 3s; the products alternate between even and odd.

MP8 **11.** What patterns do you see for the products of 9 and the factors 0–9?
Possible answers: Each product is 9 more than the product before it; you can skip-count by 9s; the products alternate between even and odd. The sum of the digits of the product is 9 for all the products.

Unit 2 ▪ Focus on Operations and Algebraic Thinking/Number and Operations in Base Ten   **109**

Writing About Math

▸ **Explore Patterns in the Real World** Have students write a paragraph about where they have seen or used patterns in the real world. Students could choose a fabric pattern, traffic pattern, or a number pattern. Encourage students to analyze the situation mathematically and determine a rule for the pattern. Have students trade their paragraphs with another classmate. Students should use their classmate's descriptions to identify the pattern and give feedback if the descriptions are not clear. Students should make changes to their descriptions, if necessary, based on their classmate's feedback.

Independent Practice

Teaching Tips

Items 12-14
Remind students that a rule includes the number to start with and how to find the next number in the pattern.

Item 16
Tell students they can use the Distributive Property to write 6 times a number *a* written as (3 × *a*) + (3 × *a*).

Independent Practice

Complete the pattern. Then name the pattern rule.

12. 7, 14, 21, _28_, _35_, _42_, _49_

    Rule: _____Start with 7. Add 7._____

13. 8, 16, 24, _32_, _40_, _48_, _54_

    Rule: _____Start with 8. Add 8._____

14. 42, 36, 30, _24_, _18_, _12_, _6_

    Rule: _____Start with 42. Subtract 6._____

MP8 15. Jean says that the product of two odd numbers is always odd. Is Jean's statement correct?

   Complete parts a, b, and c to show your work.

   a. Find the product of two odd numbers: 3 × 5.
      3 × 5 = 15

   b. Break apart the product into two addends. Can you break apart the product into two equal addends?   Possible answer: 15 = 7 + 8; 15 = 9 + 6. No, I cannot break apart the product into two equal addends.

   c. Find the products of other pairs of odd numbers. Can you break them apart into two equal addends?   No. Products will vary but students should find that the product of two odd numbers is always an odd number.

   Answer Yes, Jean's statement is correct._____

Circle the correct answer.

MP6 16. Which statement explains why 6 times a number is always even?

   a. You can break apart the product into three equal addends.

   (b.) You can break apart the product into two equal addends.

   c. You cannot break apart the product into three equal addends.

   d. You cannot break apart the product into two equal addends.

Mathematical Practices

MP6	**Attend to precision.**
Item 16: Students break apart a factor to explain why a product is even.	
MP8	**Look for and express regularity in repeated reasoning.**
Item 15: Students make a generalization about the product of two odd numbers.	

Independent Practice

Solve the problems.

MP7 **17.** Mrs. Gonzalez puts whole-wheat rolls on racks to cool. She puts 12 rolls on the first rack, 18 rolls on the second rack, 24 rolls on the third rack, 30 rolls on the fourth rack, and 36 rolls on the fifth rack. If the pattern continues, how many rolls will Mrs. Gonzalez put on the sixth rack?

▸ **Show your work.**
Possible answer: To find the pattern, I skip-counted by 6: 12, 18, 24, 30, and 36. The next number in the pattern is 6 more than 36, so it is 42.

Answer Mrs. Gonzalez will put 42 rolls on the sixth rack.

MP3 **18.** Addison uses the multiplication table to find the product of an even number and any other number. He says that sometimes the product is even and sometimes the product is odd. What mistake might Addison have made?

Answer Addison might have read the incorrect rows or columns.

▸ **Justify your answer using words, drawings, or numbers.**
Possible justification: I know from the patterns in the multiplication table that the product of an even number times a number is always even: 6 is an even number, so the product of 6 times a number is always even. Also, when I find the product of 6 and another number, I can always break it into two equal addends, which also tells me it is even.

MP8 **19.** Kwan says that the product of 9 times an odd number is always odd. Is Kwan's statement correct?

Answer Yes, Kwan's statement is correct.

▸ **Justify your answer using words, drawings, or numbers.**
Possible justification: I can find some of the products of 9 and other odd numbers and try to break them into two equal addends that are whole numbers; for example, $9 \times 5 = 45$ and $45 = 22 + 23$. Since I can't break any of the products into two equal addends that are whole numbers, I know these products are odd. I also can find the product of 9 and an odd number in the multiplication table and see that the products always end in an odd number: 1, 3, 5, 7, or 9.

Common Errors

Item 17

Some students may not recognize the pattern as *add 6* since the first term in the pattern is 12. Show them how to find a pattern rule in an arithmetic pattern by finding the difference between two consecutive terms. For example, $18 - 12 = 6$, $24 - 18 = 6$, and $30 - 24 = 6$.

Teaching Tips

Items 18–19

Students should use the multiplication table to find several factor pairs and products that follow a pattern rule before making a generalization.

Mathematical Practices

MP3	**Construct viable arguments and critique the reasoning of others.**

Item 18: Students analyze a situation to determine and correct the error.

MP7	**Look for and make use of structure.**

Item 17: Students analyze a real-world pattern then determine and extend the pattern.

MP8	**Look for and express regularity in repeated reasoning.**

Item 19: Students make a generalization about the product of 9 and an odd number.

Guided Instruction

Common Core Focus:

3.NBT.1 Use place value understanding to round whole numbers to the nearest 10 or 100.

OBJECTIVE
Use rounding to the nearest 10 or 100 to estimate.

ESSENTIAL QUESTION

Explain that an exact number is not always needed to solve problems. Rounding a number to the nearest 10 or 100 can help students estimate their answers.

PREREQUISITE SKILLS

Use Item C on page 338 of the Foundational Skills Handbook to review modeling 10 tens as 1 hundred.

FLUENCY PRACTICE

Fluency practice is available at **sadlierconnect.com**.

Concept Development

Understand: Rounding two-digit numbers to the nearest 10

■ In order to round, students need to have a solid understanding of place value. Remind students that 10 is 1 ten and 0 ones; 20 is 2 tens and 0 ones; and so on.

■ A number line is used to locate the given numbers and compare the distance to each 10. Have students identify between which two 10s each given number lies, and circle those 10s.

■ Discuss how rounding in this problem is used to estimate the sum of two numbers. Have students explain how rounding makes calculations easier.

■ Be sure students have a good understanding of the rounding rules, when a digit is 5 or greater. Since a number with a 5 in the ones place is halfway between two 10s, students may question why the number is rounded to the greater 10.

Lesson
13 Round Whole Numbers to the Nearest 10 or 100

Essential Question:
How can you round whole numbers?
3.NBT.1
Words to Know:
round

Guided Instruction

In this lesson you will round whole numbers to the nearest 10 or 100.

Understand: Rounding two-digit numbers to the nearest 10

> There are 38 third graders at recess. There are 54 fourth graders at recess. About how many students from both grades are at recess?

You can estimate to solve this problem. The word *about* in the question shows that an exact answer is not needed.

One way to estimate is to round numbers before you calculate an answer. Rounding a 2-digit number to the nearest 10 gives a number with 0 in the ones place.

> A 10 is a number you count when you skip count by 10. The 10s are 10, 20, 30 40, 50, 60, 70, 80, and 90.

Locate 38 and 54 on the number line.

The number line shows which 10 each number is closest to.

38 is closer to 40 than to 30.   54 is closer to 50 than to 60.
38 rounds to 40.   54 rounds to 50.

Now add 40 + 50 to estimate the answer: 40 + 50 = 90.

➡ About 90 students from both grades are at recess.

You can use these rules to round two-digit numbers.

> If the ones digit is 1, 2, 3, or 4, round to the lesser 10.
> If the ones digit is 5 or greater, round to the greater 10.

To round 68 using the rules, think:

> 68 is between 60 and 70. The ones digit is 8, so round to the greater 10. 68 rounds to 70.

Words to Know

round: a method to estimate by changing numbers to the nearest 10 or 100

Glossary can be found on pp. 347–350.

Lesson 13

Guided Instruction

Understand: Rounding three-digit numbers to the nearest 100

Mr. Klein's class counted birds for a science project. They counted 126 blue jays, and 271 robins. To the nearest 100, estimate how many birds the class counted?

The problem asks you to estimate to the nearest 100, so you need to round each number to the nearest 100. This gives numbers with 0 in both the ones place and the tens place.

A 100 is a number you count when you skip count by 100. The 100s are 100, 200, 300, 400, 500, 600, 700, 800, and 900.

You can use a number line to round the numbers to the nearest 100.

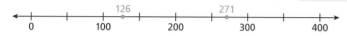

Round each number to the nearest 100.

126 is closer to 100 than 200.
126 rounds to 100.

271 is closer to 300 than to 200.
271 rounds to 300.

Now add 100 + 300 to estimate the answer.

100 + 300 = __400__ ← You can use mental math.

➡ Mr. Klein's class counted about 400 birds.

You can use these rules to round three-digit numbers.

If the tens digit is 1, 2, 3, or 4, round to the lesser 100.
If the tens digit is 5 or greater, round to the greater 100.

To round 325 using the rules, think:

325 is between 300 and 400.
The tens digit is 2, so round to the lesser 100.

325 rounds to __300__.

▶ Why does rounding let you use mental math to make an estimate?
Possible answer: I do not need to work in the places with zeros, so it is like working with 1-digit numbers and I can add and subtract 1-digit numbers with mental math.

Understand: Rounding three-digit numbers to the nearest 100

■ In this presentation, students examine how to round three-digit numbers to the nearest 100. Point out that the rounding rules are the same as rounding two-digit numbers to the nearest 10, except the rules apply to the tens digit instead of the ones digit.

■ Remind students that 100 is 1 hundred, 0 tens, and 0 ones; 200 is 2 hundreds, 0 tens, and 0 ones; 300 is 3 hundreds, 0 tens, and 0 ones; and so on. When rounding to the nearest 100, students are rounding to one of these 100s.

■ To reinforce understanding of place value, have students identify the nearer 100 for each interval on the given number line.

✏ ▶ After students have answered the question, have volunteers share their responses. As a class, discuss how rounding to the nearest 100 is similar to rounding to the nearest 10.

Support English Language Learners

Some English language learners may have difficulty with comparative language, such as *closer, nearest, lesser,* and *greater* because the endings *-est* and *-er* might not be familiar to them. Students will have experience with *greater than* and *less than* when comparing whole numbers.

Refer students to the number line on page 113. Demonstrate how to use comparative language by providing sentence frames such as: 271 is *near* 200, but 271 is *closer* to 300, and 300 is the *greater* hundred; 200 is the *lesser* hundred. Have students demonstrate their understanding of these terms by creating similar sentences. If some students are uncomfortable speaking in front of others, allow them to draw, use models, or write their sentences.

Connect: Rounding a three-digit number to the nearest 10

Use this page to help students extend their understanding of rounding to include rounding three-digit numbers to the nearest 10.

■ Remind students of the rules for rounding to the nearest 10. Explain that since a three-digit number includes both a tens digit and ones digit, a three-digit number can also be rounded to the nearest 10.

■ Extend the problem by having students estimate the number of jumping jacks by rounding 125, 152, and 136 to the nearest 100. Students should answer that to the nearest 100, the friends did 400 jumping jacks. The actual total is 413. Both estimates are close to the actual total, but the estimate to the nearest 10 is closer. Be sure students can explain why rounding to the nearest 10 is closer to the exact answer.

■ Challenge students to use the number line to find a number that, when rounded to the nearest 10, it rounds to the greater 10, but when rounded to the nearest 100, it rounds to the lesser 100. Then find a number which rounds to the lesser 10, but also rounds to the greater 100.

Lesson 13 Round Whole Numbers to the Nearest 10 or 100

Guided Instruction

Connect: Rounding a three-digit number to the nearest 10

Some friends made a table of the number of jumping jacks they did last week. They want to round to the nearest 10 to estimate how many jumping jacks they did in all. About how many jumping jacks is that?

Our Jumping Jacks	
Marta	125
Liz	152
Kate	136

One way to round to the nearest 10 is to use a number line. Locate the numbers from the problem on the number line.

```
        125           136              152
 |----|--+--|----|----|--o--|----|----|--o--|----|----|--|
120  125  130  135  140  145  150  155  160
```

125 is between 120 and __130__. 125 rounds to 130.

136 is between __130__ and 140. 136 rounds to __140__.

152 is between __150__ and __160__. 152 rounds to __150__.

You can also use rules for rounding to the nearest 10.

When you round a three-digit number to the nearest 10, look at the ones digit to decide how to round.

125 is between __120__ and 130. The ones digit is __5__, so round to the greater 10. 125 rounds to __130__.

136 is between 130 and __140__. The ones digit is 6, so round to the __greater__ 10. 136 rounds to __140__.

152 is between __150__ and __160__. The ones digit is __2__, so round to the __lesser__ 10. 152 rounds to __150__.

To solve the problem, add. 130 + 140 + 150 = __420__

➤ The friends did about __420__ jumping jacks in all.

Math-to-Travel Connection

Estimates and Overestimates Ask student to identify situations where a close estimate is needed. Point out that there are also situations where they may want to *overestimate* by always rounding to the greater number, such as when they are estimating the cost of an item to make sure they have enough money to buy it.

Explain that when planning a long road trip, it might be good to overestimate the mileage in case they get lost. It might also be good to overestimate the time it will take to reach a destination, so that they are not late. Discuss other situations where they might want to overestimate an amount.

Round to the nearest 10.

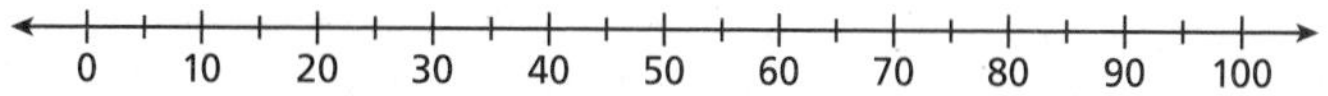

1. 18 _____20_____   2. 25 _____30_____   3. 49 _____50_____

4. 99 _____100_____   5. 7 _____10_____   6. 5 _____10_____

7. 3 _____0_____   8. 64 _____60_____   9. 65 _____70_____

10. 12 _____10_____   11. 55 _____60_____   12. 88 _____90_____

13. 137 _____140_____   14. 272 _____270_____   15. 398 _____400_____

Round to the nearest 100.

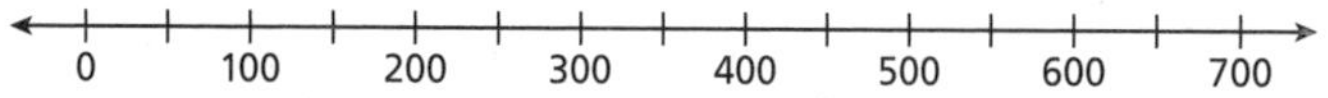

16. 373 _____400_____   17. 105 _____100_____   18. 624 _____600_____

19. 99 _____100_____   20. 650 _____700_____   21. 575 _____600_____

22. 50 _____100_____   23. 409 _____400_____   24. 14 _____0_____

25. 220 _____200_____   26. 468 _____500_____   27. 813 _____800_____

� Think•Pair•Share

MP3 28. Ismael says that 85 rounds to 100. Gabriella says that 85 rounds
to 90. Explain why both students' answers could be correct.
Possible explanation: Ismael is correct if he is rounding 85 to the nearest 100.
Gabriella is correct if she is rounding 85 to the nearest 10.

Unit 2 ■ Focus on Operations and Algebraic Thinking/Number and Operations in Base Ten **115**

Mathematical Practices

Mathematical Practice Standards underline the teaching and
understanding of all concepts and skills presented. The emphasis of
specific practices is noted throughout the guided and independent practice
of this lesson.

MP3	Construct viable arguments and critique the reasoning of others.

Item 28: Students analyze the work of two classmates and share their
reasoning about the answers.

Observational Assessment

Use page 115 to assess whether
students have an understanding of
rounding to the nearest 10 and to
nearest 100 for both two-digit and
three-digit numbers. Make note of
students who need to use the number
lines and determine if they need extra
practice with rounding rules.

� Think•Pair•Share

Peer Collaboration Have pairs
present their reasoning to the class.
Encourage class discussion and student
participation by asking the following
questions:

- *To what place value did Ismael round 85?*

- *To what place value did Gabriella round 85?*

- *Is one student's answer more accurate than the other student's answer?*

Summarize the concept by explaining
that both estimates are correct, but
rounding to the nearest 10 is more
accurate than to the nearest 100.
Determining which place value to round
to depends on the situation.

Return to the Essential Question

Reread the Lesson 13 Essential Question
on page 112: *How can you round
whole numbers?*

Ask volunteers to use what they learned
in this lesson to answer this question.
(Possible responses: I can use rounding
rules to round whole numbers to the
nearest 10 by looking at the ones
digit, or round whole numbers to the
nearest 100 by looking at the tens digit.
I can round whole numbers to either
the nearest 10 or the nearest 100 by
plotting the numbers on a number line.)

Have volunteers demonstrate their
understanding about rounding by
explaining it in their own words or by
rounding a number of their choice.

Concept Application

Students may work independently on these pages in the classroom or at home. They may refer to the first four pages of the lesson to revisit the instruction or to see a worked-out example.

Common Errors and **Teaching Tips** may help you support student learning either in the classroom or as a follow-up for work done at home.

Teaching Tips

Item 1

If students struggle with recognizing that the numbers in the 5-column should be shaded, remind them of the rule for rounding to the greater 10. Tell students to use the table to help them complete most of the exercises on the rest of this page.

Lesson 13   Round Whole Numbers to the Nearest 10 or 100

Independent Practice

Use the chart for questions 1–14.

0	1	2	3	4	5	6	7	8	9	10
10	11	12	13	14	15	16	17	18	19	20
20	21	22	23	24	25	26	27	28	29	30
30	31	32	33	34	35	36	37	38	39	40
40	41	42	43	44	45	46	47	48	49	50
50	51	52	53	54	55	56	57	58	59	60
60	61	62	63	64	65	66	67	68	69	70
70	71	72	73	74	75	76	77	78	79	80
80	81	82	83	84	85	86	87	88	89	90
90	91	92	93	94	95	96	97	98	99	100

1. Use a marker or crayon. Lightly shade all the numbers that round to the greater 10.

2. Complete the rules for rounding two-digit numbers. Write **lesser** or **greater**.

Rules for Rounding Two-Digit Numbers

a. If a number has a 1, 2, 3, or 4 in the ones place, round to the ___lesser___ 10.

b. If a number has a 5, 6, 7, 8, or 9 in the ones place, round to the ___greater___ 10.

Round to the nearest 10.

3. 6   ___10___   4. 32   ___30___   5. 78   ___80___

6. 37   ___40___   7. 15   ___20___   8. 8   ___10___

9. 84   ___80___   10. 63   ___60___   11. 1   ___0___

12. 56   ___60___   13. 95   ___100___   14. 49   ___50___

15. 557   ___560___   16. 243   ___240___   17. 185   ___190___

Writing About Math

▸ **Write an Informative Text** Have students write an informative text explaining the rounding rules for rounding to the nearest 10 and rounding to the nearest 100. Explain that informative texts often include illustrations to explain complicated information, so that the reader can more easily read and understand the material. Tell students that they should display rounding rules in a table, diagram, or other illustration.

When students are finished, have volunteers share how they displayed the rounding rules. You may want to post some of the illustrations in the classroom.

18. Complete the rules for rounding three-digit numbers. Write **lesser** or **greater**.

Rules for Rounding Three-Digit Numbers

a. If a number has a 1, 2, 3, or 4 in the tens place, round to the
   _____lesser_____ 100.

b. If a number has a 5, 6, 7, 8, or 9 in the tens place, round to the
   _____greater_____ 100.

Round to the nearest 100.

19. 702 __700__	20. 425 __400__	21. 241 __200__
22. 329 __300__	23. 650 __700__	24. 889 __900__
25. 855 __900__	26. 174 __200__	27. 817 __800__
28. 438 __400__	29. 499 __500__	30. 977 __1,000__

Round to the nearest 10 and the nearest 100.

←|++→
200   250   300   350   400   450   500   550   600   650   700

31. 422 nearest 10 __420__ nearest 100 __400__	32. 672 nearest 10 __670__ nearest 100 __700__
33. 259 nearest 10 __260__ nearest 100 __300__	34. 475 nearest 10 __480__ nearest 100 __500__
35. 272 nearest 10 __270__ nearest 100 __300__	36. 650 nearest 10 __650__ nearest 100 __700__
37. 495 nearest 10 __500__ nearest 100 __500__	38. 302 nearest 10 __300__ nearest 100 __300__

Common Errors

Items 19–30

Some students may have difficulty rounding to the nearest 100. Remind them to look at the digit in the tens place and use the rules for rounding. Alternatively, they could plot the number on a number line with intervals of 50.

Teaching Tips

Items 31–38

Explain to students that the number line has intervals of 10, so it can be used to round both to the nearest 10 and to the nearest 100.

Digital Connection

Digital Pedometer Race Provide small groups of students with digital pedometers. Each group will use the digital pedometers to track how many steps it takes each member of the group to walk around the schoolyard or classroom. Then have them work together to find the group's total number of steps by both adding the exact numbers and also by estimating the sum by rounding to the nearest 10.

Discuss the results as a class and explain that the group with the greatest number of steps wins. Then discuss which answer, the sum or the estimate, is fairer. Explain that sometimes it is better to add numbers and find the sum than to estimate and round the sum.

Independent Practice

Teaching Tips

Items 39–41
Since the numbers in each problem are two-digit numbers, suggest that students round to the nearest 10 each time.

Items 40–41
Remind students that the word "about" indicates that they should estimate to solve the problem.

Independent Practice

Solve the problems.

MP1 **39.** Janine walks several days each week. If she walked 35 miles in April and 42 miles in May, about how far did she walk in all? Estimate.

▭▭▭ · **Show your work.**
Possible answer: I can round each number to the nearest ten to get a reasonable estimate. So, I can round 35 to 40 and 42 to 40, then find the sum: 40 + 40 = 80.

Answer Janine walked about 80 miles in all.

MP8 **40.** Tamika is making a list of animals she has seen. Her list has 27 birds, 13 reptiles, and 42 mammals. About how many animals has she seen?

▭▭▭ · **Show your work.**
Possible answer: 27 rounds to 30; 13 rounds to 10, and 42 rounds to 40. 30 + 10 + 40 = 80.

Answer Tamika has seen about 80 animals.

MP6 **41.** Len buys and sells posters. At the beginning of the year, he had 63 posters. He bought 29 posters and sold 37 posters. About how many posters does he have now?

▭▭▭ · **Show your work.**
Possible answer: 63 rounds to 60; 29 rounds to 30, and 37 rounds to 40. 60 + 30 − 40 = 50.

Answer Len has about 50 posters now.

Mathematical Practices	
MP1	**Make sense of problems and persevere in solving them.**
Item 39: Students determine how to estimate to solve the problem.	
MP6	**Attend to precision.**
Item 41: Students communicate their thought process to solve a multi-step problem.	
MP8	**Look for and express regularity in repeated reasoning.**
Item 40: Students determine an estimation strategy for adding three two-digit numbers.	

Lesson 13

Independent Practice

MP6 **42.** Ms. Asato's class raised $322 in autumn and $569 in winter for a charity. About how much money did the class raise in all?

✏️ **Show your work.**

Possible answer: I can round each number to the nearest hundred dollars to get a reasonable estimate. So, I can round $322 to $300 and $569 to $600, then find the sum: $300 + $600 = $900.

Answer Ms. Asato's class raised about $900.

MP3 **43.** Jonas rounded 249 to the nearest ten and said it was 250. He rounded 249 to the nearest hundred and said it was 300. Was this correct?

Answer No. Jonas correctly rounded 249 to 250, but 249 does not round to 300.

✏️ **Justify your answer using words, drawings, or numbers.**

Possible justification: On a number line, 249 is closer to 250 than to 240, so Jonas was correct with that part of his answer. But, to round to the nearest hundred, Jonas should have rounded 249 to 200 because 249 is closer to 200 than to 300.

MP1 **44.** Mrs. Moore drives 161 miles on Friday and 179 miles on Saturday. To estimate how far she drove, first she estimated to the nearest 10 before finding the total. Then she estimated to the nearest 100 before finding the total. Which method gives the closer estimate?

Answer The method that gives the closer estimate is estimating to the nearest 10 before finding the total.

✏️ **Justify your answer using words, drawings, or numbers.**

Possible justification: When Mrs. Moore rounds to the nearest 10, she gets an estimate of 160 miles + 180 miles = 340 miles. When she rounds to the nearest 100, she gets an estimate of 200 + 200 = 400 miles. The first estimate is closer because the actual numbers are very close to the estimated numbers: 161 is very close to 160 and 179 is very close to 180. So, the first estimate, 340, is much closer to the actual total (161 + 179 = 340 miles).

Unit 2 ■ Focus on Operations and Algebraic Thinking/Number and Operations in Base Ten **119**

Teaching Tips

Items 43–44

When students are finished, have them present their justifications to the class. Discuss which justification method students find easiest to understand: words, drawings, or numbers. Have volunteers try justifying their answers using a different method.

Mathematical Practices	
MP1	**Make sense of problems and persevere in solving them.**
Item 44: Students analyze a problem and compare two results to determine the closer estimate.	
MP3	**Construct viable arguments and critique the reasoning of others.**
Item 43: Students analyze and determine the accuracy of a solution.	
MP6	**Attend to precision.**
Item 42: Students explain their reasoning to estimate a sum.	

Common Core Focus:

3.NBT.2 Fluently add and subtract within 1000 using strategies and algorithms based on place value, properties of operations, and/or the relationship between addition and subtraction.

OBJECTIVE

Use strategies to add and subtract within 1,000.

ESSENTIAL QUESTION

In this lesson, students build upon previous strategies and algorithms in order to increase fluency when adding and subtracting within 1,000.

PREREQUISITE SKILLS

Use Item D on page 338 of the Foundational Skills Handbook to review how to use place value to add two 2-digit numbers.

FLUENCY PRACTICE

Fluency practice is available at **sadlierconnect.com**.

Concept Development

Understand: Using place-value methods to add and subtract

■ In this presentation, students use place-value strategies to add and subtract two three-digit numbers. For addition, students are shown how to find partial sums by adding in each place first, beginning with the hundreds. Students are also introduced to the expanded form as an addition strategy.

■ For subtraction, students are shown to ungroup before subtracting. To apply this method, students must first look at the minuend and subtrahend and ungroup the hundreds and tens as necessary, before subtracting.

■ To reinforce the use of place value, use place-value blocks or models. Remind students that estimating can give them an idea of what the answer will be.

Lesson **14**

Add and Subtract Fluently within 1,000

Essential Question: How can you add and subtract within 1,000?

3.NBT.2

Words to Know:
Associative Property of Addition
Commutative Property of Addition

Guided Instruction

In this lesson you will use strategies to add and subtract within 1,000.

Understand: Using place-value methods to add and subtract

> At the school fair, the students bought 172 veggie burgers and 265 hamburgers. How many burgers did the students buy in all? How many more hamburgers than veggie burgers did the students buy?

To find how many burgers in all, add 172 + 265. Two strategies are: adding in each place first and using expanded form.

Add in Each Place First

```
  172
 +265
  300  ← Add the hundreds.
  130  ← Add the tens.
    7  ← Add the ones.
  437  ← Add everything.
```

Use Expanded Form

$172 \rightarrow 100 + 70 + 2$
$+265 \rightarrow 200 + 60 + 5$
$300 + 130 + 7$ ← Add each place.
$430 + 7$ ← Add 100s and 10s.
437 ← Add on the ones.

➡ The students bought 437 burgers in all.

To find how many more hamburgers than veggie burgers the students buy, you subtract. Two strategies are to ungroup first and to use expanded form.

Ungroup First

```
  1 16
  2 6 5  ← Ungroup hundreds
 −1 7 2     and tens.
    9 3
```

Use Expanded Form

$265 \rightarrow 200 + 60 + 5$
$-172 \rightarrow 100 + 70 + 2$ ← You cannot subtract the tens.
$100 + 160 + 5$ ← Ungroup the 200.
$-100 + 70 + 2$
$90 + 3$ ← Subtract.
93 ← Add.

➡ The students buy 93 more hamburgers than veggie burgers.

Words to Know

Associative Property of Addition: changing the grouping of addends does not change the sum

Example: $50 + (90 + 7) = (50 + 90) + 7$

Commutative Property of Addition: changing the order of addends does not change the sum

Example: $50 + (7 + 90) + 4 = 50 + (90 + 7) + 4$

Glossary can be found on pp. 347–350.

Lesson 14

Understand: Using properties of addition to find sums

A strategy for finding sums is to use properties of addition.

When you add, changing the grouping of addends does not change the sum. This property is called the Associative Property of Addition.

When you add, changing the order of addends does not change the sum. This property is called the Commutative Property of Addition.

Find the sum of 57 and 94.

57 + 94
(50 + 7) + (90 + 4) ← Decompose into 10s and 1s.
50 + (7 + 90) + 4 ← Use the Associative Property to change the grouping.
50 + (90 + 7) + 4 ← Use the Commutative Property to change the order.
(50 + 90) + (7 + 4) ← Use the Associative Property to change the grouping.

140 + 11 ← Add the 10s. Add the 1s.

151 ← Add to find the sum.

▶ The sum of 57 and 94 is 151.

> When you can add and subtract quickly and accurately, you can use both of these strategies to calculate mentally.

Understand: Adding on to subtract

You can add on to subtract because of the relationship between addition and subtraction.

Find 179 − 37.

37 ← Start with the number being subtracted.
37 + 3 = 40 ← Add on to go to the next 10.
40 + 60 = 100 ← Add on to go to the next 100.
100 + 79 = 179 ← Add on to go to the number being subtracted from.
142 ← The sum of the add-ons is the difference.

▶ The difference 179 − 37 is 142.

Unit 2 ■ Focus on Operations and Algebraic Thinking/Number and Operations in Base Ten   **121**

Understand: Using properties of addition to find sums

■ In this presentation, students learn how to use properties of addition to find sums. Begin by reviewing the definition of each property. Tell students that these properties will help them make mental calculations quickly and accurately as they work through the lesson.

■ This presentation builds on students' prior learning of decomposing numbers into 10s and 1s. Ask students why decomposing numbers is the first step and how it helps them apply the Associative and Commutative Properties of Addition.

Understand: Adding on to subtract

■ This presentation shows students how to utilize the relationship between addition and subtraction to subtract. Help students see that this strategy is not the same method they use to check subtraction. To check subtraction, the difference is added to the subtrahend. The sum should be the minuend. Have students check this subtraction by adding: 142 + 37 = 179.

Support English Language Learners

Students have likely encountered the term *property* in science. In science, physical properties describe attributes of an item. In social studies, *property* refers to land or something a person owns. Help students understand that properties in math are more like rules or laws.

It may be helpful to create a word wall with pictures of words that have different meanings for math class. Display these words with a picture, an example, or a definition depending upon which is clearer for students' understanding.

Guided Instruction

Connect: Add and subtract three-digit numbers

■ This presentation builds upon students' previous knowledge of place value to add and subtract three-digit numbers. To help students keep numbers organized, this presentation shows how to use a place-value chart to set up the problem. It may be helpful for students to practice subtracting three-digit numbers using a similar chart.

■ Students may also benefit from using place-value models or drawings to help them regroup.

■ It is important to display addition and subtraction both vertically and horizontally. When equations are displayed horizontally, it may help students understand how to decompose numbers and apply the Commutative and Associative Properties of Addition. When equations are displayed vertically, students can use an algorithm to add or subtract.

■ Have students find the sum or difference for the problems presented on this page using another strategy that they have learned in this lesson.

■ Remind students that subtraction can also be completed using the count on method, as when computing the amount of change after a purchase.

Guided Instruction

Connect: Add and subtract three-digit numbers

> The school librarian bought 473 books this year. He bought 419 books last year. How many books did the librarian buy in all? How many more books did he buy this year?

To answer the first question, you can add.

Find the sum. $473 + 419 = $ ■

Add the ones. Regroup 12 ones as 1 ten and 2 ones.	Add the tens.	Add the hundreds.	Subtract to check.

	h	t	o
		1	
	4	7	3
+	4	1	9
			2

	h	t	o
		1	
	4	7	3
+	4	1	9
		9	2

	h	t	o
		1	
	4	7	3
+	4	1	9
	8	9	2

	h	t	o
		8	12
	8	9	2
−	4	1	9
	4	7	3

➤ The librarian bought __892__ books in all.

To answer the second question, you can subtract.

Find the difference: $473 - 419 = $ ■.

To subtract the ones, first regroup the tens. Then subtract.	Subtract the tens.	Subtract the hundreds.	Add to check.

	h	t	o
		6	13
	4	7	3
−	4	1	9
			4

	h	t	o
		6	13
	4	7	3
−	4	1	9
		5	4

	h	t	o
		6	13
	4	7	3
−	4	1	9
	0	5	4

	h	t	o
		1	
	0	5	4
+	4	1	9
	4	7	3

➤ The librarian bought 54 more books this year.

Math-to-History Connection

Abacus An abacus is a counting frame that has been used for centuries to calculate with numbers. The abacus can also represent numbers without the use of place value. It is still widely used in Africa, the Middle East, and Asia.

Variations of the abacus have been used in many cultures throughout history. Have students work in groups to find pictures of an abacus that was used in different cultures, such as Mesopotamian, Egyptian, Persian, Greek, Roman, Chinese, and Native American.

Guided Practice

Add. Check your work.

1.

h	t	o
6	0	2
+ 3	7	3
9	7	5

2.

h	t	o
4	3	9
+ 1	4	2
5	8	1

3.

h	t	o
3	9	0
+ 4	5	9
8	4	9

4.

h	t	o
5	6	8
+ 2	9	8
8	6	6

Subtract. Check your work.

5.

h	t	o
5	9	8
− 2	9	7
3	0	1

6.

h	t	o
2	4	3
− 1	2	5
1	1	8

7.

h	t	o
9	3	5
− 6	4	8
2	8	7

8.

h	t	o
8	5	9
− 7	6	4
	9	5

Think•Pair•Share

MP4 9. Explain why you can subtract to check addition and you can add to check subtraction.
Possible explanation: You can subtract to undo addition and you can add to undo subtraction.

Observational Assessment

Use page 123 to assess whether students are able to add and subtract within 1,000. Also assess students' ability to check their answers using the opposite operation.

Think•Pair•Share

Peer Collaboration Students are asked to explain how to use the relationship between addition and subtraction to check their answers. Have volunteers share their answers with the class. Ask students question such as:

- *How do you undo addition?*
- *How do you undo subtraction?*

To summarize, remind students that addition and subtraction undo each other. Students can apply the same strategies they learned with basic addition and subtraction facts to add and subtract greater numbers.

Return to the Essential Question

Reread the Lesson 14 Essential Question on page 120: *How can you add and subtract within 1,000?*

Ask volunteers to use what they learned in this lesson to answer this question. (Possible response: I can use place value, expanded form, adding on, and properties to add and subtract greater numbers.)

Mathematical Practices

Mathematical Practice Standards underline the teaching and understanding of all concepts and skills presented. The emphasis of specific practices is noted throughout the guided and independent practice of this lesson.

MP4 **Model with mathematics.**

Item 9: Students explain the relationship between addition and subtraction.

Independent Practice

Concept Application

Students may work independently on these pages in the classroom or at home. They may refer to the first four pages of the lesson to revisit the instruction or to see a worked-out example.

Common Errors and **Teaching Tips** may help you support student learning either in the classroom or as a follow-up for work done at home.

Teaching Tips

Items 1-6

Students will likely find it helpful to rewrite the items vertically before trying to solve. Make sure students line up the numbers correctly. If students are having difficulties lining up the numbers, suggest that they use a place-value chart for their calculations.

Items 7-21

Using a place-value chart or grid paper will help students keep the numbers aligned in the proper place value.

Lesson 14 Add and Subtract Fluently within 1,000

Independent Practice

Use any strategy you like to find the sum.

1. $475 + 305 = \underline{780}$

2. $174 + 29 = \underline{203}$

3. $312 + 298 = \underline{610}$

4. $623 + 377 = \underline{1{,}000}$

5. $286 + 241 = \underline{527}$

6. $747 + 173 = \underline{920}$

Add. Check your work.

7.
```
  408
+436
────
  844
```

8.
```
  281
+405
────
  686
```

9.
```
  271
+352
────
  623
```

10.
```
  192
+339
────
  531
```

11.
```
  545
+375
────
  920
```

12.
```
  397
+228
────
  625
```

13.
```
  457
+462
────
  919
```

14.
```
  273
+140
────
  413
```

15.
```
  609
+329
────
  938
```

16.
```
  512
+127
────
  639
```

17.
```
  315
+587
────
  902
```

18.
```
  826
+ 38
────
  864
```

19.
```
  128
  205
+137
────
  470
```

20.
```
  540
  100
+139
────
  779
```

21.
```
  162
  145
+285
────
  592
```

Writing About Math

Write an Opinion Ask students to write an opinion about this lesson. Students may write about the strategy they like best, or they may choose one strategy and write about whether they think the strategy makes calculations easier. Remind students to include reasons to support their opinion.

When students have finished writing, ask volunteers to share their opinions with the class. Tell students that an opinion is neither right nor wrong, and some students will have differing opinions.

Lesson 14

Independent Practice

Use any strategy you like to find the difference.

22. $325 - 210 = \underline{115}$
23. $830 - 140 = \underline{690}$

24. $762 - 451 = \underline{311}$
25. $794 - 392 = \underline{402}$

26. $276 - 254 = \underline{22}$
27. $685 - 176 = \underline{509}$

Subtract. Check your work.

28.
$$\begin{array}{r} 64 \\ -27 \\ \hline 37 \end{array}$$

29.
$$\begin{array}{r} 75 \\ -18 \\ \hline 57 \end{array}$$

30.
$$\begin{array}{r} 41 \\ -25 \\ \hline 16 \end{array}$$

31.
$$\begin{array}{r} 408 \\ -104 \\ \hline 304 \end{array}$$

32.
$$\begin{array}{r} 519 \\ -235 \\ \hline 284 \end{array}$$

33.
$$\begin{array}{r} 635 \\ -294 \\ \hline 341 \end{array}$$

34.
$$\begin{array}{r} 235 \\ -\ 45 \\ \hline 190 \end{array}$$

35.
$$\begin{array}{r} 776 \\ -\ 59 \\ \hline 717 \end{array}$$

36.
$$\begin{array}{r} 866 \\ -371 \\ \hline 495 \end{array}$$

37.
$$\begin{array}{r} 526 \\ -371 \\ \hline 155 \end{array}$$

38.
$$\begin{array}{r} 645 \\ -293 \\ \hline 352 \end{array}$$

39.
$$\begin{array}{r} 107 \\ -\ 45 \\ \hline 62 \end{array}$$

40.
$$\begin{array}{r} 599 \\ -192 \\ \hline 407 \end{array}$$

41.
$$\begin{array}{r} 909 \\ -427 \\ \hline 482 \end{array}$$

42.
$$\begin{array}{r} 352 \\ -278 \\ \hline 74 \end{array}$$

Unit 2 ■ Focus on Operations and Algebraic Thinking/Number and Operations in Base Ten **125**

Common Errors

Items 31–42

Students may incorrectly regroup numbers to the wrong place. Suggest that students draw vertical lines between the hundreds, tens, and ones places to help align the digits correctly.

Teaching Tips

Items 22–27

When students are ready for an additional challenge, have them return to these exercises and use a different strategy to solve them a second time.

Digital Connection

Random Number Generator Have students work in pairs and use a random number generator to produce two three-digit numbers. Assign parameters for the random number generator so that only numbers between 101 and 499 can be selected. Students should use the numbers to create an addition equation and a related subtraction equation. Tell students to use one of the strategies from the lesson to add and subtract. As students work, have them explain how the addition and subtraction equations are related and how they can use the equations to check their work. If time allows, have students use another pair of numbers. Encourage students to use different strategies.

Independent Practice

Teaching Tips

Items 43-44

Some students may have difficulty explaining how they solved problems. To help, have students first solve the problem and then go back and explain what they did, rather than trying to explain the process from the beginning.

Items 45-46

It is necessary for students to have an understanding of what qualifies as a reasonable answer. If necessary, revisit the idea of reasonable and unreasonable answers before students start.

Independent Practice

MP6 **43.** Explain how to compute the sum of 382 + 130.
Possible explanation: Break the numbers into hundreds, tens, and ones. Then add the ones: 2 + 0 = 2. Add the tens: 80 + 30 = 11 tens or 110. Regroup 110 as 1 hundred and 1 ten. Add the hundreds: 300 + 100 + 100 = 500. Combine to find the sum: 382 + 130 = 512.

MP8 **44.** Explain how to compute the difference of 382 − 130.
Possible explanation: Break the numbers into hundreds, tens, and ones. Then subtract the ones: 2 − 0 = 2. Subtract the tens: 80 − 30 = 50. Subtract the hundreds: 300 − 100 = 200. Combine to find the difference: 382 − 130 = 252.

Solve the problems.

MP2 **45.** Last month Mrs. Turner's class collected 349 cans for recycling. This month the class collected 570 cans for recycling. How many cans did the class collect in all? Explain why your answer is reasonable.

▬▬· **Show your work.**   Possible explanation: To check my answer, I can round each number to the nearest hundred: 300 + 600 = 900, so the answer should be close to 900.

$$\begin{array}{r} 349 \\ +570 \\ \hline 919 \end{array}$$

919 is close to 900, so the answer makes sense.

Answer The class collected 919 cans.

MP6 **46.** Southwest Elementary has 739 students. If 382 students are boys, how many are girls? Explain why your answer is reasonable.

▬▬· **Show your work.**   Possible explanation: To check my answer, I can round: 700 − 400 = 300. So, the answer is about 300.

$$\begin{array}{r} 739 \\ -382 \\ \hline 357 \end{array}$$

357 is close to 300, so the answer is reasonable.

Answer 357 students are girls.

Mathematical Practices

MP2	**Reason abstractly and quantitatively.**
Item 45: Students explain why their answers are reasonable.	
MP6	**Attend to precision.**
Item 43: Students accurately calculate using addition.	
Item 46: Students accurately calculate using subtraction.	
MP8	**Look for and express regularity in repeated reasoning.**
Item 44: Students explain the logic used to solve a subtraction problem.	

Lesson 14

Independent Practice

MP8 **47.** Four hundred twenty-eight students came to the school fair the first day, and 355 students came the second day. How many students attended during the two days?

Show your work. Possible answer: To solve the problem, I can break the addends 428 and 355 into hundreds, tens, and ones. 400 + 300 = 700, 20 + 50 = 70, and 8 + 5 = 13. Regroup 13 ones as 1 ten and 3 ones, and add the 1 ten to the other tens: 70 + 10 = 80. So, the sum is 700 + 80 + 3 = 783.

Answer During the two days, 783 students attended the school fair.

MP3 **48.** Ramona says that 135 + 279 equals the same sum as 279 + 135. Is Ramona's statement correct?

Answer Yes, Ramona's statement is correct.

Justify your answer using words, drawings, or numbers.
Possible justification: According to the Commutative Property of Addition, numbers can be added in any order. I can show this by finding each sum.
135 + 279 = 414
279 + 135 = 414.

MP1 **49.** Jarred subtracted 540 − 365 and got a difference of 275. Give the correct answer and explain Jarred's error.

Answer The correct answer is 175.

Justify your answer using words, drawings, or numbers.
Possible justification: Jarred correctly regrouped 5 hundreds as 4 hundreds and 10 tens to get 13 tens, but he kept the 5 hundreds when he subtracted the hundreds. So, he got an answer of 275 instead of 175.

$$
\begin{array}{r}
{\scriptstyle 4\ 13\ 10}\\
\cancel{5}\,\cancel{4}\,\cancel{0}\\
-\ 3\ 6\ 5\\
\hline
1\ 7\ 5
\end{array}
$$

Unit 2 ■ Focus on Operations and Algebraic Thinking/Number and Operations in Base Ten **127**

Teaching Tips

Items 48-49

An important part of these problems is critiquing someone else's work. Make sure students identify the error (if one was made), determine the correct answer, and justify how they solved the problem.

Mathematical Practices

MP1	Make sense of problems and persevere in solving them.

Item 49: Students analyze how a problem was solved and provide the correct answer and explanation.

MP3	Construct viable arguments and critique the reasoning of others.

Item 48: Students justify another's reasoning.

MP8	Look for and express regularity in repeated reasoning.

Item 47: Students solve a word problem using addition.

Common Core Focus:

3.NBT.3 Multiply one-digit whole numbers by multiples of 10 in the range 10–90 using strategies based on place value and properties of operations.

OBJECTIVE

Multiply one-digit numbers by multiples of 10.

ESSENTIAL QUESTION

Focus students on the lesson objective by reading the Essential Question. Have students skip count by 10s from 10 to 90. Explain that these numbers are multiples of 10. In this lesson students will learn how they can use patterns and properties to multiply mentally with multiples of 10.

FLUENCY PRACTICE

Fluency practice is available at **sadlierconnect.com**.

Concept Development

Understand: What a multiple of 10 is

■ Students are expected to understand and be able to multiply one-digit whole numbers by multiples of 10. In this presentation, students learn what a multiple of 10 is and analyze number patterns in the products of one-digit factors and 10.

■ This is the first time students multiply a two-digit number. Learning to perform mental calculations by using basic facts builds a foundation for number sense and using place value to multiply other two-digit numbers.

■ Have students explain how they know whether a number is a multiple of 10. Encourage students to look at other examples to verify that any number that ends in zero must be a multiple of 10.

Essential Question:
How can you multiply a number by a multiple of 10?
3.NBT.3

Words to Know:
multiple

Guided Instruction

In this lesson you will multiply one-digit numbers by multiples of 10.

Understand: What a multiple of 10 is

> You know how to multiply a one-digit number by another one-digit number. The number 10 is the first two-digit number. What happens when you multiply 3×10?

When you multiply, you find the total of a number of equal groups.

number of groups × number in each group = number in all

| 3 | × | 10 | = | n |

To think about finding 3×10, you can draw an array.

The array shows that 3 groups of 10 is equal to 30: $3 \times 10 = 30$.

The product, 30, is called a multiple of 10. It is a number found by multiplying by 10.

When you skip count by 10s to 90, you name multiples of 10.

10, 20, 30, 40, 50, 60, 70, 80, 90

$1 \times 10 = 10$	Notice the pattern. When you multiply
$2 \times 10 = 20$	a one-digit factor by 10, the tens digit
$3 \times 10 = 30$	of the product is the same as
$4 \times 10 = 40$	that factor.
$5 \times 10 = 50$	Multiplying a one-digit factor by 10 is
$6 \times 10 = 60$	the same as moving that digit to the
$7 \times 10 = 70$	tens place and putting a 0 in the
$8 \times 10 = 80$	ones place.
$9 \times 10 = 90$	

➡ When you multiply 3×10, you get 30. The 3 moves to the tens place and a 0 goes in the ones place.

Words to Know

multiple: the product of a given whole number and another whole number

Glossary can be found on pp. 347–350.

Guided Instruction

Understand: Multiplying by a multiple of 10

> There are desks for 30 students in each of the 4 third-grade classrooms. How many desks are there in the 4 classrooms?

To answer this question, you need to multiply 4×30.

number of groups × number in each group = number in all

| 4 | × | 30 | = | d |

One way to think about finding 4×30 is to draw an array.

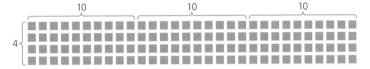

You can count all 120 squares in the array.

Another way to think about this problem is to think about groups of tens. There are 4 groups of 3 tens.

4 groups of 3 tens = ___12___ tens

$4 \times 30 =$ ___120___

➡ There are 120 desks in the 4 classrooms.

There is a faster way to multiply with multiples of 10.

$4 \times 30 = 120$

Notice that you can find 120 by multiplying 4×3 and putting a 0 to the right. When you do this, you are moving the product of 4×3 one place to the left and there is a 0 in the ones place.

✏ Find the product of 6×20 two different ways.
Possible answer: One way is to think of 6 groups of 2 tens:
6 groups of 2 tens equals 12 tens, so $6 \times 20 = 120$
Another way is to multiply the nonzero digits, $6 \times 2 = 12$, and then put a 0 in the ones place to get 120.

Unit 2 ■ Focus on Operations and Algebraic Thinking/Number and Operations in Base Ten **129**

Understand: Multiplying by a multiple of 10

■ In this presentation, students multiply by a multiple of 10. Students should interpret 4×30 as 4 groups of 3 tens and interpret the product as 12 groups of ten. Developing this understanding helps students recognize patterns in multiplying by multiples of 10.

■ Remind students that multiplication is used to find the total number of objects in equal groups. Point out to students that they can use the same strategies they have previously learned, to multiply by a two-digit number.

■ Have students identify the number of groups and the number in each group from the word problem and have them explain how to write the multiplication equation with a letter for the unknown number.

■ Emphasize the use of place value in the explanations in the presentation. Students' understanding should go beyond just writing a zero at the end of the partial product.

✏ Have students restate the expression according to the number of groups and the number in each group. Then ask them to identify the basic fact and explain how to use the fact to find the product.

Support English Language Learners

The term *multiple* is first introduced as a mathematical term in this lesson. Students may know the basic meaning of *multiple* as "more than one" or "many." This is very different from the mathematical definition of "the product of a given whole number and another whole number."

Ask students which operation they think the term is related to: addition, subtraction, multiplication, or division. Students should see that multiple and multiply have similar word structures and only differ in spelling by one letter. Tell students that to find multiples, they multiply a given number by 1, 2, 3, 4, 5, ... Have students copy the multiplication equations shown at the bottom of page 128. Explain that 10, 20, 30, 40, 50, 60, 70, 80, and 90 are some of the *multiples* of 10. A visual representation will help clarify the mathematical definition.

Connect: Using properties when multiplying by a multiple of 10 Use this page to help students strengthen their understanding of how to use properties of operations to multiply one-digit numbers by multiples of 10.

■ Students are expected to multiply using strategies based on properties of operations. In this presentation, the Distributive Property and the Associative Property of Multiplication are used to multiply a one-digit number by a multiple of 10.

■ Ask students why the Distributive Property was used to break apart 30 into 10 + 10 + 10 instead of another way, such as 10 + 20. Explain that it is easier to multiply by 10 than to multiply by a multiple of 10. Also, the resulting products (40) are all the same, so it is easier to add mentally in the final step.

■ Have students explain why they can use the Associative Property to multiply 4 × 3 first. Students should explain that the way factors are grouped does not change the product.

✎ After students have found the product using the Distributive and Associative Properties, point out that both multiplications on this page, 4 × 30 and 6 × 20, have a product of 120. Challenge students to find two more expressions that have a product of 120. Students should reason that 3 × 40 and 2 × 60 also have a product of 120.

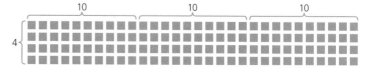

Lesson 15   **Multiply One-Digit Whole Numbers by Multiples of 10**

Guided Instruction

Connect: Using properties when multiplying by a multiple of 10

> How can the properties of multiplication help you understand multiplying a one-digit number by a multiple of 10?

To answer this question, look at the problem on page 129 again. You found the number of desks in 4 classrooms with 30 desks in each classroom. You used this diagram to visualize the problem.

You can use the Distributive Property to find the product.

$$4 \times 30 = 4 \times (10 + 10 + 10)$$
$$= (4 \times 10) + (4 \times 10) + (4 \times 10)$$
$$= 40 + 40 + 40$$
$$4 \times 30 = 120$$

You can use the Associative Property to find the product.

$$4 \times 30 = 4 \times (3 \times 10) \leftarrow \text{Rename 30 as } 3 \times 10.$$
$$= (4 \times 3) \times 10 \leftarrow \text{Use the Associative Property to change the grouping.}$$
$$= 12 \times 10 \leftarrow \text{Multiply } 4 \times 3.$$
$$4 \times 30 = 120 \leftarrow \text{Multiply } 12 \times 10.$$

➡ The properties of multiplication show what happens when a number is multiplied by a multiple of 10.

✎ Find the product of 6 × 20 using the Distributive Property and using the Associative Property.
Possible answer: Using the Distributive Property: $6 \times 20 = 6 \times (10 + 10)$
$$= (6 \times 10) + (6 \times 10)$$
$$= 60 + 60$$
$$= 120$$

Using the Associative Property: $6 \times 20 = 6 \times (2 \times 10)$
$$= (6 \times 2) \times 10$$
$$= 12 \times 10$$
$$= 120$$

130   Unit 2 ■ Focus on Operations and Algebraic Thinking/Number and Operations in Base Ten

Math-to-History Connection

Decades A *decade* is a measurement of time equivalent to 10 years. Explain to students that many time periods in history are referenced by decades. A decade can be converted to years by multiplying by 10. For example, 3 decades = 3 × 10 years = 30 years. Give students mathematical problems to solve such as:

  5 decades = _____ years   _____ decades = 80 years

Create word problems with a historical context using these facts:

• A "score" is 2 decades.

• The Gettysburg Address says, "Four score and seven years ago . . ."

• Martin Luther King, Jr.'s "I Have a Dream Speech" contains the phrase, "Five score years ago . . ."

Complete the multiplication equations to find the product.

1. 3 groups of 7 tens = __21__ tens

   3 × 70 = __210__

2. 2 groups of 8 tens = __16__ tens

   2 × 80 = __160__

3. 5 groups of 2 tens = __10__ tens

   5 × 20 = __100__

4. 4 groups of 6 tens = __24__ tens

   4 × 60 = __240__

5. 3 groups of 9 tens = __27__ tens

   3 × 90 = __270__

6. 7 groups of 6 tens = __42__ tens

   7 × 60 = __420__

7. Draw a diagram to represent 2 × 70. Then find the product.
   Show your work.   Answers will vary.
   Students should draw 2 groups of 7 tens each and explain that 2 groups of
   7 tens = 14 tens; 14 tens is 1 hundred 4 tens = 140. So, 2 × 70 = 140.

☝ Think•Pair•Share

MP4 8. Use what you know about multiplying multiples of 10 to show
   that 2 × 80 equals 8 × 20. Then find the product.
   Possible answer: I can draw arrays to show that 2 groups of 8 tens equals
   16 tens and 8 groups of 2 tens equals 16 tens, so the products are equal.
   The product is 160.

Observational Assessment

Use page 131 to assess whether students are able to multiply one-digit whole numbers by multiples of 10 by using strategies based on place value and properties of operations. Encourage students to explain these strategies aloud.

☝ Think•Pair•Share

Peer Collaboration After students have completed the problem, have students compare their answers with another student. Ask students to consider the following questions:

- *What basic fact did you use to find the products?*

- *How can you use properties of operations to write both expressions in the same way?*

- *How can you use the same array to represent both expressions?*

To summarize, encourage students to use basic facts, place value, and properties of operations as part of their reasoning when they multiply by multiples of 10.

Return to the Essential Question

Reread the Lesson 15 Essential Question on page 128: *How can you multiply a number by a multiple of 10?*

Ask volunteers to use what they learned in this lesson to answer this question. (Possible responses: I can multiply groups of tens. I can multiply the non-zero digits and place a 0 to the right of the partial product.)

Mathematical Practices

Mathematical Practice Standards underline the teaching and understanding of all concepts and skills presented. The emphasis of specific practices is noted throughout the guided and independent practice of this lesson.

MP4	**Model with mathematics.**

Item 8: Students explain the relationship between factors in related expressions.

Independent Practice

Concept Application

Students may work independently on these pages in the classroom or at home. They may refer to the first four pages of the lesson to revisit the instruction or to see a worked-out example.

Common Errors and **Teaching Tips** may help you support student learning either in the classroom or as a follow-up for work done at home.

Common Errors

Item 14

Students may forget to write the second zero at the end of the partial product, and record 10 as the product. Point out that some basic facts end in zero. For those partial products, students must remember to write a second zero.

Teaching Tips

Items 7-16

Have students use basic facts to multiply the non-zero digits and then write a 0 to the right of the partial product.

Independent Practice

Find the unknown factor to complete the equations.

1. 2 groups of __6__ tens = 12 tens
   2 × __60__ = 120

2. 3 groups of __7__ tens = 21 tens
   3 × __70__ = 210

3. 1 group of __5__ tens = 5 tens
   1 × __50__ = 50

4. 9 groups of __4__ tens = 36 tens
   9 × __40__ = 360

5. 4 groups of __8__ tens = 32 tens
   4 × __80__ = 320

6. 9 groups of __9__ tens = 81 tens
   9 × __90__ = 810

Find the product. You can use place-value models.

7. 4 × 80 = __320__

8. 9 × 40 = __360__

9. 7 × 10 = __70__

10. 0 × 30 = __0__

11. 6 × 90 = __540__

12. 7 × 70 = __490__

13. 40 × 2 = __80__

14. 20 × 5 = __100__

15. 70 × 5 = __350__

16. 90 × 5 = __450__

Writing About Math

▸ **Write an Informative Text** Have students write a "How to" paragraph explaining how to multiply by multiples of 10. Tell students to imagine that they are explaining the method to a fellow classmate who was absent for the lesson. Students can include details and examples from the lesson, as well as any illustrations that help them explain the method.

Have students trade their written directions with a partner. Students should evaluate their partner's paragraphs to make sure the directions are clear and concise and give feedback, if necessary. Students should make changes to their directions based on their partner's feedback. When students are finished, ask volunteers to share their work with the class.

Lesson 15

Independent Practice

Circle the correct answer.

17. What is the product of 8 × 40?

   a. 32

   (b.) 320

   c. 3,200

   d. 32,000

18. What is the product of 60 × 5?

   a. 300,000

   b. 30,000

   c. 3,000

   (d.) 300

19. What is the next number in the pattern?
    40, 80, 120, 160, _____

   a. 160

   b. 180

   (c.) 200

   d. 220

MP1 20. Circle all computations that do NOT help you find the product
    of 9 × 70.

   a. 9 × 7

   b. 7 × 9

   (c.) (7 + 9) × 10

   (d.) 9 + 9 + 9 + 9 + 9 + 9

Unit 2 ■ Focus on Operations and Algebraic Thinking/Number and Operations in Base Ten **133**

Teaching Tips

Item 19

Have students use a simpler pattern (basic facts) to find the pattern rule and then apply that rule to find the next number in the pattern.

Item 20

Point out that the instructions indicate that there may be more than one correct answer.

Mathematical Practices	
MP1	**Make sense of problems and persevere in solving them.**
Item 20: Students check solutions to find related expressions.	

Teaching Tips

Items 21-22

Tell students that finding the product first may help them write their explanations clearly and concisely.

Items 23-24

Have students write a word equation for each problem before solving: number of groups × number in each group = number in all.

Independent Practice

MP8 **21.** Explain how to compute the product of 20 × 3.
Possible answer: I can multiply factors in any order, so I can think of the problem as 3 × 20. Then I can find how many tens 3 groups of 2 tens each make: 3 × 2 tens = 6 tens. I know that 6 tens = 60, so 20 × 3 = 60.

MP7 **22.** Explain how to find the product of 4 × 60.
Possible answer: I can find how many tens 4 groups of 6 tens each make: 4 × 6 tens = 24 tens. I know that 6 tens equals 60. So, 4 × 60 = 240.

Solve the problems.

MP1 **23.** At the animal shelter, each box of dog food holds 30 cans. How many cans of dog food are in 6 boxes?

▶ **Show your work.**
Possible answer:
To solve the problem, I need to find the product of 6 × 30.
6 × 30 = 6 groups of 3 tens = 6 × 3 tens = 18 tens
18 tens = 180
So, 6 × 30 = 180

Answer There are 180 cans of dog food in 6 boxes.

MP2 **24.** Each sheet of stickers holds 60 stickers. If Roxanne has 8 sheets, how many stickers does she have?

▶ **Show your work.**
Possible answer:
To solve the problem, I need to find the product of 8 × 60.
8 × 60 = 8 groups of 6 tens = 8 × 6 tens = 48 tens
48 tens = 480
So, 8 × 60 = 480

Answer Roxanne has 480 stickers.

Mathematical Practices	
MP1	**Make sense of problems and persevere in solving them.**
Item 23: Students analyze a problem and plan a solution.	
MP2	**Reason abstractly and quantitatively.**
Item 24: Students represent problems using symbols.	
MP7	**Look for and make use of structure.**
Item 22: Students evaluate the structure of a problem.	
MP8	**Look for and express regularity in repeated reasoning.**
Item 21: Students make generalizations in computation.	

Lesson 15

Independent Practice

MP6 **25.** Two hundred students from the school are going on a field trip. How many buses will the school need if only 40 students can ride on each bus?

Show your work.
Possible answer:
To show the problem, I can write an equation: $40 \times b = 200$.
Then I need to find the unknown factor, b.
40 is 4 tens and 200 is 20 tens.
I know that $4 \times 5 = 20$, so 4 tens $\times 5 = 20$ tens.
So, $40 \times 5 = 200$; $b = 5$.

Answer The school will need 5 buses.

MP3 **26.** Maiko says that 6 times 50 is 30. Give the correct answer and explain her error.

Answer The correct answer is 300.

Justify your answer using words, drawings, or numbers.
Possible justification: Maiko may have correctly multiplied 6×5 to get 30, but she probably forgot to move the product one place to the left to get 300.

MP2 **27.** Kyle says that 5×80 is the same as $80 + 80 + 80 + 80 + 80$. Is his thinking correct?

Answer Yes, $5 \times 80 = 80 + 80 + 80 + 80 + 80$.

Justify your answer using words, drawings, or numbers.
Possible justification: Multiplying a number by 5 is the same as adding the same number 5 times, so Kyle is correct. Another way to think about this is to find the product and the sum and show that they are equal:
$5 \times 80 = 5 \times 8$ tens $= 40$ tens $= 400$ and $80 + 80 + 80 + 80 + 80 = 400$.

Common Errors

Item 25

Students may use 200 as a factor and incorrectly try to find 200 × 40. Help them identify this problem as an unknown factor problem with 200 as the product. Guide students to write a multiplication equation using a letter for the unknown quantity.

Teaching Tips

Item 26

Remind students that it is helpful to solve the problem correctly to identify where another student made an error. If students have trouble identifying the error, have them write Maiko's problem as 6 × 5 tens = 3 tens.

Return to the

Remind students to return to the Progress Check self-assessment, page 77, to check off additional items they have mastered during the unit.

Mathematical Practices

MP2	**Reason abstractly and quantitatively.**
Item 27: Students use symbols to relate multiplication and addition.	
MP3	**Construct viable arguments and critique the reasoning of others.**
Item 26: Students use previously established results in constructing arguments.	
MP6	**Attend to precision.**
Item 25: Students give carefully formulated explanations.	

The Common Core Review covers all the standards presented in the unit. Use it to assess your students' mastery of the unit's concepts and skills.

Depth of Knowledge

The depth of knowledge is a ranking of the content complexity of assessment items based on Webb's Depth of Knowledge (DOK) levels. The levels increase in complexity as shown below.

Level 1: Recall and Reproduction
Level 2: Basic Skills and Concepts
Level 3: Strategic Reasoning and Thinking
Level 4: Extended Thinking

Item	Standard	DOK
1	3.OA.9	2
2	3.OA.9	2
3	3.NBT.2	2
4	3.NBT.2	2
5	3.NBT.2	2
6	3.NBT.2	2
7	3.NBT.2	2
8	3.NBT.2	2
9	3.OA.9	3
10	3.OA.7	3
11	3.NBT.1	2
12	3.NBT.1	2
13	3.NBT.3	1
14	3.NBT.3	1
15	3.NBT.3	1
16	3.OA.8	3
17	3.OA.9	4
18	3.OA.8	3
19	3.OA.7	4
20	3.NBT.2	3

For exercises 1 and 2, use the number pattern below.

| 7 | 14 | 21 | 28 | 35 | 42 | 49 |

1. Write the next three numbers in the pattern.

2. What is the pattern rule? _____ Add 7; skip count by 7. _____

For exercises 3–8, add or subtract.

3.
```
  358
+ 436
-----
  794
```

4.
```
  562
+  49
-----
  611
```

5.
```
  261
  305
+ 387
-----
  953
```

6.
```
  489
- 286
-----
  203
```

7.
```
  725
- 698
-----
   27
```

8.
```
  806
- 378
-----
  428
```

9. Mike knows that $4 \times 6 = 24$. How can Mike use $4 \times 6 = 24$ to find the product of 8×6?
Possible answer: Mike can double the answer: If $4 \times 6 = 24$ and $24 + 24 = 48$, then $8 \times 6 = 48$.

10. Raisa knows that 7 groups of 9 make 63. How can Raisa use that information to find the quotient of 63 and 9?
Possible answer: Raisa can use the same three numbers to make a related division. So 63 divided by 9 is 7. Raisa can also write the multiplication fact $7 \times 9 = 63$ and use it to find the quotient for the related division $63 \div 9$.

Answer $63 \div 9 = $ ___7___

UNIT 2 Common Core Review

11. What is 35 rounded to the nearest ten?

   a. 10   b. 30

   c. 35   (d.) 40

12. What is 549 rounded to the nearest hundred?

   a. 600   b. 550

   (c.) 500   d. 100

For exercises 13–15, find the product.

13. $3 \times 50 = \underline{150}$ 14. $1 \times 90 = \underline{90}$ 15. $70 \times 4 = \underline{280}$

MP4 16. Katsu runs 2 miles each day. His goal is to run a total of 20 miles. After 7 days, how many miles does Katsu have left to run in order to meet his goal?

   Choose the equation you can use to solve the problem?

   a. $2 + 7 + n = 20$ (b.) $2 \times 7 + n = 20$

   c. $4 \times 7 + n = 20$ d. $2 + 7 \times n = 20$

   Answer Katsu has 6 miles left to run.

MP7 17. What do you notice about the numbers highlighted in green in the multiplication table? Explain the pattern using a multiplication property.

Possible answer:
The products start at 0 and increase by 7; the products are the same as you go down the column for 7 or across the row for 7. This is true because of the Commutative, or order, Property of Multiplication. The order in which you multiply factors does not matter; for example, $7 \times 4 = 28$ and $4 \times 7 = 28$.

×	0	1	2	3	4	5	6	7	8	9
0	0	0	0	0	0	0	0	0	0	0
1	0	1	2	3	4	5	6	7	8	9
2	0	2	4	6	8	10	12	14	16	18
3	0	3	6	9	12	15	18	21	24	27
4	0	4	8	12	16	20	24	28	32	36
5	0	5	10	15	20	25	30	35	40	45
6	0	6	12	18	24	30	36	42	48	54
7	0	7	14	21	28	35	42	49	56	63
8	0	8	16	24	32	40	48	56	64	72
9	0	9	18	27	36	45	54	63	72	81

Unit 2 ■ Focus on Operations and Algebraic Thinking/Number and Operations in Base Ten **137**

This chart correlates the Common Core Review items with the lessons in which the concepts and skills are presented.

Item	Lesson
1	12
2	12
3	14
4	14
5	14
6	14
7	14
8	14
9	12
10	9
11	13
12	13
13	15
14	15
15	15
16	11
17	12
18	10
19	9
20	14

Mathematical Practices

MP4	**Model with mathematics.**
Item 16: Students interpret the solution in the context of a situation.	
MP7	**Look for and make sure use of structure.**
Item 17: Students use patterns to explain their reasoning.	

Writing About Math

✏️ Direct students to respond to the Unit 2 Essential Question. (This can also be found on student page 79.)

Essential Question:
How does understanding place value help you add, subtract, and multiply?

Possible responses:
- When you add, you combine digits in like place values; you can regroup ones and tens.
- When you subtract, you can regroup hundreds and tens.
- When you multiply, you must consider the place value of the factors.

Unit Assessment

- Unit 2 Common Core Review, *pp. 136–138*
- Unit 2 Performance Task ONLINE

Additional Assessment Options

Optional Purchase:
- iProgress Monitor ONLINE
- Progress Monitor Student Benchmark Assessment Booklet

Solve the problems.

MP4 **18.** Yvette has 8 books. Darcie has twice as many books as Yvette. How many books do they have in all?

✏️ **Show your work.**
Solutions may vary. Possible answer: I can use a number line model.

8 plus 2 times 8 is 24.

0 1 2 3 4 5 6 7 8 9 10 11 12 13 14 15 16 17 18 19 20 21 22 23 24

I can write and solve equations to find the answer.
$2 \times 8 = 16$
$16 + 8 = 24$

Answer They have 24 books in all.

MP3 **19.** Tariq says that a reasonable estimate for the quotient of $55 \div 7$ is 8. Is Tariq correct?

Answer Yes, Tariq is correct.

✏️ **Justify your answer using words, drawings, or numbers.**
Possible justification: I can divide using compatible numbers, $56 \div 7 = 8$. So the quotient of $55 \div 7$ is close to 8.

MP8 **20.** Dr. Wu studies birds and goes bird watching. He counts 329 birds on the first day and 441 birds on the second day. How many birds does Dr. Wu count altogether? Explain your reasoning.

✏️ **Show your work.**
Possible answer: To solve the problem, I can break apart the addends 329 and 441 into hundreds, tens, and ones. $300 + 400 = 700$, $20 + 40 = 60$, and $9 + 1 = 10$. Regroup 10 ones as 1 ten, and add the ten to the other tens: $60 + 10 = 70$. So, the sum is $700 + 70 = 770$.

Answer Dr. Wu counts 770 birds altogether.

Mathematical Practices

MP3	**Construct viable arguments and critique the reasoning of others.**
Item 19: Students analyze an answer and share their reasoning.	
MP4	**Model with mathematics.**
Item 18: Students may use a number line to model a solution.	
MP8	**Look for and express regularity in repeated reasoning.**
Item 20: Students look for and apply problem-solving methods to find a solution.	

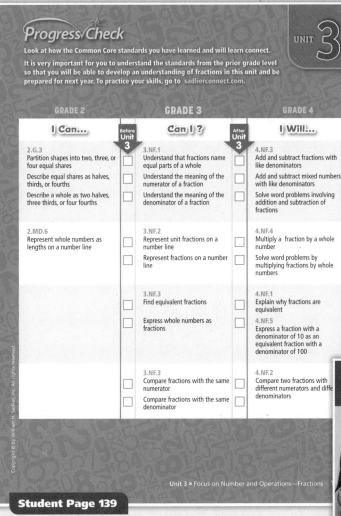

Progress Check

UNIT 3

Look at how the Common Core standards you have learned and will learn connect.

It is very important for you to understand the standards from the prior grade level so that you will be able to develop an understanding of fractions in this unit and be prepared for next year. To practice your skills, go to sadlierconnect.com.

GRADE 2			GRADE 3			GRADE 4	
I Can...	Before Unit 3		**Can I ?**	After Unit 3		**I Will...**	
2.G.3 Partition shapes into two, three, or four equal shares	☐		**3.NF.1** Understand that fractions name equal parts of a whole	☐		**4.NF.3** Add and subtract fractions with like denominators	☐
Describe equal shares as halves, thirds, or fourths	☐		Understand the meaning of the numerator of a fraction	☐		Add and subtract mixed numbers with like denominators	☐
Describe a whole as two halves, three thirds, or four fourths	☐		Understand the meaning of the denominator of a fraction	☐		Solve word problems involving addition and subtraction of fractions	☐
2.MD.6 Represent whole numbers as lengths on a number line	☐		**3.NF.2** Represent unit fractions on a number line	☐		**4.NF.4** Multiply a fraction by a whole number	☐
			Represent fractions on a number line	☐		Solve word problems by multiplying fractions by whole numbers	☐
			3.NF.3 Find equivalent fractions	☐		**4.NF.1** Explain why fractions are equivalent	☐
			Express whole numbers as fractions	☐		**4.NF.5** Express a fraction with a denominator of 10 as an equivalent fraction with a denominator of 100	☐
			3.NF.3 Compare fractions with the same numerator	☐		**4.NF.2** Compare two fractions with different numerators and diffe... denominators	☐
			Compare fractions with the same denominator	☐			

Unit 3 ■ Focus on Number and Operations—Fractions

Student Page 139

Progress Check

Progress Check is a self-assessment tool that students can use to gauge their own progress. Research shows that when students take accountability for their learning, motivation increases.

Before students begin work in Unit 3, have them check any items they know they can do well. Explain that it is fine if they don't check any of the boxes; they will have the opportunity to learn and practice all the standards through the course of the unit.

Let them know that at the end of the unit they will review their checklists to check their progress. After students have completed the last lesson of the unit, before they begin Common Core Review, you will be prompted to have students revisit this page.

HOME ◆ CONNECT...

The Home Connect feature is a way to keep parents or other adult family members apprised of what their children are learning. The key learning objectives are listed, and some ideas for related activities and discussions are included.

Explain to students that they can share the Home Connect page at home with their families. Let students know there is an activity connected to their classroom learning that they can do with their families.

Encourage students and their parents to share their experiences using the suggestions on the Home Connect. You may wish to invite students to share this work with the class.

HOME ◆ CONNECT...

A pizza pie is a great example to use with your child about fractions. Most pizza pies are pre-sliced with eight equal slices. In this example, the pizza is the whole that can be partitioned into equal parts. The slices of the pizza pie are the equal parts of the whole pizza pie. One slice of pizza represents a unit fraction, in this case $\frac{1}{8}$.

Use the following math vocabulary to talk about ways you could share this pizza pie.

• A **fraction** is a number that describes parts of a whole. A fraction contains a numerator and a denominator.

numerator tells how many equal parts you are talking about
denominator tells how many equal parts are in the whole

• A fraction that shows 1 equal part of a whole is known as a **unit fraction**. A unit fraction has 1 as the numerator. Example: $\frac{1}{8}$

Activity: Make a set of fraction strips with your child using three strips of paper in three different colors. Choose one colored strip to represent one whole. Choose a second colored strip, fold it, and cut it into two equal pieces to represent halves ($\frac{1}{2}$). Label each piece as $\frac{1}{2}$. Repeat this process of folding, cutting, and labeling equal pieces for fourths ($\frac{1}{4}$). Explore the fraction strips and find relationships among the unit and equivalent fractions.

In this unit your child will:

■ Understand that fractions name equal parts of a whole.

■ Understand the meaning of the numerator of a fraction.

■ Understand the meaning of the denominator of a fraction.

■ Represent unit fractions on a number line.

■ Represent fractions on a number line.

■ Find equivalent fractions.

■ Express whole numbers as fractions.

■ Compare fractions with the same numerator.

■ Compare fractions with the same denominator.

NOTE: All of these learning goals for your child are based on the Grade 3 Common Core State Standards for Mathematics.

Ways to Help Your Child

Make time to talk with your child's teacher. Ask about your child's level of progress, and find out if there are ways that you can assist with his or her learning at home. If your child needs extra practice, your support can really make a difference.

ONLINE
For more Home Connect activities, continue online at sadlierconnect.com

140 Unit 3 ■ Focus on Number and Operations—Fractions

Student Page 140

UNIT PLANNER

Lesson	Standard(s)	Objective
16 Understand Unit Fractions as Quantities	3.NF.1	Understand that a unit fraction is one part of a whole partitioned into equal parts.
17 Understand Fractions as Quantities	3.NF.1	Use unit fractions to form other fractions with numerators greater than one.
18 Understand Fractions on the Number Line	3.NF.2a 3.NF.2b	Understand how to represent fractions on a number line.
19 Understand Equivalent Fractions	3.NF.3a	Use a number line to understand equivalent fractions.
20 Write Equivalent Fractions	3.NF.3b	Use models to find equivalent fractions.
21 Relate Whole Numbers and Fractions	3.NF.3c	Express whole numbers as fractions and fractions as whole numbers.
22 Compare Fractions: Same Denominator	3.NF.3d	Compare two fractions that have the same denominator.
23 Compare Fractions: Same Numerator	3.NF.3d	Compare two fractions that have the same numerator.

Essential Question	Words to Know
What are unit fractions?	fraction, unit fraction, numerator, denominator
How is a unit fraction used to build other fractions?	
How can I represent a fraction on a number line?	number line
How can I use a number line to understand that two fractions are equivalent?	equivalent fractions
How can I use area models to write equivalent fractions?	
How can I relate whole numbers and fractions?	whole number
How can I compare fractions with the same denominator?	
How can I compare fractions with the same numerator?	

Unit Assessment

- Unit 3 Common Core Review, *pp. 206–208*
- Unit 3 Performance Task   (ONLINE)

Additional Assessment Options

- Performance Task 1, *pp. 209–214*
  (ALSO ONLINE)

Optional Purchase:

- iProgress Monitor   (ONLINE)
- Progress Monitor Student Benchmark Assessment Booklet

(ONLINE)   Digital Resources

- Home Connect Activities
- Unit Performance Tasks
- Additional Practice
- Fluency Practice
- Teacher Resources
- iProgress Monitor (optional purchase)

Go to SadlierConnect.com to access your Digital Resources.

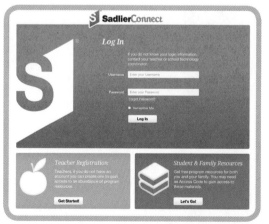

For more detailed instructions see page T3.

LEARNING PROGRESSIONS

This page provides more in-depth detail on the development of the standards across the grade levels. See also the unit Progress Check page in the Student Edition for a roadmap of the Learning Progressions.

Grade 2

- Students represent whole numbers as lengths on a number line. (2.MD.6)
- Students partition shapes into two, three, or four equal shares and describe them as halves, thirds, and fourths. (2.G.3)
- Students describe a whole as two halves, three thirds, or four fourths. (2.G.3)

Grade 3

- Students will work with fractions less than one that have denominators of 2, 3, 4, 6, and 8. (3.NF)
- Unit fractions are introduced in the first lesson and will be used later in the unit as the building block for other fractions. Students should learn that the numerator signals the number of constituent unit fractions, while the denominator signals the number of parts that make up the whole. (3.NF.1)
- Note that the word *partition* is used when working with equal parts of an object or figure. (3.NF.1)
- The lessons progress from having students work with drawings of fractional parts to discerning relative value of fractions on the number line. It is crucial for future work with the number system that students develop an understanding of fractions as numbers and are able to place them on a number line. Students who struggle with relating the model for a fraction such as $\frac{3}{8}$ to its position on the number line in Lesson 18 may need extra time and support. (3.NF.2)
- In the last two lessons, the instruction relates the concept of equal parts to fraction strips. Students must understand how equivalent fractions can be applied to representing whole numbers by equivalent fractions. (3.NF.3)
- Students compare fractions with the same numerator or denominator to write number sentences using =, <, and >. (3.NF.3d)

Grade 4

- The concept of equivalent fractions is extended to general cases. The student recognizes, generates, and explains equivalent fractions. (4.NF.1)
- The student compares two fractions that have different numerators and denominators. (4.NF.2)
- Students add and subtract fractions and mixed numbers with like denominators and solve related word problems. (4.NF.3)
- Students multiply fractions by whole numbers and solve related word problems. (4.NF.4)
- Fraction equivalence is applied to express fractions with denominators of 10 as equivalent fractions with denominators of 100. (4.NF.5)

Focus on Number and Operations—Fractions

Essential Question:
How are fractions and whole numbers alike?

Essential Question:
How are fractions and whole numbers alike?

As students become involved with the Essential Question they will begin to see fractions as quantities, like whole numbers, that can be located on the number line, that have equivalencies, and that can be compared.

Conversation Starters

Have students discuss the photograph. Ask questions such as: *What food is being served? What kinds of toppings do you see? What is your favorite topping? What is your least favorite topping?* Have students look at the pizza. *Look at how the pizza is sliced. How many slices are there on this pizza? How do you know? What do the slices look like?* (There are 8 because I can count the cuts at the center of the pizza. Each slice is part of a circle.)

Have students analyze each slice. *Which slices do you think are about to be eaten? How do you know?* (The slice on the top left and the slice on the right are about to be eaten because they are being picked up or served.) *How many slices will be left?* (There will be 6 slices left.)

Let students work in pairs to discuss how to determine how many pizzas it would take to have enough for everyone in the class to have a slice. Lead them to develop a multi-step plan for solving this problem by using addition or multiplication.

Activity

Materials: construction paper, scissors, and glue
Tell students to work in a small group to make their own pizzas from construction paper. They will minimally need a circle, but they may want to add toppings. Ask students to cut their pizzas into 4 equal pieces. Talk about folding the pizzas in half twice and cutting along the fold lines.

On the board, put a table with three columns: number of pieces, pieces eaten, and pieces left. Using their pizzas, each group should model a different number of pieces eaten: 0, 1, 2, 3, or 4. As a class, discuss what numbers will complete the table.

Common Core Focus:

3.NF.1 Understand a fraction 1/*b* as the quantity formed by 1 part when a whole is partitioned into *b* equal parts; understand a fraction *a/b* as the quantity formed by *a* parts of size 1/*b*.

OBJECTIVE

Understand that a unit fraction is one part of a whole partitioned into equal parts.

ESSENTIAL QUESTION

Remind students that in Grade 2, they partitioned circles and rectangles into equal shares and used *halves, thirds,* and *fourths* to describe those shares. Explain that in this lesson, students will learn to write a *fraction* to describe an equal share. Tell students that a fraction is a number that names part of a whole, so it is not a whole number.

PREREQUISITE SKILLS

Use Item E on page 339 of the Foundational Skills Handbook to review how to partition shapes into equal shares.

FLUENCY PRACTICE

Fluency practice is available at **sadlierconnect.com**.

Lesson
16
Understand Unit Fractions as Quantities

Essential Question:
What are unit fractions?
3.NF.1

Words to Know:
fraction
unit fraction
numerator
denominator

Guided Instruction

In this lesson you will learn about fractions and unit fractions.

Understand: The meaning of a unit fraction

> For art class Jenna partitions a square into four equal parts in different ways. Then she shades one part of each square. Here are Jenna's drawings.
>
>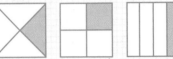
>
> What number does the shaded part in each of Jenna's drawings represent?

A fraction is a number. When a whole is partitioned, or divided, into equal parts, a unit fraction represents the quantity, or amount, in one of those equal parts.

All fractions have this form:

$$\frac{\text{numerator}}{\text{denominator}}$$ ← number of equal parts in the fraction
← number of equal parts in the whole

A unit fraction has this form:

$$\frac{1}{\text{denominator}}$$ ← 1 equal part in the fraction
← number of equal parts in the whole

Look at Jenna's drawings.
Each square has 1 equal part that is shaded.
Each square has 4 equal parts.

1 equal part in the fraction ⟶ $\frac{1}{4}$
4 equal parts in the whole ⟶

Read $\frac{1}{4}$ as "one fourth."

▷ The shaded part in each of Jenna's drawings represents the unit fraction $\frac{1}{4}$.

142 Unit 3 ▪ Focus on Number and Operations—Fractions

Concept Development

Understand: The meaning of a unit fraction

■ This is the first experience students have with writing fractions. Be mindful that students' first interaction with fractions involves unit fractions (fractions with a numerator of 1), which are formed by partitioning a whole into equal parts.

■ As you guide students through the presentation, remind them that since the squares are all the same size, and each square is divided into four equal parts, the parts must all be equal.

Words to Know

fraction: a number that names part of a whole, an area, or a group that can be expressed in the form $\frac{a}{b}$

unit fraction: represents the quantity, or amount, in one of the equal parts of a whole

numerator: the number of equal parts being considered in a fraction, shown above the bar in a fraction

denominator: the number of equal parts in the whole, shown below the bar in a fraction

Glossary can be found on pp. 347–350.

Understand: The numerator in a unit fraction

Pat and Juan want to play a board game, but the spinner is missing. Pat makes a spinner with three equal parts. $\frac{1}{3}$ of the spinner is purple. How many equal parts of the spinner are purple?

Use what you know about the form of a unit fraction.

In $\frac{1}{3}$ the numerator, 1, means one of three equal parts.

▷ So one equal part of the spinner is purple.

Understand: The denominator in a unit fraction

Manny cut out $\frac{1}{8}$ of a red paper strip. Here is what his cutout looked like.

Draw a model of the whole paper strip.

Use what you know about the denominator of a unit fraction.

In $\frac{1}{8}$ the denominator means that the whole is partitioned into 8 equal parts.

Draw a model of a strip with 8 equal parts that are the same as Manny's cutout.

▷ Here is a model of the whole paper strip.

▸ Draw a spinner that is $\frac{1}{4}$ green.
Students' drawings should show a spinner with 4 equal parts, one of which is green.

Unit 3 ▪ Focus on Number and Operations—Fractions   **143**

Understand: The numerator in a unit fraction

■ Make sure students understand that the numerator in a unit fraction represents 1 equal part of the whole, so the numerator of a unit fraction is always 1. Understanding that a fraction is a part of a whole is the basis for all fraction concepts.

■ Extend students' thinking and reinforce understanding by asking, "How many equal parts of the spinner are blue?"

Understand: The denominator in a unit fraction

■ Be sure students understand that the denominator in a unit fraction or any fraction shows that the whole is partitioned into that many equal parts. To check for understanding, have students count the number of pieces in the whole paper strip to verify that there are 8 equal pieces.

 Check for understanding to make sure students know that the unit fraction is $\frac{1}{4}$, which means to partition the spinner into 4 equal parts. As students work, make sure they draw 4 parts that are equal in size. Ask students to share how they drew equal parts. Since there are 4 parts, one method would be to draw a line to partition the spinner into two equal parts, then draw another line to partition the circle into four equal parts.

Support English Language Learners

The terms *fraction, unit fraction, numerator,* and *denominator* are all new words for students in the third grade. To help students develop a better understanding of each word, write each of these words on the board. Next, say each word aloud having students repeat after you.

Then, draw an example below each word. Point to each example and ask, "What is this?" Have students say the term for each example. Finally, erase the board and draw examples of each term and provide labels. Invite students to come to the board and label the example. Repeat this process until students grasp the meaning of each term.

Guided Instruction

Connect: What you know about unit fractions

Use this page to help students strengthen their understanding of unit fractions and develop their skills in identifying a particular unit fraction.

■ In this presentation, students are first asked to identify the denominator in Step 1, and then the numerator in Step 2. Focus attention on the meaning of denominator and numerator by recording the denominator then the numerator for the class to see. This may help students develop a deeper understanding of fractions.

■ Emphasize to students that they can only name a fraction when the whole is partitioned into equal parts.

■ Ask students to describe why the fraction of the poster board Jill paints is a unit fraction. Ensure students' answers include that the poster board is partitioned into equal parts, and that Jill painted one part of the poster board.

Guided Instruction

Connect: What you know about unit fractions

Mr. Smith buys poster board for his daughter, Jill.
He partitions the poster board into equal parts.
Jill paints one of the parts.
Use the drawing to name the fraction of the poster board Jill paints.

Jill's Poster Board

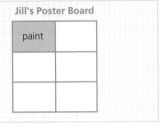

You can name the fraction because you know that the whole is partitioned into equal parts.

Step 1

Identify the denominator.

Count the number of equal parts in the whole poster board.

There are 6 equal parts in the whole poster board.

So the denominator of the fraction is 6.

> **Remember!**
> The denominator tells how many equal parts are in the whole.

Step 2

Identify the numerator.

Count the number of equal parts with paint.

There is 1 equal part with paint.

So the numerator of the fraction is 1.

Write the numerator and denominator to show the fraction.

$$\frac{1}{6}$$

 Jill paints $\frac{1}{6}$ of the poster board.

144   Unit 3 ■ Focus on Number and Operations—Fractions

Math-to-Math Connection

Different Uses of "Unit" The word *unit* has many different uses in mathematics. In general, a unit is to represent "one" of something. A unit fraction has a numerator of 1; a unit square has side lengths of 1 unit and an area of 1 square unit; and a unit cube has a side length of 1 unit and a volume of 1 cubic unit.

Units are also used to represent a particular quantity in measurement. For example, if an object measures 4 inches, the unit is 1 inch, which represents the quantity by which the object is measured; 4 inches is 4 times the length of 1 inch.

Guided Practice

Each model represents a whole. Write a unit fraction for the shaded part of each model.

1.  $\frac{1}{3}$

2. 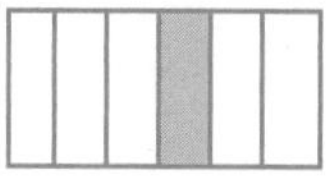 $\frac{1}{6}$

3. 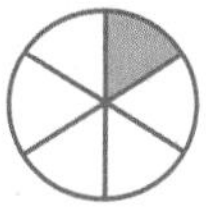 $\frac{1}{6}$

Use the model at the right for exercises 4–6.

Possible drawing:

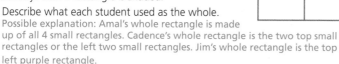

4. Draw lines in the square to show fourths.
5. How many equal parts are in your model? 4
6. Write a unit fraction that represents one equal part of your model. $\frac{1}{4}$

Solve the problem.

7. Rita makes a flower garden and divides it into three equal sections. She plants $\frac{1}{3}$ of the garden with yellow flowers. Draw a model to show the fraction of the garden Rita plants with yellow flowers.

Possible drawing:

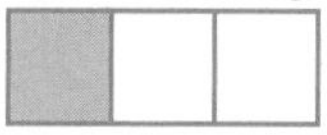

Think•Pair•Share

MP3 8. Amal says that $\frac{1}{4}$ of a rectangle is shaded. Cadence says that $\frac{1}{2}$ of a rectangle is shaded. Jim says that 1 rectangle is shaded. Describe what each student used as the whole.

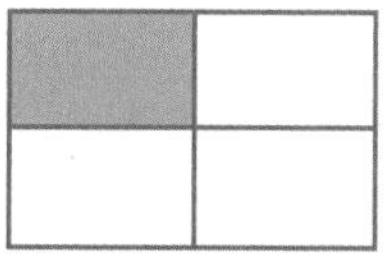

Possible explanation: Amal's whole rectangle is made up of all 4 small rectangles. Cadence's whole rectangle is the two top small rectangles or the left two small rectangles. Jim's whole rectangle is the top left purple rectangle.

Mathematical Practices

Mathematical Practice Standards underline the teaching and understanding of all concepts and skills presented. The emphasis of specific practices is noted throughout the guided and independent practice of this lesson.

MP3	**Construct viable arguments and critique the reasoning of others.**

Item 8: Students analyze a problem and explain the reasoning behind how each person arrived at each given answer.

Observational Assessment

Use page 145 to assess whether students understand how to create and write unit fractions. Check to see that students know the correct placement of the numerator and denominator. Note those students who struggle with item 7, as students must draw a model of a unit fraction on their own. Check that students completed their model by shading one part of their model.

Think•Pair•Share

Peer Collaboration Have students work in pairs to analyze the problem and determine what whole each person used. Have students share their answers with the class to make sure there is agreement on the correct answer. Ask questions such as:

- *How did the denominator of each unit fraction help you to determine the whole?*
- *Could any of the unit fractions be represented by more than one whole?*

To summarize, ask for volunteers to draw the rectangles that Amal, Cadence, and Jim each used as the whole.

Return to the Essential Question

Reread the Lesson 16 Essential Question on page 142: *What are unit fractions?*

Ask volunteers to use what they learned in this lesson to answer this question. (Possible response: A unit fraction represents 1 of the equal parts of a whole.)

Invite volunteers to the board to draw a model of a shape divided into equal parts, and give an example of a unit fraction from their model.

Concept Application

Students may work independently on these pages in the classroom or at home. They may refer to the first four pages of the lesson to revisit the instruction or to see a worked-out example.

Common Errors and **Teaching Tips** may help you support student learning either in the classroom or as a follow-up for work done at home.

Common Errors

Item 4

Students may incorrectly select choice b or choice d as the answer because the models are divided into thirds. Remind students to look for the model that shows 3 equal parts with 1 part shaded. A student who chooses choice a, will need more practice identifying unit fractions.

Item 5

Students may select choice d as the correct answer because the numbers are correct, but the numerator and denominator have been switched. Redirect students to the definitions of *numerator* and *denominator.*

Independent Practice

Each figure represents one whole. Write the unit fraction that the shaded part of each figure represents.

1. $\frac{1}{2}$ 2. $\frac{1}{3}$ 3. $\frac{1}{6}$

4. Look at the shaded part of each model. Which model represents the fraction $\frac{1}{3}$?

a.   b.

(c.)   d.

5. Which fraction does the shaded part of the circle represent?

(a.) $\frac{1}{8}$ b. $\frac{1}{4}$

c. $\frac{1}{1}$ d. $\frac{8}{1}$

Writing About Math

▸ **Write an Explanatory Text** Ask students to write an explanation of what a unit fraction is and give two examples. Have students choose their audience and purpose for writing. For example, a student might write an explanation of unit fraction to a classmate who has been absent or to a new classmate.

When the papers are completed, have students trade papers with a partner. Ask students to read their partner's paper and determine if the explanation is correct.

Independent Practice

Partition each figure into the given number of equal parts.
Shade one part. Then write the fraction for the shaded part.

6. 2 equal parts

Answer ____ $\frac{1}{2}$ ____

7. 4 equal parts

Answer ____ $\frac{1}{4}$ ____

8. Show two different ways to partition a square into thirds.
Shade 1 equal part of each square. Write the fraction that
one equal part represents. Possible answers:

Answer ____ $\frac{1}{3}$ ____

Answer ____ $\frac{1}{3}$ ____

9. This square is $\frac{1}{6}$ of a whole.
Draw a model of the whole.
Label each unit fraction.

$\boxed{\frac{1}{6}}$

Possible answer:

$\boxed{\frac{1}{6} \mid \frac{1}{6} \mid \frac{1}{6} \mid \frac{1}{6} \mid \frac{1}{6} \mid \frac{1}{6}}$

Common Errors

Item 8

Students may partition the square into
3 unequal parts. Remind students that
each third of the same square must
be the same size. Help students by
demonstrating how to partition a square
into 3 equal parts. Then shade 1 part to
illustrate 1 third.

Item 9

Students may label each equal part
in succession ($\frac{1}{6}$, $\frac{2}{6}$, $\frac{3}{6}$, . . .). Remind
students to label each part with the unit
fraction $\frac{1}{6}$.

Digital Connection

Random Number Generator Use a search engine to find a random
number generator Web site. Assign parameters for the random number
generator to select two numbers between 2 and 10. Have students
work in pairs to write two different unit fractions, using the randomly
generated numbers as the denominators. Students should then draw
a model for each unit fraction. Encourage students to use a different
geometric shape for each model. Challenge students to choose one of
their models and draw it in another way, such as a rectangle with vertical
lines and a rectangle with horizontal lines.

Independent Practice

Teaching Tips

Item 10

Remind students that unit fractions will have 1 as their numerator. Tell students they should write two different unit fractions. Encourage students to tell how the two fractions are the same and how they are different.

Item 11

Tell students that their pictures must show equal parts, and only 1 part should have a picture on it. Students may choose to draw their pictures on any one of the equal parts.

Independent Practice

10. Think of two unit fractions. Possible answers shown.

    a. Write the fractions. $\frac{1}{6}$ $\frac{1}{8}$

    b. Tell how the two fractions are alike.

       Both have 1 as the numerator and are each one part of a whole.

    c. Tell how the two fractions are different. Their denominators are

       different, so the number of parts in each whole is different.

Solve the problems.

MP4 11. Steve writes a letter to his grandparents. He folds the paper into 6 equal parts. He draws a picture on 1 part. What fraction of the paper does Steve draw on?

✏️ **Show your work.** Possible answer:

Answer Steve draws on $\frac{1}{6}$ of the paper.

MP6 12. Mina has a rope. She wants to cut it into 8 equal parts. What fraction of the rope will each part be?

✏️ **Show your work.** Possible answer:

Answer Each part will be $\frac{1}{8}$ of the rope.

Mathematical Practices		
MP4	**Model with mathematics.**	
Item 11: Students draw a model of sixths and then identify $\frac{1}{6}$ as 1 of 6 equal parts.		
MP6	**Attend to precision.**	
Item 12: Students accurately draw and partition a model into 8 equal parts.		

Solve the problems.

MP5 **13.** The Thompson family eats a whole pot pie for dinner.

• The pot pie is cut into equal parts.

• Each part is $\frac{1}{3}$ of the pot pie.

• Each person eats 1 part.

How many people are in the Thompson family?

▭· **Show your work.** Possible answer:

Answer There are 3 people in the Thompson family.

MP3 **14.** Jorge has a large sheet of paper. He cuts it into pieces to make airplanes. Each piece is $\frac{1}{8}$ of the whole sheet. If it takes one piece to make an airplane, how many airplanes can Jorge make?

Answer Jorge can make 8 airplaines.

▭· **Justify your answer using words, drawings, or numbers.**

Possible justification:
$\frac{1}{8}$ means that the whole sheet of paper has 8 equal parts, or pieces.

MP2 **15.** Teresa cuts a ribbon into equal pieces. She gives one piece to each of her friends: Tomás, Nick, and Linda. Teresa takes the last piece for herself. "We each get $\frac{1}{3}$ of the ribbon," she said. Does Teresa's statement make sense?

Answer No. Theresa's statement does not make sense.

▭· **Justify your answer using words, drawings, or numbers.**

Possible justification:
Teresa forgot to count herself. Four people get an equal piece, or $\frac{1}{4}$, of the ribbon.

Item 15
Students may not read the problem carefully and draw the model divided into thirds. Redirect them to determine the number of people in the problem.

Teaching Tips

Item 14
Remind students that $\frac{1}{8}$ is a unit fraction. This means that the whole sheet of paper is divided into 8 equal parts. Point out that each equal part will make one airplane.

Mathematical Practices

MP2	**Reason abstractly and quantitatively.**

Item 15: Students consider the total number of equal parts and the quantity formed by one part.

MP3	**Construct viable arguments and critique the reasoning of others.**

Item 14: Students construct an argument to justify their answers using drawings or models.

MP5	**Use appropriate tools strategically.**

Item 13: Students use paper and pencil to draw a model to support their answers.

Common Core Focus:

3.NF.1 Understand a fraction 1/*b* as the quantity formed by 1 part when a whole is partitioned into *b* equal parts; understand a fraction *a/b* as the quantity formed by *a* parts of size 1/*b*.

OBJECTIVE

Use unit fractions to form other fractions with numerators greater than one.

ESSENTIAL QUESTION

Students have previously learned about identifying unit fractions. This lesson will help students develop an understanding of fractions with numerators greater than 1. Understanding fractions will provide students with a foundation to generate equivalent fractions.

PREREQUISITE SKILLS

Use Item E on page 339 of the Foundational Skills Handbook to review how to partition shapes into equal shares.

FLUENCY PRACTICE

Fluency practice is available at **sadlierconnect.com.**

Concept Development

Understand: Using unit fractions to form other fractions

■ This presentation shows that when a whole is partitioned into equal parts, the quantity of one or more parts is a fraction of the whole. Students will also see that 1 part of the whole can be represented as a unit fraction.

■ Review the meaning of *numerator* and *denominator* with students. The numerator tells the number of equal parts in the fraction. The denominator tells the number of equal parts in the whole.

Essential Question:
How is a unit fraction used to build other fractions?
3.NF.1

Guided Instruction

In this lesson you will learn about fractions with numerators greater than 1.

Understand: Using unit fractions to form other fractions

Mindy draws three identical rectangles and partitions each rectangle into fourths. Then she shades different parts of each rectangle.

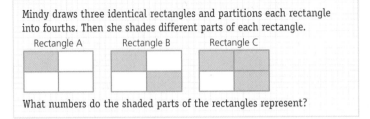

Rectangle A   Rectangle B   Rectangle C

What numbers do the shaded parts of the rectangles represent?

The numbers are fractions. Use what you know about a fraction.

$\dfrac{\text{numerator}}{\text{denominator}}$ ← number of equal parts in the fraction
← number of equal parts in the whole

Mindy's rectangles are divided into 4 equal parts. She shades a different number of parts in each rectangle.

In Rectangle A, count to find that 1 equal part is shaded.

$\dfrac{1}{4}$ ← 1 equal part in the fraction
← 4 equal parts in the whole

> The shaded part of Rectangle A represents the fraction $\frac{1}{4}$.

In Rectangle B, count to find that 2 equal parts are shaded.

$\dfrac{2}{4}$ ← 2 equal parts in the fraction
← 4 equal parts in the whole

> The shaded part of Rectangle B represents the fraction $\frac{2}{4}$.

In Rectangle C, count to find that 3 equal parts are shaded.

$\dfrac{3}{4}$ ← 3 equal parts in the fraction
← 4 equal parts in the whole

When you counted, you found the number of unit fractions of $\frac{1}{4}$ that are in $\frac{1}{4}$, in $\frac{2}{4}$, and in $\frac{3}{4}$.

> The shaded part of Rectangle C represents the fraction $\frac{3}{4}$.

➡ The shaded parts of the figures represent the numbers $\frac{1}{4}$, $\frac{2}{4}$, and $\frac{3}{4}$.

Support English Language Learners

In this unit, students are first introduced to fractions. Not knowing how to say a fraction correctly may keep students from participating in class. Create a fraction poster with examples to help students know how to read and talk about fractions. In one column, write examples of fractions such as $\frac{1}{2}$, $\frac{2}{3}$, $\frac{3}{4}$, $\frac{4}{5}$, and so on, using denominators to 10. In the second column write the word form of the fraction: *one half, two thirds, three fourths, four fifths,* and so on. Have students practice reading the fractions and offer support to students who have difficulty in pronunciation.

Lesson 17

Guided Instruction

Connect: What you know about fractions

Marc ordered a pizza with mushrooms on some of the slices. The pizza was cut into equal slices. Use the picture to name the fraction of the pizza that has mushrooms.

Each slice is an equal part, so you can write a fraction to answer the question.

Step 1

Identify the denominator.

Count the number of equal parts in the whole pizza.

There are 8 equal parts in the pizza.

So the denominator of the fraction is __8__.

Step 2

Identify the numerator.

Count the number of equal parts with mushrooms.

There are 3 equal parts with mushrooms.

So the numerator of the fraction is __3__.

Use the numerator and denominator to write the fraction. $\dfrac{3}{8}$

➡ The part of the pizza that has mushrooms is $\frac{3}{8}$.

Another way to name the fraction is to count the unit fractions. For this problem, the slices are the unit fractions.

Count 3 slices or 3 unit fractions of $\frac{1}{8}$ to get $\frac{3}{8}$.

✏ Use the picture to name the fraction of the pizza that has no mushrooms. $\frac{5}{8}$

Math-to-Math Connection

Geometric Shapes A strong understanding of equal shares will enable students to better understand fractions. Allow students to partition a variety of geometric shapes into equal parts. Students should explain how to write fractions to represent each model. Discuss with students that as the number of equal parts of a shape increases, the size of each part decreases. Explain that a shape can be partitioned equally in more than one way.

Connect: What you know about fractions

■ This presentation helps students strengthen their understanding of how fractions are represented with numerical symbols.

■ Remind students that each slice of pizza is an equal part and one slice can be represented as a unit fraction. Encourage students to make the connection that the total number of equal parts in the pizza is the denominator.

■ Explain that each individual slice with mushrooms can also be represented as a unit fraction. Demonstrate that counting the number of unit fractions representing slices with mushrooms, will give you the numerator for the fraction that represents the part of the whole pizza with mushrooms.

✏ Explain to students that another fraction is shown on the pizza. Ask students to name the fraction of the pizza that has no mushrooms. Explain to students that this is similar to naming a fraction that is represented by the un-shaded portion of a shape.

To reinforce understanding, show a drawing of a pizza partitioned into 6 equal slices, and explain that the denominator of any fraction for the figure is 6. Then make the connection that the numerator in the fraction represents the number of slices with mushrooms. Ask students to explain what the numerator would be if there were 5 slices with mushrooms.

Observational Assessment

Use pages 152–153 to assess whether students are able to name the fraction represented by the shaded portion of each model, and to assess student's ability to shade pictures to represent fractions. If students are having difficulty determining the numerator or the denominator, remind them that the numerator represents the number of parts that are shaded.

Guided Practice

Each model represents a whole. Count the unit fractions to name the shaded part of each model.

1.

2.

3.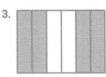

Each model represents one whole. Shade the model to represent the fraction. Possible answers shown.

4. $\frac{2}{3}$

5. $\frac{2}{6}$

6. $\frac{5}{8}$

7. $\frac{4}{6}$

8. $\frac{5}{8}$

9. $\frac{3}{6}$

Talking About Math

Report on a Topic Tell students that they will be writing a paragraph about how to form a non-unit fraction from a unit fraction, and present their work to the class. Students should explain how they determined the numerator and the denominator of their non-unit fraction. Presentations should include colorful visual models that represent both the unit fraction and the non-unit fraction.

As students present their work, ask if there is another way they could partition the shape into equal parts to show the same fractions.

10. Shade $\frac{2}{6}$ of each shape. Possible answers shown.

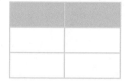

Use the model at the right for exercises 11–13.

11. Divide the rectangle into equal parts to show eighths. Check students' drawings.

12. How many equal parts did you make? __8__

13. Shade 7 equal parts. Write the fraction for the parts you shaded. __$\frac{7}{8}$__

Solve the problem.

14. Jaime designed a flag. He colored $\frac{3}{4}$ of the flag blue and $\frac{1}{4}$ of the flag green. Draw a picture that shows the flag that Jaime designed.
Check students' drawings. Drawings should have 4 equal parts with 3 colored blue and 1 colored green.

Think•Pair•Share

MP4 15. Keiko says that three $\frac{1}{8}$ unit fractions are shaded in the figure. Jordan says that $\frac{3}{8}$ of the figure is shaded. Explain why both students' answers are correct.
Possible explanation: Each shaded part is $\frac{1}{8}$ of the figure. So the shaded part of the figure is $\frac{3}{8}$ of the figure and is made up of three $\frac{1}{8}$ unit fractions.

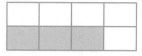

Think•Pair•Share

Peer Collaboration Encourage students to think about Keiko's response and Jordan's response in the problem. Have students explain in writing why both Keiko and Jordan are correct. Have students work with partners to discuss their explanations. Ask questions such as:

- *How many equal parts are in the whole?*

- *How many equal parts are in Keiko's fraction?*

- *How many equal parts are in Jordan's fraction?*

To summarize, have students explain how to write the fraction for the shaded part of the figure two different ways.

Return to the Essential Question

Reread the Lesson 17 Essential Question on page 150: *How is a unit fraction used to build other fractions?*

Ask volunteers to use what they learned in this lesson to answer the question. (Possible response: I can count the number of unit fractions that are shaded in a figure to build a fraction that represents the total shaded amount.)

Invite volunteers to express ideas about using a unit fraction to build other fractions.

Mathematical Practices

Mathematical Practice Standards underline the teaching and understanding of all concepts and skills presented. The emphasis of specific practices is noted throughout the guided and independent practice of this lesson.

MP4	**Model with mathematics.**

Item 15: Students interpret two different solutions within the context of fractions.

Independent Practice

Concept Application

Students may work independently on these pages in the classroom or at home. They may refer to the first four pages of the lesson to revisit the instruction or to see a worked-out example.

Common Errors and **Teaching Tips** may help you support student learning either in the classroom or as a follow-up for work done at home.

Common Errors

Items 1-2

Some students may write $\frac{1}{2}$ to represent the shaded part of the figures. Encourage students to explain why this answer is also acceptable.

Teaching Tips

Items 1-6

The fraction used to name the shaded part for each item is a total of the shaded unit fractions within each figure. Encourage students to label each shaded part with the unit fraction, then count the unit fractions to find the total.

Independent Practice

Each figure represents one whole. Write the fraction that the shaded part of each figure represents.

1.
$\frac{2}{4}$

2.
$\frac{3}{6}$

3.
$\frac{5}{8}$

4. In which model do the shaded parts represent the fraction $\frac{3}{8}$?

a.

b.

c.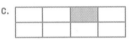

d.

5. Which fraction does the shaded part of the rectangle represent?

a. $\frac{1}{6}$ b. $\frac{4}{6}$

c. $\frac{6}{4}$ d. $\frac{6}{1}$

6. Which fraction does the shaded part of the square represent?

a. $\frac{4}{8}$ b. $\frac{3}{4}$

c. $\frac{5}{6}$ d. $\frac{4}{4}$

Digital Connection

Interactive Whiteboard Use Interactive Whiteboard software to create a visual representation of a pizza. Partition the pizza into equal slices. Create visual representations of various toppings. Allow volunteers to add toppings to some slices of the pizza. Ask students to write the fraction represented by the slices with toppings.

Independent Practice

Partition each figure into the given number of equal parts. Shade two parts. Then write the fraction for the shaded part.

7. 4 equal parts

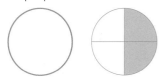

Answer $\frac{2}{4}$

8. 3 equal parts

Answer $\frac{2}{3}$

9. Show two different ways to partition a square into fourths. Shade 3 equal parts of each square. Write the fraction that the 3 equal parts represent. Partitioning will vary. Check students' drawings.

Answer $\frac{3}{4}$

Answer $\frac{3}{4}$

Make a drawing to represent the fraction.
Check students' drawings.

10. $\frac{5}{6}$

11. $\frac{4}{8}$

Common Errors

Items 10 and 11

Students might partition their shapes into the correct number of parts, but of varying sizes. Remind students that shapes must be partitioned into equal parts to represent a fraction.

Teaching Tips

Item 9

Students might have difficulty determining two ways to partition the square. Guide students to use vertical lines in one square and horizontal lines in the other. Ask students whether the vertical parts are the same size as the horizontal parts. Students should be able to explain that one part of each figure represents $\frac{1}{4}$, so the parts are the same size.

Math-to-Statistics Connection

Circle Graphs Students are familiar with bar graphs and picture graphs as a way to display data. Introduce students to another type of graph, the circle graph. Provide students with a circle graph that is divided into equal parts. Then give students data that represents the results of a survey, such as $\frac{2}{8}$ of the class prefer hot chocolate and $\frac{3}{8}$ prefer juice. Have students shade the circle graph using different colors for each result.

Independent Practice

Common Errors

Item 14

Students may say that both figures have 2 parts of 3 parts shaded so they each show $\frac{2}{3}$. Remind students that a fraction names one or more equal parts of a whole. The figure on the right is not partitioned into equal parts.

Teaching Tips

Items 12-15

Make sure students understand the meaning of *unit fraction*. It may be helpful for students to start with the unit when solving problems like these.

Lesson 17   Understand Fractions as Quantities

Independent Practice

MP6 **12.** Explain two ways to find the fraction of the square that is green. Possible answers given.

One way is to see that the unit fraction is $\frac{1}{8}$ and count 4 green unit fractions to get $\frac{4}{8}$.

Another way is to count all the equal parts, which is 8, and count all the green parts, which is 4, and make the fraction $\frac{4}{8}$.

MP4 **13.** Write a unit fraction and another fraction with the same denominator. How are they alike? How are they different?
Possible answer: They are alike in that they both have the same denominator. Both represent the same number of parts in the whole. They are different in that their numerators are not the same. They represent a different number of parts of the whole.

Solve the problems.

MP7 **14.** Sarah says that $\frac{2}{3}$ of each figure is shaded. Do you agree?
Explain your answer.
Possible explanation: No, I disagree. The figure on the right is not divided into equal parts.

MP4 **15.** Omar is using a board to make a plaque with the letters of his name on it. He divides the board into 6 equal parts. He writes each letter of his name on a different part. What fraction of the board has a letter from Omar's name on it? What fraction of the board does not have a letter from Omar's name?

▶ **Show your work.**   Possible drawing.

O	M	A	R		

Answer $\frac{4}{6}$ of the board has a letter from Omar's name on it, and $\frac{2}{6}$ of the board does not have a letter from Omar's name on it.

156   Unit 3 ▪ Focus on Number and Operations—Fractions

Mathematical Practices	
MP4	**Model with mathematics.**
Item 13: Students apply an understanding of the structure of a fraction to determine similarities and differences between two different fractions.	
Item 15: Students write fractions to match both the shaded and unshaded portions of a shape.	
MP6	**Attend to precision.**
Item 12: Students explain two methods for describing an illustrated fraction.	
MP7	**Look for and make use of structure.**
Item 14: Students evaluate given illustrations of a fraction.	

Independent Practice

Solve the problems.

MP4 **16.** Mrs. Turan makes some pita breads for her family's dinner.

- Each pita bread is cut into equal slices.

- Each slice is $\frac{1}{4}$ of the pita bread.

- Each person in the family eats 3 slices.

- There are 4 people in the family.

How many pita breads does Mrs. Turan make?

Answer Mrs. Turan makes 3 pita breads.

▸ **Justify your answer using words, drawings, or numbers.**

Possible justification: Each person had three $\frac{1}{4}$ slices, or $\frac{3}{4}$ of a pita bread. I drew a picture and used 4 names until I came out with a whole number of pita breads.

MP2 **17.** The Green family's garden is divided into 8 equal size plots. The Greens plant vegetables in 5 of the plots and flowers in the other plots. What fraction of the garden has flowers?

▸ **Show your work.** Possible drawing.

vegetables	vegetables	vegetables	vegetables
vegetables	flowers	flowers	flowers

Answer There are flowers in $\frac{3}{8}$ of the garden.

MP7 **18.** Katya is making designs by shading the same amount in each square. Make a different design in the blank square that represents the same fraction shaded as in Katya's designs.

Answer Check students' drawings.

  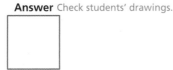

▸ **Justify your answer using words.**

Possible justification: There are 8 equal pieces in each square and 2 equal pieces in each square are shaded. So I need to divide the third square into 8 equal pieces and shade $\frac{2}{8}$ of the pieces. **Unit 3** ■ Focus on Number and Operations—Fractions **157**

Teaching Tips

Items 16-17

Remind students that they can explain their reasoning using words, drawings, or numbers. Students should choose the method that works best for them.

Item 18

Encourage students to determine which fraction is shown by the first two drawings before creating their own drawing. Be sure students understand that as long as each same-size figure is divided into equal parts, the size of each part in the first figure is the same size of each part in the second figure, even though the equal parts are different shapes.

Mathematical Practices	
MP2	**Reason abstractly and quantitatively.**
Item 17: Students use fraction notation to solve a problem.	
MP4	**Model with mathematics.**
Item 16: Students justify the solution to an everyday problem.	
MP7	**Look for and make use of structure.**
Item 18: Students evaluate fraction designs and partition a shape to create a design for the same fraction.	

Common Core Focus:

3.NF.2a Represent a fraction 1/*b* on a number line diagram by defining the interval from 0 to 1 as the whole and partitioning it into *b* equal parts. Recognize that each part has size 1/*b* and that the endpoint of the part based at 0 locates the number 1/*b* on the number line; **3.NF.2b** Represent a fraction *a*/*b* on a number line diagram by marking off *a* lengths 1/*b* from 0. Recognize that the resulting interval has size *a*/*b* and that its endpoint locates the number *a*/*b* on the number line.

OBJECTIVE

Understand how to represent fractions on a number line.

ESSENTIAL QUESTION

Students have used number lines to represent whole numbers, and to add and subtract whole numbers. Explain to students that they will learn how to represent a fraction on a number line.

PREREQUISITE SKILLS

Use Item F on page 339 of the Foundational Skills Handbook to review using a number line to add.

FLUENCY PRACTICE

Fluency practice is available at **sadlierconnect.com**.

Lesson 18

Understand Fractions on the Number Line

Essential Question:
How can I represent a fraction on a number line?

3.NF.2a, 3.NF.2b

Words to Know:
number line

Guided Instruction

In this lesson you will learn how to represent a fraction on a number line.

Understand: Representing a unit fraction on a number line

> Tyler knows that $\frac{1}{4}$ is a number. How can he locate $\frac{1}{4}$ on the number line?

To do this, you can find the whole and make equal parts on the number line.

Step 1

Find the whole on the number line. The whole is the distance from 0 to 1.

Step 2

Divide the whole into 4 equal parts. Make 4 parts because the denominator is 4. The size of each part is $\frac{1}{4}$.

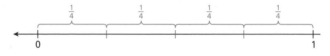

Step 3

Look at the first $\frac{1}{4}$ part. It has one endpoint at 0. Its size is $\frac{1}{4}$. So its other endpoint is located at the point for $\frac{1}{4}$.

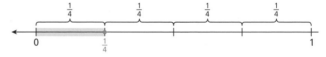

➡ Tyler can locate $\frac{1}{4}$ at the red point on the number line.

Concept Development

Understand: Representing a unit fraction on a number line

■ In this presentation, students represent unit fractions on a number line and then extend this understanding to represent non-unit fractions on a number line.

■ Have students explain in their own words how the intervals between 0 and 1 on the number line are similar to partitioning a shape into four equal parts.

Words to Know

number line: A line used to show the order of numbers. The numbers are represented by points that are spaced equally.

Example:

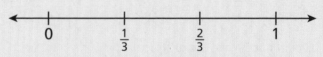

Glossary can be found on pp. 347–350.

Lesson 18

Guided Instruction

Understand: Representing a fraction on a number line

> Fumi knows that $\frac{7}{6}$ is a number. How can she locate $\frac{7}{6}$ on the number line?

You can find the whole and use equal parts to locate $\frac{7}{6}$.

Step 1

Find the whole. The whole is the distance from 0 to 1.

Step 2

Divide the whole into 6 equal parts. Find the point for $\frac{1}{6}$.

Step 3

Count unit fractions of $\frac{1}{6}$ until you reach $\frac{7}{6}$. $\frac{7}{6}$ is the same as seven $\frac{1}{6}$ unit fractions.

➡ Fumi can locate $\frac{7}{6}$ at the red point on the number line.

✏ Compare finding $\frac{7}{6}$ on the number line with finding 7 on the number line. Possible answer: To find $\frac{7}{6}$ or to find 7 on the number line, you count 7 units. For $\frac{7}{6}$, the units are $\frac{1}{6}$. For 7, the units are 1.

Unit 3 ■ Focus on Number and Operations—Fractions **159**

Understand: Representing a fraction on a number line

■ Using the number line to represent fractions may be difficult for some students to understand. Point out that this number line is similar to the number line for whole numbers that students have used before, except this time, the area between whole numbers is enlarged to show how it can be partitioned into equal parts. Each equal part is a fraction of the whole number.

■ Connect this presentation to prior learning. The denominator of the fraction tells the number of equal parts in the whole. The whole is the distance between two whole numbers.

■ Help students see that $1 = \frac{6}{6}$. To get to $\frac{7}{6}$, you need one more sixth between 1 and 2. Point out that $\frac{7}{6}$ is between the whole numbers 1 and 2, so it is greater than 1.

✏ After students have answered this question, ask volunteers to read their answers aloud. Make sure students recognize that when counting unit fractions, the numerators increase by 1, just as with counting whole numbers. The denominator remains the same.

Support English Language Learners

A *number line* is an important tool in mathematics. It is used to represent many different mathematical concepts. The underlying concept of a number line is to represent distance or length. Draw a line on the board with arrows at each end and explain that it is a straight line that extends in both directions. Add tick marks and label the number line, then discuss how the number line can be used.

Guided Instruction

Connect: Using number lines to identify fractions

Use this page to help students strengthen their understanding of identifying fractions on a number line.

■ In this presentation, students are given a point and have to determine what fraction it represents. Remind students of the steps used to locate points. These steps will help them identify the point they are given.

■ Ask students what fraction they could write for 1 on the number line. Be sure students understand that the fraction for 1 has the same numerator and denominator—in this case $\frac{8}{8}$.

■ This example introduces the idea of using letters to label points on the number line. Explain to students that this type of labeling makes it easy for others to identify the points you are describing.

✏ ‣ Have students explain the steps they followed to identify the fraction. Watch for students who count the number of lines between 0 and 1 instead of the intervals to determine the denominator.

Guided Instruction

Connect: Using number lines to identify fractions

Amanda drew point A on a number line to show the distance in miles that she lives from her school.

What does point A on the number line represent?

Point A represents a fraction. Use the meaning of a fraction to identify the fraction.

Step 1

Count the number of parts between 0 and 1.

There are 8 equal parts.

Step 2

Since there are 8 equal parts, label the number line in ___eighths___.

Step 3

Identify the fraction at point A.

The fraction at point A is $\frac{5}{8}$.

➤ Point A represents $\frac{5}{8}$ mile, the distance Amanda lives from her school.

✏ ‣ Identify the fraction at point B to find the distance in miles that Amanda lives from the park.
Point B represents $\frac{2}{3}$ mile, the distance Amanda lives from the park.

Math-to-Sports Connection

Track Tell students that each lap around a running track is $\frac{1}{4}$ mile. Have students create a number line and locate the point for $\frac{1}{4}$. Ask students to use their number lines to determine how many laps they will need to run if they want to run $\frac{3}{4}$ of a mile. Then have students extend their number lines and locate the point that represents running 5 laps ($\frac{5}{4}$). Have students explain how they located each point. Students should understand that each lap represents counting unit fractions of $\frac{1}{4}$.

Lesson 18

Guided Practice

1. Write the missing fractions on the number line.

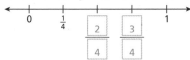

Use the number line for exercises 2 and 3.

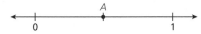

2. Into how many parts is the number line equally divided? __2__

3. What fraction is represented by point A? __$\frac{1}{2}$__

Use the number line for exercises 4 and 5.

4. Into how many parts is the number line equally divided? __8__

5. What fraction is represented by point B? __$\frac{3}{8}$__

Solve the problem.

6. Will draws a number line to represent a fraction.

What fraction does the point on Will's number line represent?

The point represents the fraction $\frac{4}{6}$. _____

ⓦ Think·Pair·Share

MP4 7. Work with a partner. Represent a fraction with a point on the number line. Have your partner identify the fraction for the point and explain how he or she arrived at the answer. Check students' drawings.

Mathematical Practices

Mathematical Practice Standards underline the teaching and understanding of all concepts and skills presented. The emphasis of specific practices is noted throughout the guided and independent practice of this lesson.

MP4	**Model with mathematics.**

Item 7: Students represent a fraction on a number line.

Observational Assessment

Use page 161 to assess whether students are able to represent a fraction on a number line. As the amount of scaffolding in the problems drops off, note those students who need additional help labeling the intervals on the number lines.

ⓦ Think·Pair·Share

Peer Collaboration Have pairs of students share their fractions with the class. Ask questions such as:

- *How did you determine the denominator of the fraction?*

- *How did you determine the numerator of the fraction?*

- *What unit fraction represents the size of each interval on your number line?*

Keep a list of fractions that students used and discuss the list. Draw a few examples of the fractions on a number line and use these examples to review what students have learned about locating fractions on a number line.

Return to the Essential Question

Reread the Lesson 18 Essential Question on page 158: *How can I represent a fraction on a number line?*

Ask volunteers to use what they learned in this lesson to answer the question. (Possible response: I can partition the distance between 0 and 1 on the number line into equal parts. The number of equal parts depends on the denominator. The size of each part is a unit fraction. I can count unit fractions to represent other fractions that have a numerator other than 1.)

Invite volunteers to express ideas about using a number line to represent a fraction.

Independent Practice

Concept Application

Students may work independently on these pages in the classroom or at home. They may refer to the first four pages of the lesson to revisit the instruction or to see a worked-out example.

Common Errors and **Teaching Tips** may help you support student learning either in the classroom or as a follow-up for work done at home.

Common Errors

Items 3–5

Students may count the number of lines instead of the number of intervals. For example, in item 4, students might choose $\frac{4}{6}$ as the answer instead of $\frac{3}{6}$. Remind students that the whole number 1 can be represented by a fraction that has the same numerator and denominator, in this case $\frac{6}{6}$. Suggest that students check their work by counting back from 1 by unit fractions to the point on the number line.

Independent Practice

1. Write the missing fractions on the number line.

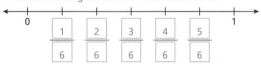

2. Write the missing fractions on the number line.

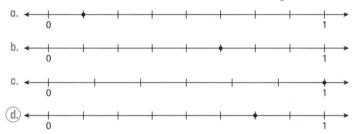

3. On which number line does a point represent the fraction $\frac{6}{8}$?

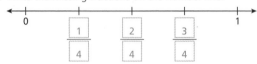

4. Which fraction does the point on the number line represent?

   a. $\frac{1}{3}$ b. $\frac{3}{6}$

   c. $\frac{4}{6}$ d. $\frac{3}{4}$

5. Which fraction does the point on the number line represent?

   a. $\frac{1}{4}$ b. $\frac{1}{2}$

   c. $\frac{5}{8}$ d. $\frac{3}{4}$

Writing About Math

Compare and Contrast Have students write a paragraph describing the similarities and differences of representing a whole number and representing a fraction on a number line. Students may use specific examples in their writing; for example, compare how to represent 3 and $\frac{3}{5}$ on a number line. Encourage students to include an illustration.

MORE ONLINE sadlierconnect.com   Lesson 18

Independent Practice

Use the number line for exercises 6 and 7.

6. What fraction is represented by point *A*?

   Answer $\frac{1}{4}$

7. What fraction is represented by point *B*?

   Answer $\frac{2}{4}$

Use the number line for exercises 8 and 9.

8. What fraction is represented by point *A*?

   Answer $\frac{3}{8}$

9. What fraction is represented by point *B*?

   Answer $\frac{7}{8}$

Draw a number line. Use a point to locate the given fraction.

10. $\frac{3}{4}$

11. $\frac{3}{6}$

Teaching Tips

Items 6–11

Students may struggle with identifying the points on a number line. It may be helpful to guide them through labeling the number line. After students have numbered the entire number line they can identify given points more easily.

Digital Connection

Drawing Tools Have students use a drawing program or a word processing program with drawing capabilities to create their own number lines. Next, have students create a word problem using their labeled number lines. Have students work in pairs to solve the word problems using the number lines.

Independent Practice

Common Errors

Item 13

Students may label the number line with whole numbers instead of fractions. Have students write the fraction for Point *L*. Have students use what they know about unit fractions to determine the size of each interval and label the rest of the number line.

Teaching Tips

Item 15

Some students may not understand how to find the amount of milkshake that is left. Tell them that 1 represents the whole milk shake. They can use the number line to find the distance or the amount between $\frac{3}{4}$ and 1.

Independent Practice

MP6 **12.** Compare your number lines in exercises 10 and 11. How are they alike? How are they different?
Possible answer: They are alike because both number lines have a dot at the end of the third part since both fractions have a numerator of 3. They are different because the number lines are divided into different numbers of parts since they have different denominators.

MP1 **13.** Point *L* on the number line represents $\frac{6}{8}$. Which point represents 1?

  a. *J*   b. *K*   c. *M*   d. *N*

Solve the problems.

MP4 **14.** Hudson buys some muffins. He draws a number line to show what fraction of the muffins he buys are blueberry muffins.

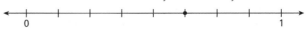

What fraction of the muffins Hudson buys are blueberry muffins?

Answer The fraction of muffins that are blueberry muffins is $\frac{5}{8}$.

MP4 **15.** Ella makes a strawberry milk shake. She drinks $\frac{3}{4}$ of it. Draw a number line to show how much of the milk shake Ella drinks. Then find what fraction of the milkshake Ella has left.
Check students' drawings.

Answer Ella has $\frac{1}{4}$ of the milkshake left.

Mathematical Practices	
MP1	**Make sense of problems and persevere in solving them.**
Item 13: Students identify fractions on a number line.	
MP4	**Model with mathematics.**
Items 14 and 15: Students solve word problems using fractions on a number line.	
MP6	**Attend to precision.**
Item 12: Students explain the similarities and differences between two given number lines.	

Independent Practice

Teaching Tips

Item 16
Help students identify the whole in this problem. It may be helpful for students to think of a whole container that contains 8 cups of milk.

Items 16–18
Show students how to use the number line to determine how much is left. They should represent the fraction that is used and then count on to the whole, 1.

Solve the problems. Check students' drawings.

MP2 **16.** Lily has 8 cups of milk. She used 2 cups of milk for a recipe. What fraction of the milk is left? Use a number line to represent the problem. Explain your reasoning.

Answer: The fraction of milk left is $\frac{6}{8}$. Possible explanation: Lily used $\frac{2}{8}$ of the milk, so I put a dot at $\frac{2}{8}$. Then I counted the eighths between $\frac{2}{8}$ and 1 and got $\frac{6}{8}$.

MP4 **17.** Victor has a rope that is 3 yards long. He cut off 1 yard of the rope. What fraction of the rope is left? Use a number line.

Answer: The fraction of rope left is $\frac{2}{3}$. Possible explanation: Victor cut off $\frac{1}{3}$ of the rope, so I put a dot at $\frac{1}{3}$. Then I counted the thirds between $\frac{1}{3}$ and 1 and got $\frac{2}{3}$.

MP1 **18.** Ariana's necklace has 6 beads. The necklace broke and all the beads fell off. She could only find 5 of the beads. What fraction of the beads did she lose? Use a number line.

Answer: Ariana lost $\frac{1}{6}$ of the beads. Possible explanation: She found $\frac{5}{6}$ of the beads, so I put a dot at $\frac{5}{6}$. Then I counted the sixths between $\frac{5}{6}$ and 1 and got $\frac{1}{6}$.

Unit 3 ■ Focus on Number and Operations—Fractions **165**

Mathematical Practices

MP1	**Make sense of problems and persevere in solving them.**

Item 18: Students use a number line to solve a word problem.

MP2	**Reason abstractly and quantitatively.**

Item 16: Students represent a word problem using a number line and explain their reasoning.

MP4	**Model with mathematics.**

Item 17: Students use a number line to model and solve an everyday word problem.

Common Core Focus:

3.NF.3a Understand two fractions as equivalent (equal) if they are the same size, or the same point on a number line.

OBJECTIVE

Use a number line to understand equivalent fractions.

ESSENTIAL QUESTION

Have volunteers share the meaning of *equivalent* in their own words. Tell students that two fractions are equivalent if they are equal in size. Using equivalent fractions is an essential skill to master for future work in mathematics.

FLUENCY PRACTICE

Fluency practice is available at **sadlierconnect.com**.

Concept Development

Understand: Equivalent fractions on a number line

■ In Grade 3, students should use number lines or models to explore equivalent fractions, instead of using algorithms or other procedures.

■ Expectations in this lesson are limited to fractions with denominators of 2, 3, 4, 6, and 8.

■ It is important that students reason about the size of fractions. Emphasize that even though equivalent fractions have different numerators and different denominators they are the same size. One way to determine whether two fractions are equivalent is to check if they name the same point on a number line.

▭▬▶ After students have answered this question, they should circle both fractions on the number lines to show that the fractions label the same point. To illustrate the equivalent fractions, students can highlight the distance from 0 for both fractions on the number lines.

In this lesson you will learn how to find equivalent fractions.

Understand: Equivalent fractions on a number line

> Nuts come in bags that weigh $\frac{1}{6}$ pound. Ashton wants to buy $\frac{1}{3}$ pound of nuts. How many bags weighing $\frac{1}{6}$ pound does Ashton need to buy?

You can use number lines to find fractions that have different names but are at the same point on the number line. These are called equivalent fractions.

Notice that the distance from 0 to 1 is the same on both number lines.

Find $\frac{1}{3}$ on the number line on top. Find the equivalent fraction in sixths directly below it on the number line on the bottom.

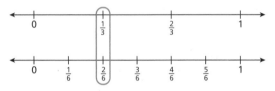

▶ $\frac{1}{3} = \frac{2}{6}$, so Ashton needs to buy two bags weighing $\frac{1}{6}$ pound each.

▭▬▶ Find $\frac{2}{3}$ on the top number line above.

What fraction is directly below it? $\frac{4}{6}$

Write an equation to show that the fractions are equivalent.

$\frac{2}{3} = \frac{4}{6}$

Words to Know

equivalent fractions: fractions that have different names but are at the same point on the number line

Example: $\frac{1}{3} = \frac{2}{6}$

Glossary can be found on pp. 347–350.

MORE ONLINE sadlierconnect.com   Lesson 19

Connect: How you can use equivalent fractions

Yolanda and Tony shared a pizza. Yolanda ate $\frac{1}{4}$ of the pizza and Tony ate $\frac{2}{8}$ of the pizza. Did Yolanda and Tony eat the same amount of pizza?

You can use number lines to find the answer.

Step 1

Draw a number line in fourths.

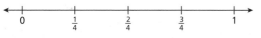

Remember!
To compare fractions using number lines, the distance from 0 to 1 must be the same on both number lines.

Step 2

Draw a number line in eighths.

Step 3

Find $\frac{1}{4}$ on the number line in Step 1. Find the equivalent fraction in eighths directly below it on the number line in Step 2. $\frac{1}{4} = \frac{2}{8}$

➤ Yolanda and Tony ate the same amount of pizza.

▬▬ · What if Yolanda eats $\frac{1}{2}$ of a small pizza and Tony eats $\frac{1}{2}$ of a large pizza? Do they eat the same amount of pizza? Explain your answer.
No, they do not. Possible explanation: $\frac{1}{2}$ of a small pizza would be less than $\frac{1}{2}$ of a large pizza.

Unit 3 ▪ Focus on Number and Operations—Fractions **167**

Connect: How you can use equivalent fractions Use this page to help students strengthen their understanding of real-life applications of equivalent fractions.

■ Be sure students understand that if you cut a slice of pizza into two slices, the size of each slice of pizza has changed, but the amount of pizza has not changed.

■ Have students look at one slice of each pizza. This is a good opportunity to discuss that $\frac{1}{8}$ of a pizza is smaller than $\frac{1}{4}$ of the same-size pizza because when a pizza is cut into 8 equal pieces, the pieces are smaller than when the pizza is cut into 4 equal pieces.

■ Remind students that the intervals on a number line must be equally spaced.

✎ · After students have answered this question, ask volunteers to read their answers aloud. Explain that the size of fractions is relative to the size of the whole, and that fractions are only comparable if the whole is the same size.

Support English Language Learners

The term *equivalent fraction* may present some difficulties for some students. *Equivalent* means to be equal or the same. This could confuse some students, because when we write equivalent fractions they have different numerators and denominators. Write the term *equivalent* on the board. Say the word and have students repeat it aloud. Have students brainstorm a list of other math words that begin with *equ* such as equal, equation, and equality. Make sure students understand that all of these words represent relationships that are the same or balanced.

Guided Practice

Observational Assessment

Use pages 168–169 to assess whether students are able to use a number line to identify equivalent fractions. Students should realize that equivalent fractions must line up vertically on the number lines, and the distance from 0 to 1 on both number lines must be the same.

For each item, have students write an equation to show the fractions are equivalent.

Guided Practice

Find and circle equivalent fractions on each pair of number lines.

1.
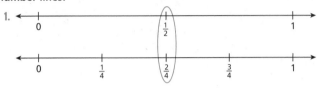

2.
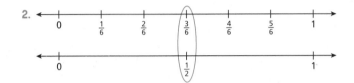

3.
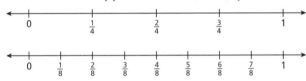

Solve the problem.

4. Sharona buys $\frac{3}{4}$ yard of ribbon. Use the number lines to find an equivalent fraction for how many yards of ribbon Sharona buys.

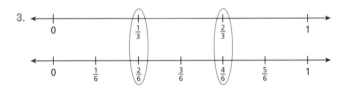

Answer The equivalent fraction is $\frac{6}{8}$ yard.

168 Unit 3 ■ Focus on Number and Operations—Fractions

Math-to-Cooking Connection

Recipes Most recipes use fractional measurements for some of the ingredients. Ask students if they have ever used a recipe to bake or cook something. Tell students that when they are following a recipe, it is very important to measure accurately. Have students share any experiences they may have had using a measuring cup.

Have students imagine that they are making a recipe for muffins. The recipe calls for $\frac{1}{2}$ cup of milk but they can only find a measuring cup that measures $\frac{1}{4}$ cup. Have them discuss in groups how they can still get the correct amount of milk using the $\frac{1}{4}$ cup. Students should conclude that they could fill the cup twice to make $\frac{2}{4}$ cup, which is equivalent to $\frac{1}{2}$ cup. Ask students how they could use only the $\frac{1}{4}$ cup to measure 1 cup of milk. Encourage students to explain their thinking.

Lesson 19

Guided Practice

5. Colin walks $\frac{2}{6}$ mile from his house to the library. Use the number lines to find an equivalent fraction for how many miles Colin walked.

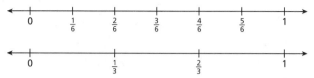

Answer The equivalent fraction is $\frac{1}{3}$ mile.

6. Jill buys $\frac{4}{8}$ pound of trail mix. Use the number lines to find an equivalent fraction for how many pounds of trail mix Jill buys.

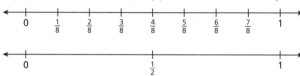

Answer The equivalent fraction is $\frac{1}{2}$ pound.

ꙮ Think•Pair•Share

MP4 **7.** Francesco looks at the number lines below. He says that no fractions between 0 and 1 shown on these number lines are equivalent. Do you agree? Explain your answer.

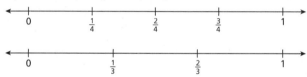

Yes, I agree. Possible explanation: None of the fractions line up.

ꙮ Think•Pair•Share

Peer Collaboration After students have answered the question, have them choose a partner and discuss their answers. Have partners ask each other questions such as:

- *How is one whole represented on each number line?*
- *Is the distance from 0 to 1 the same on both number lines?*
- *Are the fractions correctly spaced on the number line?*

To summarize, point out that when the the distance from 0 to 1 on each number line is the same, equivalent fractions represent the same distance from 0.

Return to the Essential Question

Reread the Lesson 19 Essential Question on page 166: *How can I use a number line to understand that two fractions are equivalent?*

Ask volunteers to use what they learned in this lesson to answer this question. (Possible response: I can use a number line and determine which two fractions line up. Equivalent fractions label the same point on a number line.)

Mathematical Practices

Mathematical Practice Standards underline the teaching and understanding of all concepts and skills presented. The emphasis of specific practices is noted throughout the guided and independent practice of this lesson.

MP4	**Model with mathematics.**

Item 7: Students explain the relationship of quantities by comparing fractions on a number line.

Independent Practice

Concept Application

Students may work independently on these pages in the classroom or at home. They may refer to the first four pages of the lesson to revisit the instruction or to see a worked-out example.

Common Errors and **Teaching Tips** may help you support student learning either in the classroom or as a follow-up for work done at home.

Teaching Tips

Items 1–4

Help students recall how to plot fractions on a number line. Encourage them to label all points, if necessary. Remind students that when labeling fractions on a number line the denominator stays the same. The distance between each tick mark is the size of the unit fraction.

Independent Practice

Plot each fraction on a number line. Determine if the fractions are equivalent.

Answer The fractions are not equivalent.

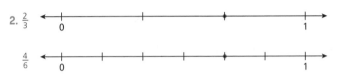

Answer The fractions are equivalent: $\frac{2}{3} = \frac{4}{6}$.

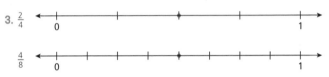

Answer The fractions are equivalent: $\frac{2}{4} = \frac{4}{8}$.

Answer The fractions are not equivalent.

Talking About Math

Report on a Topic Have students work in small groups to prepare a presentation on equivalent fractions. Students should decide roles for each group member.

Tell students that their presentation should include the following:

- a description of what it means for two fractions to be equivalent,
- how to determine if two fractions are equivalent,
- examples of equivalent fractions,
- examples of fractions that are not equivalent, and
- visual models.

When groups are finished, have them present their work to the class. Students should be prepared to answer questions from the rest of the class.

Lesson 19

Independent Practice

Use these number lines to find equivalent fractions.

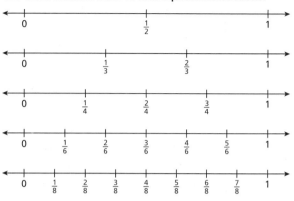

Teaching Tips

Items 5–14

Remind students that equivalent fractions label the same point on a number line. Suggest that students use a ruler to help them line up the equivalent fractions from the different number lines. Point out that equivalent fractions would be the same points if the number lines on page 171 were placed on top of each other.

Item 15

Remind students that fractions can only be compared if the sizes of the wholes are the same. The distance between 0 and 1 represents a whole on the number lines.

5. $\frac{1}{2} = \frac{3}{6}$

6. $\frac{4}{6} = \frac{2}{3}$

7. $\frac{4}{8} = \frac{2}{4}$

8. $\frac{1}{3} = \frac{2}{6}$

9. $\frac{3}{4} = \frac{6}{8}$

10. $\frac{2}{4} = \frac{3}{6}$

11. $\frac{2}{8} = \frac{1}{4}$

12. $\frac{1}{2} = \frac{2}{4}$

13. $\frac{4}{8} = \frac{1}{2}$

14. $\frac{3}{6} = \frac{4}{8}$

15. Explain why you can use the number lines above to find equivalent fractions.

Answer Possible explanation: The distance between 0 and 1 is the same for all the number lines, so equivalent fractions are the same point on each number line.

Digital Connection

Online Games Use a search engine to find games for equivalent fractions at the third-grade level. There are several matching games that use fraction models and other activities that have students build equivalent fractions. Students will benefit from the additional practice of using concrete models to represent equivalent fractions.

Independent Practice

Teaching Tips

Items 16-18

Remind students to identify the fractions from the illustrations first, and then use the number lines on page 171 to look for equivalent fractions. Discuss what other fractions could also be equivalent, according to the number lines.

It may be helpful to make copies of the number lines on page 171, so that students can refer directly to the number lines as they work, eliminating the need to flip back and forth and possibly lose their place.

Independent Practice

Use the number lines on page 171 to solve the problems.

16. Justin shaded 2 parts of a square. Which fraction is equivalent to the shaded part of the square?

   (a.) $\frac{1}{4}$ b. $\frac{1}{2}$

   c. $\frac{6}{8}$ d. $\frac{3}{4}$

17. Maria shaded 2 parts of a circle. Which fraction is equivalent to the shaded part of the circle?

   a. $\frac{2}{6}$ b. $\frac{1}{3}$

   c. $\frac{3}{6}$ (d.) $\frac{4}{6}$

18. Liam shaded 2 parts of a parallelogram. Which fraction is equivalent to the shaded part of the parallelogram?

   (a.) $\frac{1}{2}$ b. $\frac{1}{3}$

   c. $\frac{1}{4}$ d. $\frac{1}{6}$

Math-to-Math Connection

Computation with Fractions It is important for students to become fluent renaming equivalent fractions as they will be using this skill to add or subtract fractions later on. When adding or subtracting fractions, it will be necessary for students to first rewrite the expressions so that each fraction contains a common denominator. Each fraction must represent the whole partitioned into equal-sized parts. For example, $\frac{3}{4} - \frac{1}{3}$ must first be rewritten as $\frac{9}{12} - \frac{4}{12}$, so that a student can see that $\frac{4}{12}$ are being taken away from $\frac{9}{12}$, leaving $\frac{5}{12}$.

Teaching Tips
Item 21
Students may become confused by having to label fractions with different denominators on one number line. Walk students through this by first having them label the eighths, then the fourths, and last labeling one half.

Use the number lines on page 171 to solve the problems.

MP3 **19.** Sandria shades 3 parts of a rectangle. She says that the shaded part of the rectangle represents more than one fraction. Do you agree?

Answer Yes, I agree.

▶ **Justify your answer using words, drawings, or numbers.**

Possible justification: $\frac{1}{2}$, $\frac{2}{4}$, and $\frac{4}{8}$ are all equivalent fractions for $\frac{3}{6}$.

MP3 **20.** Joe cuts a pizza into 8 equal slices. He gives 2 slices to each of his friends: Brent, Lisandra, and Paco. Joe also takes 2 slices for himself. "We each get $\frac{1}{3}$ of the pizza," he said. Is Joe right?

Answer No, Joe is not right.

▶ **Justify your answer using words, drawings, or numbers.**

Possible justification: Each person got 2 of the 8 slices, or $\frac{2}{8}$ of the pizza. $\frac{2}{8}$ is not equivalent to $\frac{1}{3}$ but is equivalent to $\frac{1}{4}$.

MP4 **21.** Place the following fractions on the number line: $\frac{1}{2}$, $\frac{1}{4}$, $\frac{2}{4}$, $\frac{3}{4}$, $\frac{1}{8}$, $\frac{2}{8}$, $\frac{3}{8}$, $\frac{4}{8}$, $\frac{5}{8}$, $\frac{6}{8}$, and $\frac{7}{8}$.

Explain why there is more than one fraction at some of the points on the number line.

Answer Some points on the number line can be named by two or more equivalent fractions.

▶ **Justify your answer using words, drawings, or numbers.**

Possible justification: Equivalent fractions show the same amount or distance. The fractions $\frac{1}{4}$ and $\frac{2}{8}$ are equivalent fractions; $\frac{1}{2}$, $\frac{2}{4}$, and $\frac{4}{8}$ are equivalent fractions; and $\frac{3}{4}$ and $\frac{6}{8}$ are equivalent fractions.

Unit 3 ■ Focus on Number and Operations—Fractions **173**

Mathematical Practices

MP3	Construct viable arguments and critique the reasoning of others.

Items 19 and 20: Students construct arguments using drawings, and explain an approach to solving the problem.

MP4	Model with mathematics.

Item 21: Students explain the relationship of quantities between fractions.

Common Core Focus:

3.NF.3b Recognize and generate simple equivalent fractions. Explain why the fractions are equivalent.

OBJECTIVE

Use models to find equivalent fractions.

ESSENTIAL QUESTION

Visualizing fractions helps students analyze and evaluate the relationship between fractions. Using different kinds of models to explore fractions provides opportunities for students to see fractions as flexible in a real-world context. These various models help deepen a student's understanding of how to manipulate fractions, which is essential in everyday life.

FLUENCY PRACTICE

Fluency practice is available at **sadlierconnect.com**.

Concept Development

Understand: Using fraction strips to find equivalent fractions

■ Have fraction strips or fraction tiles available for students to use so they can work along with the instruction on this page.

■ Have students use a straightedge to show how equivalent fraction lengths align. Remind students to count each unit fraction to find the total length of the fractional part of the whole.

■ Encourage students to find a pattern in equivalent fractions. For example, the fraction strips show four equivalent fractions for $\frac{1}{2}$. Ask students to consider the relationship between the numerators and the denominators.

■ Use the models on the page to show that each whole is the same size. As the value of the denominators increase in each consecutive model, the size of the individual parts of each whole decreases.

Lesson
20 Write Equivalent Fractions

Essential Question:
How can I use area models to write equivalent fractions?
3.NF.3b

Guided Instruction

In this lesson you will learn how to find equivalent fractions.

Understand: Using fraction strips to find equivalent fractions

> Eda wants to use fraction strips to find some equivalent fractions for $\frac{1}{2}$. How can she do this?

To find equivalent fractions, look for lengths that are the same.

Line up the fraction strips under the 1.

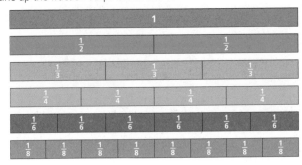

Start with a $\frac{1}{2}$ strip.

Find sets of strips that are exactly the same length as the $\frac{1}{2}$ strip. Look at the set of fraction strips or pull out some to compare.

Fraction strips showing $\frac{2}{4}$, $\frac{3}{6}$, and $\frac{4}{8}$ have the same length as the $\frac{1}{2}$ fraction strip.

➡ Eda finds that $\frac{2}{4}$, $\frac{3}{6}$, and $\frac{4}{8}$ are equivalent fractions for $\frac{1}{2}$ because they are all the same length.

Support English Language Learners

Explain that an *area* is a region with specific boundaries. Allow students to use diagrams or maps to explore and identify what *areas* of the universe, world, country, state, city and/or neighborhood they live in.

Explain that *area models* are used in math to relate a smaller region or part, to a larger region or part. Although area models can be any shape, some shapes are easier to work with than others. Have students trace a variety of geometric tiles on sheets of paper. Ask students to choose a shape and draw a line to separate it into two equal parts. Have them shade one part. Guide them to write the comparison of shaded parts to total parts as the fraction $\frac{1}{2}$. Continue with other shapes, total number of equal parts, and shaded fractional parts. Have students share their understanding of the meaning of area models.

Guided Instruction

Understand: Using number lines to find equivalent fractions

> Jorge wants to use number lines to find some equivalent fractions for $\frac{1}{2}$. How can he do this?

To find equivalent fractions, look for numbers that are at the same place on the number line.

Draw number lines with halves, thirds, fourths, sixths, and eighths.

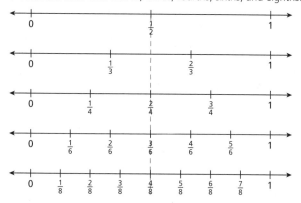

Find the fractions that are at the same place as $\frac{1}{2}$ on the number line. Draw a line going straight down from $\frac{1}{2}$. The fractions it crosses are equivalent to $\frac{1}{2}$.

The fractions $\frac{2}{4}$, $\frac{3}{6}$, and $\frac{4}{8}$ are equivalent to $\frac{1}{2}$. Each point is the same distance from 0.

▶ Jorge finds that ____$\frac{2}{4}$, $\frac{3}{6}$, and $\frac{4}{8}$____ are equivalent fractions for $\frac{1}{2}$ because they are all at the same place on the number line.

✏ • Why is there no equivalent fraction for $\frac{1}{2}$ that has 3 as its denominator? Possible answer: None of the three equal parts of the line from 0 to 1 ends at $\frac{1}{2}$, so there is no way to have an equivalent fraction for $\frac{1}{2}$ with a 3 as the denominator.

Understand: Using number lines to find equivalent fractions

■ This presentation uses number lines to show the same fractions as shown on page 174. Students often interpret fraction strips to represent physical objects of equal lengths. Using number lines encourages students to extend their understanding of fractions to measurable lengths or distances.

■ Remind students that the label of each tick mark on the number line represents the total number of equal parts from 0. For example, the tick mark at $\frac{2}{4}$ means there are 2 equal $\frac{1}{4}$ parts between the tick mark and 0. Ask students to describe the meaning of $\frac{3}{4}$ and $\frac{4}{8}$ as the number of unit fractions from 0.

■ Students should realize that denominators represent the number of equal parts in one whole and numerators represent the number of equal parts being used. Make sure students understand that they should count the number of parts, not the number of tick marks.

■ Point out that the numerator increases by 1 with each consecutive tick mark. Eventually the numerator and denominator will be the same: $\frac{2}{2}$, $\frac{3}{3}$, $\frac{4}{4}$, $\frac{6}{6}$, and $\frac{8}{8}$. Number lines usually represent these fractions as 1. Students will learn more about this in the next lesson.

✏ • Have students find fractions on the number lines that do not show equivalent fractions.

Math-to-Measurement Connection

Rulers Have students compare a ruler with tick marks showing eighths, to a number line partitioned into eight equal parts. Draw an enlarged part of the ruler on the board, with tick marks indicating eighths, and labels for 0 and 1. Have students help you label the tick marks for each eighth. Point to the tick marks on the board that are labeled $\frac{2}{8}$, $\frac{4}{8}$, and $\frac{6}{8}$. Have students use the number lines on page 175 to name equivalent fractions for these measurements. Use colored chalk to show that the distance between the tick marks for fourths is greater than the distance between the tick marks for eighths. Tell students that when they measure objects, the measurement can be read using different denominators, but the standard is to use the measurement with the least denominator.

Guided Instruction

Connect: **Using models to represent equivalent fractions** This presentation focuses on rectangular fractional models because they are an easy shape for students to partition into equal parts.

■ Students should understand that there are many ways to represent fractions. Fraction strips allow students to identify and visualize fractions with the numerator 1. Number lines depict fractions as part of a whole using linear measurements. Shape models may be used to present fractions as an area that is partitioned into equal parts.

■ Remind students to read word problems carefully. Careful reading reveals there is only one whole lasagna. Both fractional parts came from the same whole.

■ This question reinforces that fractions must refer to the same whole, or wholes that are the same size. Draw two different-size rectangles on the board. Divide and shade $\frac{1}{4}$ of each model. Ask students to discuss whether the shaded parts are equal. They both represent the same fraction of the whole model, but because the sizes of the whole models are not equal, the shaded parts are not equal.

Lesson 20   Write Equivalent Fractions

Guided Instruction

Connect: **Using models to represent equivalent fractions**

> Henry and his sister Lucy made a small lasagna. Henry ate $\frac{1}{4}$ of the lasagna and Lucy ate $\frac{2}{8}$ of the lasagna. Did Henry and Lucy eat the same amount of lasagna?

To find out whether Henry and Lucy ate the same amount of lasagna, check whether $\frac{1}{4}$ and $\frac{2}{8}$ are equivalent fractions.

Step 1

Draw a rectangle to represent the lasagna. Show the part of the lasagna that Henry ate. Divide the rectangle into fourths. Shade $\frac{1}{4}$ of the rectangle.

Step 2

Draw another rectangle of the same size to represent the lasagna. Show the part of the lasagna that Lucy ate. Divide the rectangle into eighths. Shade $\frac{2}{8}$ of the rectangle.

Step 3

Compare the amounts shaded in each rectangle.

The amounts shaded are the same, so $\frac{1}{4} = \frac{2}{8}$.

➡ Lucy and Henry ate the same amount of lasagna.

■ Why is it important to draw rectangles that are the same size?
Possible answer: The rectangles represent the whole lasagna. If they are not the same, then you are not comparing parts of the same whole.

176 Unit 3 ■ Focus on Number and Operations—Fractions

Math-to-Money Connection

Equivalent Amounts Provide students with 4 quarters, 10 dimes, and 20 nickels. Demonstrate how 2 quarters, 5 dimes, and 10 nickels all represent $\frac{1}{2}$ of a dollar. Show students that $\frac{2}{4}$ of the 4 quarters, $\frac{5}{10}$ of the 10 dimes, and $\frac{10}{20}$ of the 20 nickels all show $\frac{1}{2}$, and are all equivalent fractions. Challenge students to find other equivalent fractions using coins.

Lesson 20

Guided Practice

Use the fraction strips. Find an equivalent fraction.

1. $\frac{1}{3}$ = $\frac{2}{6}$

2. $\frac{2}{4}$ = $\frac{1}{2}$, $\frac{3}{6}$, or $\frac{4}{8}$

3. $\frac{4}{6}$ = $\frac{2}{3}$

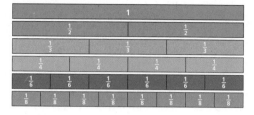

Use the number lines. Find an equivalent fraction.

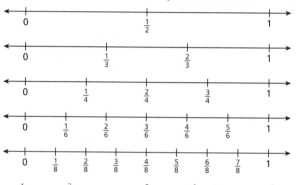

4. $\frac{1}{4}$ = $\frac{2}{8}$ 5. $\frac{2}{3}$ = $\frac{4}{6}$ 6. $\frac{3}{4}$ = $\frac{6}{8}$

7. Doriano planted $\frac{1}{6}$ of his garden with green peppers and $\frac{1}{6}$ with red peppers. He said that he planted $\frac{1}{3}$ of the garden with peppers. Use the models to show why Doriano's thinking is correct.

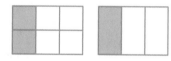

☆☆☆ **Think•Pair•Share**

MP3 8. Compare using fraction strips, number lines, and rectangles as models to find equivalent fractions. Tell which one you like to use and why. See Additional Answers.

Unit 3 ■ Focus on Number and Operations—Fractions **177**

Mathematical Practices

Mathematical Practice Standards underline the teaching and understanding of all concepts and skills presented. The emphasis of specific practices is noted throughout the guided and independent practice of this lesson.

MP3	**Construct viable arguments and critique the reasoning of others.**

Item 8: Students share reasoning with others.

Observational Assessment

Use page 177 to assess whether students understand how to use fraction strips, number lines, and area models to find equivalent fractions. Note which fractional representations students seem least comfortable with and provide additional support as needed.

☆☆☆ Think•Pair•Share

Peer Collaboration Encourage partners to discuss how to use each model to find equivalent fractions. Once students have decided on their favorite, ask:

- *How are fraction strips, number lines, and rectangles as models similar and different?*

- *Which do you think is easiest to use and why?*

- *How does each model represent a whole?*

To summarize, explain that even though these models are different, they can all be used to find equivalent fractions.

Return to the Essential Question

Reread the Lesson 20 Essential Question on page 174: *How can I use area models to write equivalent fractions?*

Ask volunteers to use what they learned in this lesson to answer this question. (Possible response: Fraction strips, number lines, and rectangles as models all help me visualize and explain fractions. It is easier to see how big a fraction is with the help of area models.)

Additional Answers

Item 8. Possible answer: Fraction strips can be moved around and you can line them up to see which ones have the same length. Number lines are easy to draw if you use graph paper. Rectangles take longer to draw but are sometimes better to show equal parts. I like to use number lines because I can put fractions with different denominators on the same number line if I am careful.

Independent Practice

Concept Application

Students may work independently on these pages in the classroom or at home. They may refer to the first four pages of the lesson to revisit the instruction or to see a worked-out example.

Common Errors and **Teaching Tips** may help you support student learning either in the classroom or as a follow-up for work done at home.

Common Errors

Items 4–11

Students may misinterpret fractions when the numerator in the given fraction is greater than 1. Remind students that the numerator represents the number of equal parts being compared.

Teaching Tips

Items 1–13

Equivalent fractions represent equal amounts of equal wholes. If needed, suggest students use a straightedge to align the lengths of the fraction strips to determine if the fractions are equivalent.

Item 10

Point out that there is more than one equivalent fraction for this exercise.

Lesson 20 Write Equivalent Fractions

Independent Practice

Use the fraction strips for the problems on this page.

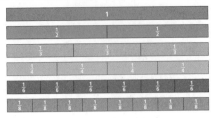

Complete the equivalent fraction.

1. $\frac{1}{4} = \frac{2}{8}$

2. $\frac{1}{2} = \frac{3}{6}$

3. $\frac{1}{2} = \frac{4}{8}$

4. $\frac{2}{6} = \frac{1}{3}$

5. $\frac{2}{8} = \frac{1}{4}$

6. $\frac{4}{8} = \frac{2}{4}$

Write an equivalent fraction.

7. $\frac{2}{6} = \frac{1}{3}$

8. $\frac{2}{3} = \frac{4}{6}$

9. $\frac{2}{8} = \frac{1}{4}$

10. $\frac{4}{8} = \frac{1}{2}$ or $\frac{2}{4}$ or $\frac{3}{6}$

11. $\frac{6}{8} = \frac{3}{4}$

12. $\frac{1}{3} = \frac{2}{6}$

13. Find 3 equivalent fractions for $\frac{1}{2}$.
$\frac{2}{4} \qquad \frac{3}{6} \qquad \frac{4}{8}$

14. Why is there no equivalent fraction for $\frac{3}{4}$ that has a denominator of 3?
Possible answer: Two $\frac{1}{3}$ strips are too short to match $\frac{3}{4}$ and three $\frac{1}{3}$ strips are too long. There is no way to make an equivalent fraction for $\frac{3}{4}$ with thirds.

15. Describe any pattern you notice in the set of fraction strips.
Possible answers: The greater a denominator of a unit fraction is, the shorter its strip is. You can use strips for unit fractions that can be divided by 2 to make equivalent fractions for $\frac{1}{2}$.

178 Unit 3 ■ Focus on Number and Operations—Fractions

Talking About Math

Collaborative Conversations Ask students to share with a partner what they have learned about equivalent fractions. Students should talk about what an equivalent fraction is and what equivalent fractions might look like. They should be able to discuss how to use number lines, fraction strips, and area models to find equivalent fractions. Students should also discuss which model they prefer. Remind students that they are giving their opinion to another person, so there is no right or wrong answer. It is acceptable for students to disagree about which model they prefer.

Independent Practice

Use the number lines for the problems on this page.

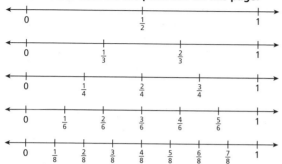

Complete the equivalent fraction.

16. $\frac{1}{2} = \frac{4}{8}$

17. $\frac{1}{3} = \frac{2}{6}$

18. $\frac{1}{4} = \frac{2}{8}$

19. $\frac{2}{8} = \frac{1}{4}$

20. $\frac{2}{4} = \frac{3}{6}$

21. $\frac{4}{8} = \frac{1}{2}$

Write an equivalent fraction.

22. $\frac{2}{4} = \frac{1}{2}$ or $\frac{3}{6}$ or $\frac{4}{8}$

23. $\frac{3}{4} = \frac{6}{8}$

24. $\frac{2}{6} = \frac{1}{3}$

25. $\frac{4}{6} = \frac{2}{3}$

26. $\frac{6}{8} = \frac{3}{4}$

27. $\frac{2}{8} = \frac{1}{4}$

28. Find 4 equivalent fractions and explain how you found them.

$\frac{1}{2}$ $\frac{2}{4}$ $\frac{3}{6}$ $\frac{4}{8}$

Possible explanation: I looked for fractions that were the same distance from 0 on the number lines.

29. Describe any pattern you notice in the number lines.

Possible explanation: The distances between the fractions get smaller as the number of fractions between 0 and 1 gets greater. The first fraction on each line gets closer to 0 and the last fraction on each line gets closer to 1 as you go down the set of number lines.

Unit 3 ■ Focus on Number and Operations—Fractions **179**

Common Errors

Items 16–27

Some students may approximate and think that if fractions are approximately the same length they are equivalent. This becomes more difficult as denominators and pieces of the whole get smaller. For example, $\frac{5}{6}$ and $\frac{7}{8}$ are close but not exactly the same length. They are not equivalent.

Teaching Tips

Item 22

Encourage students to find more than one equivalent fraction.

Digital Connection

Interactive Whiteboard Students can use the fraction models and number lines from the tools section of the interactive whiteboard to create equivalent fractions. Divide students into pairs. Have pairs of students work together at the whiteboard. Give the students a fraction. Have one student model an equivalent fraction using a model and the other student model an equivalent fraction on a number line.

Independent Practice

Common Errors

Items 30–32

Page 176 presented the idea that the whole of equivalent fractions needs to be the same size, which may cause confusion for students as they work on these exercises.

Explain that students are considering the equivalence of the fractional parts of individual shapes rather than equivalence among the shapes. Suggest students write a fraction for the shaded part of each figure. Then have them compare the fractions rather than the shaded parts.

Teaching Tips

Items 30–32

Students have used rectangles to explore fractional area models, but these problems include other shapes. These varied experiences with different shapes are crucial to a deeper understanding of fractions. Explain that as long as the individual parts of the area model represent equivalent areas, each part represents an equivalent fraction of the whole.

Remind students to circle each correct answer for each exercise.

Independent Practice

For each question, circle any figures that have a shaded part equivalent to the given fraction.

30. $\frac{1}{2}$

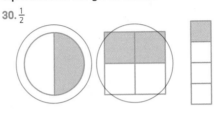

31. $\frac{1}{3}$

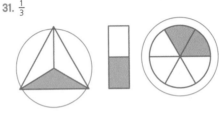

32. $\frac{1}{4}$

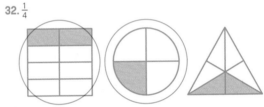

MP1 33. Explain how you decided which figure is not equal to $\frac{1}{2}$ in exercise 30.
Possible explanation: The rectangle is divided into 4 equal parts and 1 part is shaded. This is equivalent to 1 out of 4 parts shaded, which is $\frac{1}{4}$, not $\frac{1}{2}$.

MP3 34. Explain how you decided which figure is not equal to $\frac{1}{4}$ in exercise 32.
Possible explanation: The triangle is divided into 6 equal parts and 2 parts are shaded. This is equivalent to 1 out of 3 parts shaded which is $\frac{1}{3}$, not $\frac{1}{4}$.

Mathematical Practices	
MP1	Make sense of problems and persevere in solving them.
Item 33:	Students refer to pictures to explain relationships.
MP3	Construct viable arguments and critique the reasoning of others.
Item 34:	Students share their reasoning with others.

MORE ONLINE sadlierconnect.com   Lesson 20

Independent Practice

Solve the problems.

MP2 **35.** Jaime and Serena are painting a room. So far Jaime has painted $\frac{2}{6}$ of one wall. Serena has painted the same amount of that wall. Write an equivalent fraction to represent how much of the wall Serena has painted.

Answer <u>Serena has painted $\frac{1}{3}$ of the wall.</u>

▸ **Justify your answer using words, drawings, or numbers.**

Possible justification: I can draw a model showing $\frac{2}{6}$ and find an equivalent fraction. $\frac{2}{6}$ and $\frac{1}{3}$ are equivalent fractions.

MP4 **36.** Sophie, Ethan, and Ava each have a garden.

Sophie's Garden

roses	tulips
daffodils	pansies

Ethan's Garden

roses	daffodils
tulips	pansies
pansies	tulips
daffodils	roses

Ava's Garden

tulips	roses
roses	daffodils

Which two people have the same amount of roses planted in their gardens?

Answer <u>Sophie and Ethan have the same amount of roses planted in their gardens.</u>

▸ **Justify your answer using words, drawings, or numbers.**

Possible justification: $\frac{1}{4}$ of Sophie's garden is roses. $\frac{2}{8}$ of Ethan's garden is roses and $\frac{2}{8}$ and $\frac{1}{4}$ are equivalent fractions.

MP7 **37.** Bobby only has a $\frac{1}{4}$-cup measuring cup. He needs to measure $\frac{4}{8}$ cup of flour. Explain how he can do it with the $\frac{1}{4}$-cup measuring cup.

Answer <u>Bobby can use the $\frac{1}{4}$-cup measuring cup twice to measure $\frac{4}{8}$ cup of flour.</u>

▸ **Justify your answer using words, drawings, or numbers.**

Possible justification: The fraction $\frac{4}{8}$ is equivalent to the fraction $\frac{1}{2}$ and the fraction $\frac{2}{4}$ is equivalent to the fraction $\frac{1}{2}$. Since both $\frac{4}{8}$ and $\frac{2}{4}$ are equivalent to $\frac{1}{2}$, Bobby can use two $\frac{1}{4}$-cup scoops of flour.

Unit 3 ▪ Focus on Number and Operations—Fractions **181**

Common Errors
Item 36
Students may consider the position of the equal parts rather than the number of equal parts. Ethan's roses are not next to each other; however, they still take up a certain area of the garden.

Teaching Tips
Item 37
Encourage students to draw a visual or use real measuring cups to test their ideas.

Mathematical Practices

MP2	**Reason abstractly and quantitatively.**

Item 35: Students pay attention to the meaning of quantities to make sense of a problem.

MP4	**Model with mathematics.**

Item 36: Students relate mathematics to everyday problems.

MP7	**Look for and make use of structure.**

Item 37: Students evaluate the structure of a problem to find a solution.

Common Core Focus:

3.NF.3c Express whole numbers as fractions, and recognize fractions that are equivalent to whole numbers.

OBJECTIVE

Express whole numbers as fractions and fractions as whole numbers.

ESSENTIAL QUESTION

This lesson builds upon students' knowledge of equivalent fractions. Students will express whole numbers as fractions and recognize fractions that are equivalent to whole numbers. Have students compare the number lines in this lesson to the number lines in the previous lesson. Point out that in this lesson, a fraction is also used to represent 1.

FLUENCY PRACTICE

Fluency practice is available at **sadlierconnect.com**.

Concept Development

Understand: Recognizing fractions equivalent to whole numbers

■ This presentation will help students develop an understanding of fractions as numbers by focusing on the relationship between fractions and whole numbers. Renaming fractions as whole numbers and whole numbers as fractions builds a foundation for working with mixed numbers in later grades.

■ Ask students how they know that $\frac{2}{2}$ and 1 are equivalent. Students should explain that they name the same point on the number line.

■ For students who are struggling, it may be helpful to use real-world objects, such as two straws cut in half, to represent the dowels.

✏ Ask volunteers to draw a number line and explain the strategy they used to the rest of the class.

Lesson 21 — Relate Whole Numbers and Fractions

Essential Question: How can I relate whole numbers and fractions?

3.NF.3c

Words to Know: whole number

Guided Instruction

In this lesson you will learn to express whole numbers as fractions and recognize fractions that are equivalent to whole numbers.

Understand: Recognizing fractions equivalent to whole numbers

> Naomi is using wooden dowels to make axles for two model cars she is building. She cuts each dowel in half and makes four pieces.
>
>
>
> How many dowels did Naomi use?

Naomi made 4 halves. To find the number of dowels, find the whole number that is equivalent to $\frac{4}{2}$.

Use a number line. Count 4 unit fractions of $\frac{1}{2}$.

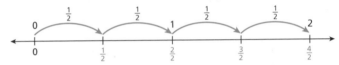

The number line shows that the whole number 2 is equivalent to $\frac{4}{2}$.

▶ Naomi used 2 dowels.

Another way to find the whole number that a fraction is equivalent to is to divide the numerator by the denominator.

$\frac{4}{2} \longrightarrow 4 \div 2 = 2$

$\frac{4}{2}$ is equivalent to 2

✏ How can you use a number line to find the whole number that is equivalent to $\frac{8}{4}$? Possible answer: Draw a number line in fourths to $\frac{8}{4}$. Then find the whole number that is equivalent to $\frac{8}{4}$. $\frac{8}{4} = 2$.

Words to Know

whole number: any of the numbers 0, 1, 2, 3, 4, 5, and so on

Glossary can be found on pp. 347–350.

Understand: Expressing a whole number as a fraction

Burnell, Candace, and Jake are sharing equal parts of 2 seed pots.

You need to write 2 as a fraction in thirds.
Each person gets $\frac{1}{3}$ of a seed pot.
How many thirds are in the 2 seed pots?

Label the parts of the seed pots.

Count the number of thirds in the 2 seed pots.
There are 3 thirds in the first seed pot and
3 thirds in the second seed pot.

3 thirds + 3 thirds = 6 thirds

➡ The 2 seed pots contain 6 thirds. $2 = \frac{6}{3}$

Another way to express a whole number as a
fraction is to multiply the whole number by the
denominator you want. Use the product as the
numerator with the denominator you want.

Remember!
The denominator of a
fraction tells how many
parts the whole is
divided into.

Express 6 as a fraction in fourths.
    The denominator you want is 4.
    $6 \times 4 = 24$.
    6 is equivalent to $\frac{24}{4}$.

How can you use a number line to find the number of thirds in 2?
Possible answer: Draw a number line in thirds. Label the thirds and the whole
numbers. There are 6 thirds in 2.

Unit 3 ■ Focus on Number and Operations—Fractions **183**

Understand: Expressing a whole number as a fraction

■ In this presentation, students build
upon the previous presentation where
they recognized fractions equivalent
to whole numbers. Students will now
express a whole number as a fraction.

■ It may be helpful to review the parts
of a fraction and what the numbers
mean. Remind students that the
denominator tells how many parts
are in the whole. Make sure students
understand that there are two wholes
in the model. Each seed pot represents
1 third. Some students may incorrectly
think that the model represents sixths.

✏ Ask a few students to
demonstrate for the rest of the class
how they would draw a number line to
find the number of thirds in 2. Be sure
students understand that when drawing
a number line for thirds, each whole has
3 equal parts.

Support English Language Learners

As students build their knowledge of fractions it may be helpful to have
English language learners create a set of fractions they typically use.
Give students notecards and have them write a fraction on one side of
each card. On the other side of the card have students write the word
form and draw a diagram to illustrate the fraction. Having this set of
fraction cards will give students a reference as they continue to build their
understanding and use of fractions.

It may also be helpful to work on the pronunciation of their fraction
cards. Take turns showing either side of the cards and asking students
to recite the fraction aloud. Repeat this process to improve the
pronunciation of fractions.

Guided Instruction

Connect: Writing 1 as a fraction Use this page to help students strengthen their understanding of whole numbers and fractions.

■ This presentation shows students different ways to write 1 as a fraction. Have students give examples of additional ways to write 1 as a fraction.

■ Ask students to explain why $1 = \frac{2}{2} = \frac{3}{3} = \frac{4}{4}$. Make sure students can read the number lines in this presentation. Point out that the length of each number line is the same, and each number line represents 1 whole.

Connect: Writing a whole number as a fraction with 1 as the denominator

■ It is important for students to understand the meaning of a fraction with a denominator of 1. Emphasize that this is another way to write a whole number as a fraction. Guide students to draw a model for $\frac{8}{1}$.

■ Have students practice writing additional whole numbers as fractions. Some students will quickly see that you just write the whole number in the numerator and write 1 in the denominator. Ask students to draw models for some of the fractions to emphasize the meaning of the fraction.

Connect: Writing 1 as a fraction

Isaac looked at these number lines and said, "I can write 1 as a fraction in many different ways. I see a pattern I can use."

Find the pattern. Find ways to write 1 as a fraction.

Find a pattern for writing 1 as fraction in different ways. Look at the fractions at the same place on the number lines as 1. Each numerator is the same as the denominator.

Write the fractions.

$$1 = \frac{2}{2} = \frac{3}{\boxed{3}}$$

Continue the pattern:

$$\frac{4}{4} = \frac{\boxed{5}}{5} = \frac{9}{\boxed{9}}$$

➤ The pattern is that the numerator and denominator are the same. Some ways to write 1 as a fraction are $\frac{2}{2}$, $\frac{3}{3}$, $\frac{5}{5}$, $\frac{10}{10}$, and $\frac{47}{47}$.

Connect: Writing a whole number as a fraction with 1 as the denominator

How can Alana write 8 as a fraction with 1 in the denominator?

The denominator tells how many parts in the whole. To have a denominator of 1, the whole can have only 1 part. The fraction $\frac{8}{1}$ shows there are 8 parts in the fraction and each part is 1 whole.

➤ Alana can write 8 as $\frac{8}{1}$. To write a whole number as a fraction with 1 as the denominator, use the whole number as the numerator.

Math-to-Math Connection

Liquid Volume Have students work with measuring cups to relate how many fractional measurements make a whole cup. Bring in measuring cups for $\frac{1}{3}$ cup, $\frac{1}{4}$ cup, 1 cup, and 2 cups. Have students use what they know about fractions and whole numbers to guess how many $\frac{1}{4}$ cups are in 1 cup and how many $\frac{1}{4}$ cups are in 2 cups. Check students' guesses by using the $\frac{1}{4}$ cup to fill 1 cup and 2 cups. Have students count the number of times you have to fill the $\frac{1}{4}$ cup. Repeat the activity with the $\frac{1}{3}$ measuring cup.

Lesson 21

Guided Practice

Use the number line to find the whole number for each fraction.

1. $\frac{2}{2}$ = __1__   2. $\frac{6}{2}$ = __3__

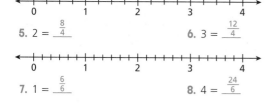

3. $\frac{3}{3}$ = __1__   4. $\frac{6}{3}$ = __2__

Use the number line to find the fraction for each whole number.

5. 2 = $\frac{8}{4}$ 6. 3 = $\frac{12}{4}$

7. 1 = $\frac{6}{6}$ 8. 4 = $\frac{24}{6}$

Solve the problem.

9. Makaela plants $\frac{3}{4}$ of her herb garden with basil and $\frac{1}{4}$ with sage. Explain why the fraction strips show that the whole garden is planted with basil and sage.

One Whole			
$\frac{1}{4}$	$\frac{1}{4}$	$\frac{1}{4}$	$\frac{1}{4}$

Answer Possible explanation: The fraction strips show that three $\frac{1}{4}$ strips for the basil and one $\frac{1}{4}$ strip for the sage are equal to one whole.

Think·Pair·Share

MP3 10. Work with a partner. Explain how you can find whole numbers for $\frac{8}{8}$, $\frac{16}{8}$, $\frac{24}{8}$, and $\frac{32}{8}$. Share your ideas with your class. Possible explanation: I would make and label a number line from 0 to 4 in eighths. I would label $\frac{8}{8}$ as 1, $\frac{16}{8}$ as 2, $\frac{24}{8}$ as 3, and $\frac{32}{8}$ as 4.

Unit 3 ■ Focus on Number and Operations—Fractions **185**

Mathematical Practices

Mathematical Practice Standards underline the teaching and understanding of all concepts and skills presented. The emphasis of specific practices is noted throughout the guided and independent practice of this lesson.

MP3	Construct viable arguments and critique the reasoning of others.

Item 10: Students explain how to write whole numbers as fractions and share their reasoning with others.

Observational Assessment

Use page 185 to assess whether students are able to use a number line to express a fraction as a whole number, and a whole number as a fraction. To express a whole number as a fraction, make sure students are correctly identifying the number of equal parts in one whole, and using that as the denominator in their fractions.

Think·Pair·Share

Peer Collaboration As each pair of students shares their ideas with the class, ask questions such as:

- *Did you use the same strategy or different strategies?*
- *Can you find a pattern in the fractions?*
- *How can you represent the fractions on a number line?*

To summarize, draw different models to represent the fractions. Have students identify the whole in each model.

Return to the Essential Question

Reread the Lesson 21 Essential Question on page 182: *How can I relate whole numbers and fractions?*

Ask volunteers to use what they learned in this lesson to answer this question. (Possible responses: I can use a number line to show how many unit fractions are in a whole number. I can multiply the whole number by the denominator I want.)

Independent Practice

Concept Application

Students may work independently on these pages in the classroom or at home. They may refer to the first four pages of the lesson to revisit the instruction or to see a worked-out example.

Common Errors and **Teaching Tips** may help you support student learning either in the classroom or as a follow-up for work done at home.

Teaching Tips

Items 1–8

It may be helpful for students to label each part as they count. When writing the fraction, remind them to use the number of equal parts as the denominator.

Independent Practice

Write the fraction and whole number for the parts that are shaded.

1.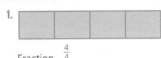

   Fraction $\frac{4}{4}$

   Whole number $\underline{1}$

2.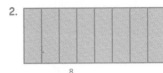

   Fraction $\frac{8}{8}$

   Whole number $\underline{1}$

3.

   Fraction $\frac{6}{6}$

   Whole number $\underline{1}$

4.

   Fraction $\frac{6}{3}$

   Whole number $\underline{2}$

Shade each whole. Then write the fraction and whole number for the parts that are shaded.

5.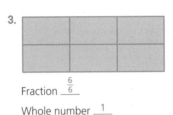

   Fraction $\frac{4}{4}$

   Whole number $\underline{1}$

6.

   Fraction $\frac{5}{5}$

   Whole number $\underline{1}$

7.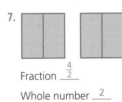

   Fraction $\frac{4}{2}$

   Whole number $\underline{2}$

8.

   Fraction $\frac{3}{3}$

   Whole number $\underline{1}$

186   Unit 3 ■ Focus on Number and Operations—Fractions

Writing About Math

▸ **Write an Informative Text** Ask students to write a paragraph about how to rewrite a fraction as a whole number and how to rewrite a whole number as a fraction. When students are finished, have them trade papers with a partner. The partner should try to write a fraction and a whole number based on their partner's instructions. If there is a part missing from the explanation, students should revise their paragraphs.

MORE ONLINE | sadlierconnect.com

Lesson 21

Independent Practice

9. Which whole number does the point on the number line represent?

a. 1

b. 3

c. 4

d. 12

10. Which fraction does the point on the number line represent?

a. $\frac{20}{4}$

b. $\frac{16}{4}$

c. $\frac{12}{4}$

d. $\frac{4}{4}$

11. Which fraction is not equivalent to 1?

a. $\frac{3}{3}$

b. $\frac{6}{6}$

c. $\frac{18}{6}$

d. $\frac{18}{18}$

12. Write 3 fractions that are equivalent to the whole number 3.

Answer Possible answer: $\frac{3}{1}, \frac{6}{2}, \frac{9}{3}$ _____

13. Write 3 fractions that are equivalent to the whole number 4.

Answer Possible answer: $\frac{4}{1}, \frac{8}{2}, \frac{12}{3}$ _____

14. Write 3 fractions that are equivalent to the whole number 5.

Answer Possible answer: $\frac{5}{1}, \frac{10}{2}, \frac{15}{3}$ _____

15. Write 3 fractions that are equivalent to the whole number 6.

Answer Possible answer: $\frac{6}{1}, \frac{12}{2}, \frac{18}{3}$ _____

Unit 3 ■ Focus on Number and Operations—Fractions **187**

Teaching Tips

Item 10

It may be helpful for students to write the fractions on the number line. Students should first identify how many equal groups are between 0 and 1 and then use that number as their denominator.

Items 12–15

Struggling students may find it helpful to draw and label number lines. Remind them to use the number of equal groups in one whole as the denominator.

Digital Connection

Drawing Fractions Ask students to use an art program to draw fraction strips. They should use a different color to show different fractions. For example, halves might be red and thirds might be blue. The scale of their strips should be proportionally accurate. Most art programs will have measuring tools to help with the accuracy of student drawings. Students should begin with the whole strip and then partition strips of the same size into equal parts. Fractions with greater denominators will have smaller parts.

Common Errors

Item 16

Students may forget to count both lasagnas. They may see *sixths* and end up with an answer of 6 instead of 12. Remind students that they must express 2 as an equivalent fraction.

Teaching Tips

Item 18

After drawing a model, students could also draw a number line to solve the word problem. Encourage students to translate information from their model to the number line and then fill in the other numbers.

Independent Practice

Solve the problems.

MP4 **16.** Lauren bakes 2 lasagnas. She cuts each lasagna into sixths. How many pieces does she have? Draw or use fraction strips to express 2 as a fraction in sixths. Write the equivalent fractions.
Check students' drawings.

Answer $12; \frac{2}{1} = \frac{12}{6}$

MP5 **17.** Marco makes 6 personal pizzas. He cuts each pizza into thirds. How many pieces does he have? Draw a number line to express 6 as a fraction in thirds. Write the equivalent fractions. Check students' drawings.

Answer $18; \frac{6}{1} = \frac{18}{3}$

MP6 **18.** Joanie bakes 3 pies. She cuts each pie into eighths. How many pieces does she have? Draw a model to express 3 as a fraction in eighths. Write the equivalent fractions. Check students' drawings.

Answer $24; \frac{3}{1} = \frac{24}{8}$

Mathematical Practices	
MP4	**Model with mathematics.**
Item 16: Students draw a model to represent fractional quantities.	
MP5	**Use appropriate tools strategically.**
Item 17: Students use a number line to solve a word problem.	
MP6	**Attend to precision.**
Item 18: Students express a whole number as a fraction.	

Independent Practice

MP4 **19.** Mrs. Becker bakes an apple pie for her family. Mr. Becker eats $\frac{2}{8}$, Josh eats $\frac{3}{8}$, Randi eats $\frac{1}{8}$, and Mrs. Becker eats $\frac{1}{8}$. Did they eat the whole pie?

Answer No, they did not eat the whole pie.

◗ · Justify your answer using words, drawings, or numbers.
Possible justification: I used fraction strips. I lined up two $\frac{1}{8}$ strips for Mr. Becker, three $\frac{1}{8}$ strips for Josh, one $\frac{1}{8}$ strip for Randi, and one $\frac{1}{8}$ strip for Mrs. Becker under a 1 whole strip. Since they did not line up completely under the 1 whole strip, the Beckers did not eat the whole pie.

MP2 **20.** Liat, Kevin, and Chandler each baked corn bread in the same size pan. The pictures show how each person cuts the corn bread in the pan.

Liat's Pan   Kevin's Pan   Chandler's Pan

Chandler says he bakes the most corn bread. Do you agree?

Answer No, I disagree.

◗ · Justify your answer using words, drawings, or numbers.
Possible justification: They all baked the same amount of corn bread. Liat's pan represents $\frac{4}{4}$ = 1. Kevin's pan represents $\frac{8}{8}$ = 1. Chandler's pan represents $\frac{12}{12}$ = 1.

MP3 **21.** Parker says that the shading in the figure represents the fraction $\frac{3}{3}$. Maddie says the shading in the figure represents the fraction $\frac{6}{6}$. Who do you agree with?

Answer I agree with Maddie.

◗ · Justify your answer using words, drawings, or numbers.
Possible justification: The triangle is divided into 6 equal parts, so the shading represents $\frac{6}{6}$. Parker may have counted the number of sides of the triangle instead of the number of equal parts.

Justifying answers is a critical skill in math. Tell students that they can choose the way that works best for them to justify their answers, but they should practice trying different ways.

Mathematical Practices

MP2	**Reason abstractly and quantitatively.**

Item 20: Students analyze a model, solve a word problem, and justify their reasoning.

MP3	**Construct viable arguments and critique the reasoning of others.**

Item 21: Students solve a word problem and construct an argument to explain their solution.

MP4	**Model with mathematics.**

Item 19: Students relate mathematics to everyday problems and use words, drawings, or numbers to justify their thinking.

Common Core Focus:

3.NF.3d Compare two fractions with the same numerator or the same denominator by reasoning about their size. Recognize that comparisons are valid only when the two fractions refer to the same whole. Record the results of comparisons with the symbols >, =, or <, and justify the conclusions.

OBJECTIVE
Compare two fractions that have the same denominator.

ESSENTIAL QUESTION
Students learn to use a number line and fraction models to visually compare fractions with the same denominator. Remind students of how to use the *greater than* and *less than* symbols to compare whole numbers. Students will apply this understanding to comparing fractions.

FLUENCY PRACTICE
Fluency practice is available at **sadlierconnect.com**.

Concept Development

Understand: Comparing fractions on a number line

■ Be sure students understand that on a number line, the fraction to the right is always greater than the fraction to the left. Discuss how the > and < symbols can be used to show a single comparison two different ways.

■ It may be helpful to show students that another way to compare fractions is to relate the fraction to 0. The closer the fraction is to 0, the lesser the fraction.

▸ Ask for volunteers to demonstrate how they used fraction models to compare the fractions. Explain that there are different models that can be used.

Lesson 22 Compare Fractions: Same Denominator

Essential Question: How can I compare fractions with the same denominator? 3.NF.3d

Guided Instruction

In this lesson you will learn to compare two fractions that have the same denominator.

Understand: Comparing fractions on a number line

Tamara is ordering a large pizza with mushrooms on $\frac{5}{8}$ of the slices and pineapple on $\frac{3}{8}$ of the slices. Does the pizza have more mushrooms or more pineapple?

Compare $\frac{5}{8}$ and $\frac{3}{8}$ to answer the question.

Look at the number line.

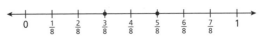

$\frac{5}{8}$ is to the right of $\frac{3}{8}$ on the number line, so $\frac{5}{8}$ is greater than $\frac{3}{8}$.

To show this comparison, write $\frac{5}{8} > \frac{3}{8}$.

$\frac{3}{8}$ is to the left of $\frac{5}{8}$ on the number line, so $\frac{3}{8}$ is less than $\frac{5}{8}$.

To show this comparison, write $\frac{3}{8} < \frac{5}{8}$.

Remember! > means is greater than and < means is less than.

➡ The pizza has more mushrooms.

▸ How can you compare $\frac{5}{8}$ and $\frac{3}{8}$ using fraction models? Possible answer: Draw 2 identical rectangles and divide both into 8 equal parts. Shade 5 parts of one rectangle and 3 parts of the other rectangle. Count to compare the shaded parts. You find that $\frac{5}{8} > \frac{3}{8}$ and $\frac{3}{8} < \frac{5}{8}$.

Support English Language Learners

The term *greater than* is not often used in everyday speech, and therefore may be confusing for English language learners. Some students may think that "greater" means "better" and be confused as to which is the better number.

Provide a sentence frame to help students relate the terms *greater than* and *less than* to the context of the lesson. For example, _____ *is greater than* _____, or _____ *is less than* _____. Select two non-equivalent numbers at random and have students use the sentence frame to describe the relationship between the numbers. Repeat the process to ensure students become familiar with the terms *greater than* and *less than*.

Lesson 22

Guided Instruction

Understand: Using fraction strips to compare fractions with the same denominator

> Bryce bought $\frac{2}{4}$ pound of American cheese and $\frac{3}{4}$ pound of Swiss cheese. Compare the amounts of cheese that Bryce bought.

You can use fraction strips to represent $\frac{2}{4}$ pound and $\frac{3}{4}$ pound.

Step 1

Use two $\frac{1}{4}$ fraction strips for $\frac{2}{4}$.

Use three $\frac{1}{4}$ fraction strips for $\frac{3}{4}$.

	1			
American cheese	$\frac{1}{4}$	$\frac{1}{4}$	$\frac{1}{4}$	$\frac{1}{4}$
Swiss cheese	$\frac{1}{4}$	$\frac{1}{4}$	$\frac{1}{4}$	$\frac{1}{4}$

Step 2

Compare the lengths.

The length of the fraction strips for $\frac{3}{4}$ is greater than the length of the fraction strips for $\frac{2}{4}$.

The length of the fraction strips for $\frac{2}{4}$ is less than the length of the fraction strips for $\frac{3}{4}$.

Step 3

Compare the fractions. Use < and >.

$\frac{3}{4} > \frac{2}{4}$ $\qquad$ $\frac{2}{4} < \frac{3}{4}$

➡ Bryce bought more Swiss cheese than American cheese.
Bryce bought less American cheese than Swiss cheese.

✏ Why can you compare two fractions two ways?
Possible answer: If a fraction is greater than another fraction, then the other fraction is less than the first fraction.

Understand: Using fraction strips to compare fractions with the same denominator

■ In this presentation, students examine how to use fraction strips to represent and compare fractions. You may wish to have fractions strips available for students to use to model the instruction on this page. Manipulating the strips may help students compare two fractions and determine the greater and lesser fraction.

■ Be sure students understand that only fractions of the same-size whole can be compared in order to have a true comparison.

✏ Students may need guidance to answer this question. Provide appropriate scaffolding and prompt them to see that if one fraction is greater and one fraction is lesser, the sign that is used (> or <) depends on which fraction is written first.

Math-to-Measurement Connection

Time Students can use a number line to compare increments of time. For example, using time increments of $\frac{1}{4}$ hour, help students keep track of what they did for an hour in school, and then determine which activity took the longest. If they read for $\frac{3}{4}$ of an hour, practiced math for $\frac{1}{4}$ of an hour, and had recess for $\frac{1}{4}$ of an hour, which activity did they spend the greatest amount of time on? Remind students to compare the fractions.

Connect: Reasoning about fractions with the same denominator Use this page to help students strengthen their understanding of how fractions with the same denominator can be compared.

■ Remind students that if the denominators are the same they can simply compare the numerators.

■ Discuss with students the definition of *denominator* as the number of equal parts in the whole.

Connect: Reasoning about the size of the whole Use this section to help students strengthen their understanding of how the size of the whole matters when comparing fractions.

■ Remind students that they can only compare fractions of wholes that are the same size. Once they determine that the wholes are equal in size, they can compare fractions of each whole.

■ Emphasize that the denominators of two same-size wholes partitioned into the same number of equal parts, will be the same, even though the parts may not have the same shape.

■ Ask students to explain why they cannot use fractions to compare fractions of a large pizza and a small pizza. Students should understand that the wholes are not the same size, so for example, $\frac{1}{8}$ of each pizza would not be the same size. The comparisons would not make sense.

Connect: Reasoning about fractions with the same denominator

> Uma has to compare $\frac{2}{6}$ and $\frac{4}{6}$, but she does not have any fraction strips or number lines to use. How can Uma compare the fractions?

To compare fractions with the same denominator, use what you know about the fractions.

The denominators tell you that the parts that make up each fraction are the same size. The numerators tell you how many parts you are comparing. You can compare the fractions by comparing the numerators.

Compare $\frac{2}{6}$ and $\frac{4}{6}$. $2 \underline{<} 4$ $4 \underline{>} 2$ $\boxed{\text{You can write the comparison of two numbers two ways.}}$

$\frac{2}{6} \underline{<} \frac{4}{6}$ $\frac{4}{6} \underline{>} \frac{2}{6}$

➡ Uma can compare $\frac{2}{6}$ and $\frac{4}{6}$ by comparing the numerators.

Connect: Reasoning about the size of the whole

> In which two rectangles can you compare the fractions represented by the shaded parts?
>
>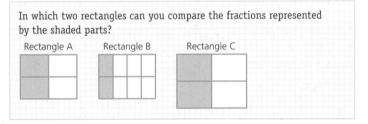
> Rectangle A   Rectangle B   Rectangle C

To compare fractions, the wholes must be the same size.

Each rectangle represents the whole for a fraction. Rectangle C is larger than Rectangles A and B. Rectangles A and B are the same size, so the wholes are the same size.

➡ The fractions represented by the shaded parts in Rectangles A and B can be compared. $\frac{2}{4} > \frac{2}{8}$ and $\frac{2}{8} < \frac{2}{4}$.

192   Unit 3 ▪ Focus on Number and Operations—Fractions

Math-to-Math Connection

Arithmetic and Geometry A strong understanding of the relationship between the sizes of the wholes will be helpful when students compare fractions. Students can compare the different sizes of geometric shapes, such as squares. Given two squares of different sizes, students can divide each into half. Ask them to compare the halves. The half of the larger square will obviously be larger than the half of the smaller square. This should lead into a discussion of the necessity of comparing fractions from the same-size whole.

MORE ONLINE sadlierconnect.com

Lesson 22

Guided Practice

Use the number line to compare the fractions. Write < or >.

1. $\frac{7}{8}$ ⊙ $\frac{4}{8}$ $\frac{4}{8}$ ⊙ $\frac{7}{8}$ 2. $\frac{1}{8}$ ⊙ $\frac{6}{8}$ $\frac{6}{8}$ ⊙ $\frac{1}{8}$

Use the models to compare the fractions. Write < or >.

3.

$\frac{1}{3}$ ⊙ $\frac{2}{3}$ $\frac{2}{3}$ ⊙ $\frac{1}{3}$

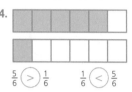

4.

$\frac{5}{6}$ ⊙ $\frac{1}{6}$ $\frac{1}{6}$ ⊙ $\frac{5}{6}$

Solve the problem.

5. Molly bought $\frac{1}{4}$ yard of blue ribbon and $\frac{3}{4}$ yard of red ribbon. Compare the amounts of ribbon Molly bought. Make a drawing to support your answer. Answers will vary. Check students' drawings.

Answer _Molly bought more red ribbon than blue ribbon because $\frac{3}{4} > \frac{1}{4}$ or Molly bought less blue ribbon than red ribbon because $\frac{1}{4} < \frac{3}{4}$._

👑 Think•Pair•Share

MP4 6. Work with a partner. Arrange 3 rows of fraction strips on a desk. In row one, place one $\frac{1}{3}$ fraction strip. In row two, place two $\frac{1}{3}$ fraction strips. In row three, place three $\frac{1}{3}$ fraction strips.

• Write the fractions that the fraction strips represent in order from least to greatest.

• What do you notice about the denominators?

• What do you notice about the numerators?

• How do the numerators relate to the number of fraction strips?
$\frac{1}{3}, \frac{2}{3}, \frac{3}{3}$; the denominators are the same; the numerators grow by 1s. The numerators show the number of fraction strips that were used.

Unit 3 ■ Focus on Number and Operations—Fractions **193**

Observational Assessment

Use page 193 to assess whether students are able to compare fractions with the same denominator. Look for evidence that students can correctly use the >, <, and = symbols.

👑 Think•Pair•Share

Peer Collaboration Ask each student to work with a partner to model the fractions. As students work, ask questions such as:

• *Are the wholes equal?*

• *How can fraction strips be used to demonstrate this?*

In summary, students should be able to show and also explain their thinking.

Return to the Essential Question

Reread the Lesson 22 Essential Question on page 190: *How can I compare fractions with the same denominator?*

Ask volunteers to use what they learned in this lesson to answer this question. (Possible response: I can use a number line or fraction strips to model fractions of same-size wholes and determine which fraction is greater and which is lesser.)

Mathematical Practices

Mathematical Practice Standards underline the teaching and understanding of all concepts and skills presented. The emphasis of specific practices is noted throughout the guided and independent practice of this lesson.

MP4	Model with mathematics.

Item 6: Students explain the relationships of quantities represented by fraction strips.

Independent Practice

Concept Application

Students may work independently on these pages in the classroom or at home. They may refer to the first four pages of the lesson to revisit the instruction or to see a worked-out example.

Common Errors and **Teaching Tips** may help you support student learning either in the classroom or as a follow-up for work done at home.

Teaching Tips

Items 1-4
Remind students that on the number line, the number to the right is the greater fraction because it is closer to the whole number.

Items 5-10
Help students see that the models for each pair of fractions show the same-size whole, which is a prerequisite for comparing fractions.

Independent Practice

Use the number line to compare the fractions. Write < or >.

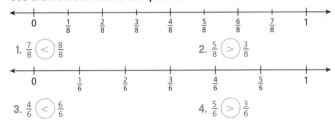

1. $\frac{7}{8}$ (<) $\frac{8}{8}$ 2. $\frac{5}{8}$ (>) $\frac{3}{8}$

3. $\frac{4}{6}$ (<) $\frac{6}{6}$ 4. $\frac{5}{6}$ (>) $\frac{3}{6}$

Use the models to compare the fractions. Write < or >.

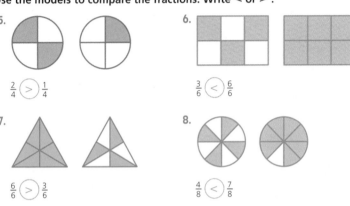

5. $\frac{2}{4}$ (>) $\frac{1}{4}$ 6. $\frac{3}{6}$ (<) $\frac{6}{6}$

7. $\frac{6}{6}$ (>) $\frac{3}{6}$ 8. $\frac{4}{8}$ (<) $\frac{7}{8}$

Find the fractions shown by each model. Then compare the fractions. Use <, >, or =.

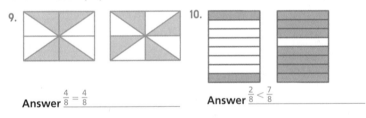

9. **Answer** $\frac{4}{8} = \frac{4}{8}$ 10. **Answer** $\frac{2}{8} < \frac{7}{8}$

Writing About Math

▸ **Write an Opinion Text** Ask students to write a paragraph giving their opinion on whether they think it is easier to use a number line or fraction strips to compare fractions. Have students provide reasons that support their opinions.

Ask volunteers to read their paragraphs aloud. Remind students that these are opinion paragraphs, so there is no right or wrong answer.

Lesson 22

Independent Practice

Teaching Tips

Items 13–14

If students are struggling, ask them to draw and label a number line with the fractions used. This should allow them to see where the fractions are in relation to one another.

Shade the figures to compare the fractions. Write <, >, or =.

11.

$\frac{1}{6}$ < $\frac{3}{6}$ $\frac{3}{6}$ > $\frac{1}{6}$

12.

$\frac{4}{4}$ > $\frac{3}{4}$ $\frac{3}{4}$ < $\frac{4}{4}$

13. Which fraction is greater than $\frac{6}{8}$?

a. $\frac{1}{8}$ b. $\frac{3}{8}$

c. $\frac{5}{8}$ (d.) $\frac{9}{8}$

14. Which fraction is NOT less than $\frac{5}{6}$?

(a.) $\frac{6}{6}$ b. $\frac{4}{6}$

c. $\frac{2}{6}$ d. $\frac{1}{6}$

Compare. Write <, >, or =. Use a number line or model if needed.

15. $\frac{2}{2}$ > $\frac{1}{2}$ 16. $\frac{1}{6}$ < $\frac{3}{6}$

17. $\frac{2}{3}$ < $\frac{3}{3}$ 18. $\frac{5}{6}$ > $\frac{2}{6}$

19. $\frac{3}{8}$ < $\frac{8}{8}$ 20. $\frac{4}{4}$ = $\frac{3}{3}$

21. Write 3 fractions that are less than $\frac{4}{6}$.

Answer Possible answer: $\frac{1}{6}, \frac{2}{6}, \frac{3}{6}$

22. Write 3 fractions that are greater than $\frac{5}{8}$.

Answer Possible answer: $\frac{6}{8}, \frac{7}{8}, \frac{11}{8}$

Digital Connection

Whiteboard Activity Use the interactive whiteboard to practice writing number lines with students. Students are often provided the number lines that they are to work with. Set the parameters for each number line and have different students label each fractional increment.

Independent Practice

Common Errors

Item 23

Students may confuse the number of problems (12) with the denominators (sixths) and not understand how to solve the problem. Tell students that the fractions $\frac{4}{6}$ and $\frac{5}{6}$ tell how much homework each student has finished. Suggest that students draw number lines, fraction strips, or geometric shapes such as circles or rectangles to model the problem.

Since the denominators are the same, students may notice that they need only to compare the numerators to determine which fraction is greater, and therefore which student finished more homework.

Teaching Tips

Item 24

Some students might not recognize that they need to determine the lesser fraction to solve the problem. Point out that the paint can that is "less full" is the lesser fraction. Since the fractions have the same denominators, the lesser numerator indicates the lesser fraction.

Lesson 22 **Compare Fractions: Same Denominator**

Independent Practice

Solve the problems.

MP4 **23.** Before dinner, Prana finishes $\frac{4}{6}$ of her homework and Julieta finishes $\frac{5}{6}$ of her homework. There are 12 problems for homework. Who has finished more homework? Draw a model. Then compare the fractions. Check students' drawings.

Answer Julieta finishes more of her homework. $\frac{5}{6} > \frac{4}{6}$

MP2 **24.** Garrett paints his bedroom blue and white. He has $\frac{3}{8}$ gallon of white paint left and $\frac{2}{8}$ gallon of blue paint left. Draw a model to show the paint cans. Which paint can is less full? Then compare the fractions. Check students' drawings.

Answer The can of blue paint is less full. $\frac{2}{8} < \frac{3}{8}$

MP7 **25.** Kwame runs $\frac{5}{8}$ mile on Friday, $\frac{7}{8}$ mile on Saturday, and $\frac{4}{8}$ mile on Sunday. Draw number lines to compare the distances Kwame runs each day. On which day does Kwame run the longest distance? Then write the fractions in order from least to greatest. Check students' drawings.

Answer Kwame runs the longest distance on Saturday. $\frac{4}{8}, \frac{5}{8}, \frac{7}{8}$

196   Unit 3 ▪ Focus on Number and Operations—Fractions

Mathematical Practices		
MP2	**Reason abstractly and quantitatively.**	
Item 24: Students analyze the information in a problem, model the problem, and represent the solution using symbols.		
MP4	**Model with mathematics.**	
Item 23: Students relate mathematics to real-world problems.		
MP7	**Look for and make use of structure.**	
Item 25: Students evaluate the structure of the problem in order to solve it.		

MORE ONLINE sadlierconnect.com   Lesson 22

Independent Practice

MP3 **26.** Lauren eats $\frac{1}{2}$ of a small pizza. Jared eats $\frac{1}{2}$ of a large pizza. Jared says that they both eat the same amount of pizza because $\frac{1}{2} = \frac{1}{2}$.

Do you agree? Explain your answer.

Answer No, I disagree. _____

 Justify your answer using words, drawings, or numbers.

Possible justification: The pizzas are different sizes: $\frac{1}{2}$ of a small pizza is not equivalent to $\frac{1}{2}$ of a large pizza.

MP3 **27.** Is this fraction comparison true or false?

$$\frac{2}{8} > \frac{6}{8}$$

Use the models to help you decide. Check students' drawings.

Answer It is false. _____

 Justify your answer using words, drawings, or numbers.

Possible justification: $\frac{6}{8} > \frac{2}{8}$ since the amount in 6 shaded equal parts is greater than the amount in 2 shaded equal parts.

Teaching Tips

Item 26
Students may have difficulty justifying their answer. Encourage them to use the drawings provided to frame their response.

Item 27
Students may need help using words to justify their answer. Provide scaffolding in the form of a sentence frame such as "The size of the wholes are equal, so . . . ."

Mathematical Practices		
MP3	**Construct viable arguments and critique the reasoning of others.**	

Item 26: Students analyze a problem and justify their reasoning.

Item 27: Students construct arguments by using drawings.

Common Core Focus:

3.NF.3d Compare two fractions with the same numerator or the same denominator by reasoning about their size. Recognize that comparisons are valid only when the two fractions refer to the same whole. Record the results of comparisons with the symbols >, =, or <, and justify the conclusions.

OBJECTIVE

Compare two fractions that have the same numerator.

ESSENTIAL QUESTION

Discuss with students the different ways they have learned to compare fractions.

FLUENCY PRACTICE

Fluency practice is available at **sadlierconnect.com**.

Concept Development

Understand: Using number lines and models to compare fractions with the same numerator

■ When using area models, encourage students to begin by drawing a rectangle, partitioning it into a number of equal parts determined by the denominator, then shading the number of parts in the numerator. If they run out of parts to shade, students need to draw another rectangle and continue this process until they have shaded the correct number of parts being used.

■ · Students should write whole numbers as fractions to help visualize the number of parts being used compared to the number of parts in the whole. Keeping consistent denominators will be more effective than having to switch back and forth from fractions to whole numbers, back to fractions.

Lesson 23 Compare Fractions: Same Numerator

Essential Question:
How can I compare fractions with the same numerator?
3.NF.3d

Guided Instruction

In this lesson you will learn to compare two fractions that have the same numerator.

Understand: Using number lines and models to compare fractions with the same numerator

> At a farm club meeting, Luke says that he collected $\frac{3}{4}$ dozen eggs that morning. Polly says that she collected $\frac{3}{2}$ dozen eggs. Who collected more eggs?

To find the answer, you can use a number line to compare $\frac{3}{4}$ and $\frac{3}{2}$.

Label the top of the number line with fractions in $\frac{1}{2}$s. Label the bottom of the number line with fractions in $\frac{1}{4}$s. When you do this, you can compare two fractions on the same number line.

The point for $\frac{3}{2}$ is to the right of the point for $\frac{3}{4}$, so $\frac{3}{2}$ is greater than $\frac{3}{4}$.

➡ Polly collected more eggs.

You can also use models to compare $\frac{3}{4}$ and $\frac{3}{2}$.

Draw rectangles and use shading to show $\frac{3}{4}$ and $\frac{3}{2}$.

When you compare the sizes, you can see that $\frac{3}{2} > \frac{3}{4}$ and that $\frac{3}{4} < \frac{3}{2}$.

■ · When you use models to work with fractions, how do you work with fractions that are greater than 1? Possible answer: I do not need to think about whether a fraction is greater or less than 1, because I just use the denominator to find the kind of equal parts and the numerator to find the number of those parts.

Remember!
Each whole must be the same size in order to compare them.

198 Unit 3 ■ Focus on Number and Operations—Fractions

Support English Language Learners

Help English language learners understand that the term *compare* means to examine two things to see how they are similar and how they are different.

This term is often used in math exploration. To compare in math also means to communicate the similarities and differences between two things. In this lesson, comparing is done by comparing numerators and denominators, and using >, <, or = symbols to describe the comparison.

Practice using the comparative symbols and the phrases *greater than*, *less than*, and *equal to* will help reinforce the meaning of the symbols.

Understand: Using number strips to compare fractions with the same numerator

Haley used $\frac{3}{4}$ cup of wheat flour and $\frac{3}{6}$ cup of rye flour in a recipe. Compare the amounts of the flours that Haley used.

Step 1

Use fraction strips to represent $\frac{3}{4}$ cup and $\frac{3}{6}$ cup.

Use three $\frac{1}{4}$ fraction strips for $\frac{3}{4}$.

Use three $\frac{1}{6}$ fraction strips for $\frac{3}{6}$.

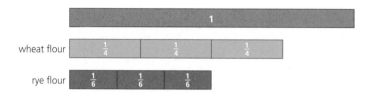

Step 2

Compare the lengths.

The length of the fraction strips for $\frac{3}{4}$ is greater than the length of the fraction strips for $\frac{3}{6}$.

Step 3

Compare the fractions two ways. Use $<$ and $>$.

$$\frac{3}{4} > \frac{3}{6} \qquad \frac{3}{6} < \frac{3}{4}$$

➡ Haley used more wheat flour than rye flour in the recipe.

✏ What does using the 1 strip help you remember?
Possible answer: You can only compare fractions when the whole is the same for both fractions.

Unit 3 ■ Focus on Number and Operations—Fractions **199**

Understand: Using number strips to compare fractions with the same numerator

■ Using different visual models allows students to experience fractions in different contexts and provides flexibility in reasoning and explaining strategies.

■ If necessary, have student stack fraction strips on top of each other, to better visualize their size. This process is also similar to creating an area model.

■ Encourage students to use the definitions of numerator (the number of equal parts being used) and denominator (the number of equal parts in the whole) when comparing fractions. This scaffolds understanding for the next section.

✏ When comparing fractions, it is important to think about the whole, since fractions are parts of the whole. Visualizing the whole when comparing fractions will deepen understanding about the relationship between numerators and denominators. In visual models, such as number lines and area models, the whole is represented. Therefore, it is important to be consistent in this concept and portray it when using fraction strips.

Math-to-Science Connection

Deforestation Relating real-world problems to math builds problem-solving skills. Pollution and deforestation are issues that need to be explored in a science context, and integrating math will provide a quantitative understanding.

Have students imagine that their class and another class will both be planting new trees in recently cleared forests. If one class plants $\frac{5}{8}$ of an area with maple trees, and another class plants oak trees on $\frac{5}{6}$ of another area the same size, how can students determine which class planted more trees? Have students choose an effective strategy for solving the problem, by using a visual model to represent the problem, and explaining their thinking. Encourage students to explore what the relationship between the numerators and denominators can tell us about a fraction.

Guided Instruction

Connect: Reasoning about fractions with the same numerator Use this page to help students strengthen their understanding of comparing fractions with the same numerator.

■ When the numerator is the same, students need to focus on the denominator. Comparing the denominators will determine how the fraction compares—the greater denominator determines the lesser fraction.

■ Visual models are presented on this page for support, but should be faded out as students master the concept. It is essential that students are able to think critically about numerators, denominators, and their relationships.

■ Students should understand that the greater the denominator, the smaller the parts. The greater the numerator, the more parts being used. Encourage students to explain why $\frac{2}{8}$ is smaller than $\frac{2}{4}$ of the same whole. Explaining their thinking aloud can help students build a deeper understanding of fractions.

✏ When comparing fractions with the same numerator, the number of parts stays the same, but the size of the parts might change. When comparing fractions with the same denominator, the size of the parts are the same. To explore this idea, have students draw visual models of fractions with the same numerator followed by fractions with the same denominator.

Additional Answers

Guided Instruction

Connect: Reasoning about fractions with the same numerator

> Alex has to compare $\frac{2}{4}$ and $\frac{2}{8}$, but he wants to do it mentally. How can Alex compare the fractions?

To compare fractions with the same numerator, use what you know about the fractions.

The numerators tell you that there are the same number of parts to compare.

The denominators tell you about the size of the equal parts of the whole.

• The equal parts of a fraction with a greater denominator are smaller because the whole is divided into more parts.

This means that the fraction with the greater denominator will be the lesser fraction.

$\frac{2}{4}$

$\frac{2}{8}$

Notice that eighths are smaller than fourths.

• The equal parts of a fraction with a lesser denominator are larger because the whole is divided into fewer parts.

This means that the fraction with the lesser denominator will be the greater fraction.

$\frac{2}{4}$

$\frac{2}{8}$

Notice that fourths are larger than eighths.

To compare $\frac{2}{4}$ and $\frac{2}{8}$, think about the denominators.

$4 < 8$ $8 > 4$

$\frac{2}{4} > \frac{2}{8}$ $\frac{2}{8} < \frac{2}{4}$

➡ Alex can compare $\frac{2}{4}$ and $\frac{2}{8}$ by thinking about the denominators.

✏ How is comparing fractions with the same numerator different from comparing fractions with the same denominator?
See Additional Answers.

Math-to-Reading Connection

Reading Have students imagine that a third grade class is having a reading race to see who can finish a book first. The class is trying to guess who will finish first, so they want to compare the contestants' progress. They judge their progress based on how many of the 8 chapters have been read in a week. Ray has read $\frac{3}{8}$ of the book, Marci has finished $\frac{7}{8}$, and Larissa is $\frac{5}{8}$ done. Have students use visual models to determine which student has read the most and share their ideas. Have students discuss what needs to be true about each chapter, in order for the book to be split into 8 parts. (The chapters all need to be the same number of pages. If it is not, the fractions of their progress do not accurately reflect who has read more.)

Lesson 23

Guided Practice

Use the number lines to compare the fractions. Write < or >.

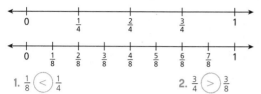

1. $\frac{1}{8}$ $<$ $\frac{1}{4}$

2. $\frac{3}{4}$ $>$ $\frac{3}{8}$

Use the models to compare the fractions. Write < or >.

3.

$\frac{1}{3}$ $>$ $\frac{1}{4}$

4.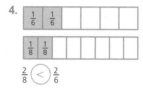

$\frac{2}{8}$ $<$ $\frac{2}{6}$

Solve the problem.

5. Zach walks $\frac{6}{2}$ blocks to the library. Lily walks $\frac{6}{3}$ blocks to the gym. Compare the distances they walk. Use a model to represent the problem. Check students' drawings.

Answer ___ Zach walks farther than Lily because $\frac{6}{2} > \frac{6}{3}$ or Lily walks less than Zach because $\frac{6}{3} < \frac{6}{2}$.

☗ Think·Pair·Share

MP4 6. Arrange fraction strips of $\frac{1}{2}$, $\frac{1}{3}$, $\frac{1}{4}$, $\frac{1}{6}$, and $\frac{1}{8}$ on a desk. Place the longest strip at the top and the shortest strip at the bottom.

  • What do you notice about the numerators?

  • What do you notice about the denominators?

  • How do the denominators relate to the size of the fraction strips? $\frac{1}{2}$, $\frac{1}{3}$, $\frac{1}{4}$, $\frac{1}{6}$, $\frac{1}{8}$; the numerators are the same. The denominators get smaller. The smaller the denominator, the longer the fraction strip.

Observational Assessment

Use page 201 to assess whether students understand how to compare fractions with the same numerator. Using different models and strategies will encourage students to think critically about comparing fractions. Symbols help students explain their reasoning.

☗ Think·Pair·Share

Peer Collaboration Ask pairs to share their strategies with each other, then the class. Asking questions while students work in pairs and then as a class, will give all students an opportunity to share effectively.

• *What changes as the denominator gets larger?*

• *What does ordering unit fraction strips from least to greatest denominator show us?*

To summarize, point out that the smaller the denominator, the longer the fraction strip.

Return to the Essential Question

Reread the Lesson 23 Essential Question on page 198: *How can I compare fractions with the same numerator?*

Ask volunteers to use what they learned in this lesson to answer this question. (Possible response: When the numerator is the same, the number of parts used stays the same. To compare the fractions, you need to look at the denominator to see how many parts are in the whole. The smaller the denominator, the greater the fraction.)

Mathematical Practices

Mathematical Practice Standards underline the teaching and understanding of all concepts and skills presented. The emphasis of specific practices is noted throughout the guided and independent practice of this lesson.

MP4	Model with mathematics.

Item 6: Students use fraction strips to visualize how larger denominators reduce the size of a unit fraction. Ordering the fractions by denominators will further the understanding of the relationship of quantities.

Concept Application

Students may work independently on these pages in the classroom or at home. They may refer to the first four pages of this lesson to revisit the instruction or to see a worked-out example.

Common Errors and **Teaching Tips** may help you support student learning either in the classroom or as a follow-up for work done at home.

Teaching Tips

Items 1–2

Suggest that students mark each fraction on the number line. Remind students that the fraction closer to 1 on the number line is the greater fraction.

Items 3–8

Have students first label each model with the fraction the shaded part represents. To challenge students, have them flip the order of the fractions written then fill in the correct inequality symbol.

Independent Practice

Use the number lines to compare the fractions. Write < or >.

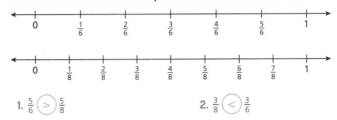

1. $\frac{5}{6}$ ⟩ $\frac{5}{8}$

2. $\frac{3}{8}$ ⟨ $\frac{3}{6}$

Use the models to compare the fractions. Write < or >.

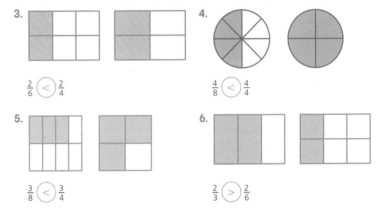

3. $\frac{2}{6}$ ⟨ $\frac{2}{4}$

4. $\frac{4}{8}$ ⟨ $\frac{4}{4}$

5. $\frac{3}{8}$ ⟨ $\frac{3}{4}$

6. $\frac{2}{3}$ ⟩ $\frac{2}{6}$

Write the fractions shown by each model. Then compare the fractions two ways. Use < and >.

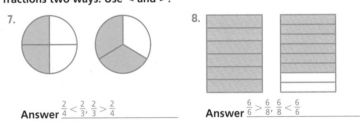

7. **Answer** $\frac{2}{4} < \frac{2}{3}, \frac{2}{3} > \frac{2}{4}$

8. **Answer** $\frac{6}{6} > \frac{6}{8}, \frac{6}{8} < \frac{6}{6}$

Writing About Math

▭ · **Write Explanatory Text** Ask students to write a paragraph explaining which model they find most useful when comparing fractions. Encourage students to justify their answers by discussing how easy it is to create the model, and identify any errors they might face when using the model.

Have students share their work with a partner and respond to the ideas given.

Independent Practice

Shade the figures to compare the fractions. Write < or >.

9.

$\frac{2}{3}$ ⊘ $\frac{2}{6}$ $\frac{2}{6}$ ⊘ $\frac{2}{3}$

$\frac{2}{3} > \frac{2}{6}$ $\frac{2}{6} < \frac{2}{3}$

10.

$\frac{3}{8} < \frac{3}{4}$ $\frac{3}{4} > \frac{3}{8}$

11. Which fraction is less than $\frac{1}{6}$?

   a. $\frac{1}{8}$ **b.** $\frac{1}{4}$

   c. $\frac{1}{3}$ **d.** $\frac{1}{2}$

12. Which fraction is less than $\frac{3}{6}$?

   a. $\frac{3}{3}$ **b.** $\frac{3}{4}$

   c. $\frac{3}{5}$ **d.** $\frac{3}{8}$

13. Which fraction is NOT less than $\frac{4}{2}$?

   a. $\frac{4}{8}$ **b.** $\frac{4}{6}$

   c. $\frac{4}{3}$ **d.** $\frac{4}{1}$

Compare. Write < or >. Use a number line or model if needed.

14. $\frac{3}{3} > \frac{3}{4}$ 15. $\frac{4}{6} > \frac{4}{8}$

16. Write 3 fractions with a numerator of 1 that are less than $\frac{1}{2}$.

   Answer Possible answer: $\frac{1}{3}, \frac{1}{4}, \frac{1}{6}$

17. Write 3 fractions with a numerator of 3 that are greater than $\frac{3}{8}$.

   Answer Possible answer: $\frac{3}{3}, \frac{3}{4}, \frac{3}{6}$

Common Errors

Items 9-10

Students might record the same symbol for the two comparisons in each problem. Point out that the two fractions below the models are the same, but in reverse order. Reinforce the translation of the symbols by encouraging students to say the fractions and symbols as a sentence. For example, "$\frac{2}{3}$ is greater than $\frac{2}{6}$; $\frac{2}{6}$ is less than $\frac{2}{3}$."

Teaching Tips

Items 11-13

Encourage students to write each comparison using inequality symbols. Challenge students to use the opposite symbol to show another way to compare the fractions.

Items 14-15

Have students read the comparison aloud.

Items 16-17

Students should see that there is more than one answer for each item.

Digital Connection

Interactive Fraction Strips Use a search engine or smart board to find images of fraction strips. Have students work in pairs, groups, or as a class to create a visual model of one fraction without saying the fraction aloud, then ask students to find another fraction that is either *greater than* or *less than* the given fraction.

Independent Practice

Common Errors

Items 18-20

Students may determine the fraction with the greater denominator to be the greater fraction, and neglect to draw a model. Tell students to begin by drawing a model. When creating area models, students should begin by drawing the wholes first. Then, they should partition each whole into an equal number of parts, determined by each denominator. The numerators tell how many of the parts to shade.

Teaching Tips

Items 18-19

Remind students to record their answers with >, <, or = symbols.

Item 20

Tell students they can compare three fractions the same way they compare two fractions.

Independent Practice

Solve the problems. Draw models to represent the problems.

MP4 **18.** Will runs $\frac{3}{6}$ mile around a track. Olivia runs $\frac{3}{4}$ mile around the track. Who runs farther? Compare the fractions. Check students' drawings.

Answer Olivia ran farther. $\frac{3}{4} > \frac{3}{6}$

MP7 **19.** Ben makes a punch. He uses $\frac{2}{3}$ quart of pineapple juice and $\frac{2}{8}$ quart of orange juice in the punch. Which juice does Ben use less of? Compare the fractions. Check students' drawings.

Answer Ben uses less orange juice than pineapple juice: $\frac{2}{8} < \frac{2}{3}$

MP1 **20.** Melody buys three pieces of ribbon to make hair bows. She buys $\frac{4}{8}$ foot of blue ribbon, $\frac{4}{4}$ foot of yellow ribbon, and $\frac{4}{6}$ foot of red ribbon. Compare the lengths of the ribbons. Write the fractions in order from least to greatest. Check students' drawings.

Answer Possible answer: The yellow ribbon is longer than the red ribbon. The red ribbon is longer than the blue ribbon. $\frac{4}{8}, \frac{4}{6}, \frac{4}{4}$

Mathematical Practices

MP1	**Make sense of problems and persevere in solving them.**

Item 20: Students relate the comparison of two fractions to compare three fractions with the same numerator.

MP4	**Model with mathematics.**

Item 18: Students relate mathematics to everyday problems to analyze the size of two fractions.

MP7	**Look for and make use of structure.**

Item 19: Students use common numerators to determine how to compare fractions.

Independent Practice

Solve the problems.

MP7 **21.** Tawana drinks $\frac{5}{8}$ cup of milk. Jarrett drinks $\frac{5}{4}$ cup of milk. Who drinks more milk?

Answer Jarrett drinks more milk.

▸ **Justify your answer using words, drawings, or numbers.**

Possible justification: Jarrett drinks more milk than Tawana because $\frac{5}{4} > \frac{5}{8}$.

MP3 **22.** Anna says that she has more pizza with peppers than Kai has.

Anna's Pizza   Kai's Pizza

Do you agree? Explain your answer.

Answer Yes, I agree.

▸ **Justify your answer using words, drawings, or numbers.**

Possible justification: Anna's pizza has a greater fraction of peppers than Kai's pizza because $\frac{3}{6}$ of Anna's pizza has peppers and $\frac{3}{8}$ of Kai's pizza has peppers. $\frac{3}{6} > \frac{3}{8}$.

MP6 **23.** Depak says that $\frac{2}{4} < \frac{2}{8}$ because $4 < 8$. Do you agree? Use the rectangles to show $\frac{2}{4}$ and $\frac{2}{8}$.

Answer No, I disagree.

Check students' drawings.

▸ **Justify your answer using words, drawings, or numbers.**

Possible justification: $\frac{2}{4}$ is greater than $\frac{2}{8}$ because each fraction has 2 equal parts. If an object is divided into 4 equal parts, the size of each equal part will be larger than if the object were divided into 8 equal parts. So, 2 larger equal parts are more than 2 smaller equal parts.

Unit 3 ■ Focus on Number and Operations—Fractions **205**

Common Errors

Item 22

Students may think that both pizzas have an equal amount of peppers. Point out the location of the peppers on both pizzas. Anna's pizza is partitioned into 6 equal parts with peppers on 3 parts, so $\frac{3}{6}$ of the pizza has peppers. Kai's pizza is partitioned into 8 equal parts, with peppers on 3 parts, so $\frac{3}{8}$ of Kai's pizza has peppers. Since the numerators are the same, students must look at the denominators and conclude that $\frac{3}{8}$ is less than $\frac{3}{6}$. So Anna has more pizza with peppers.

Teaching Tips

Item 21

Encourage students to think about the relationship between the numerator and denominator of the given fractions. Help them see that $\frac{5}{4}$ is more than 1 and $\frac{5}{8}$ is less than 1. Therefore, $\frac{5}{4}$ is greater than $\frac{5}{8}$.

Return to the

Progress Check

Remind students to return to the Progress Check self-assessment, page 139, to check off additional items they have mastered during the unit.

Mathematical Practices

MP3	Construct viable arguments and critique the reasoning of others.

Item 22: Students justify their reasoning about the size of a model by explaining an approach to a problem.

MP6	Attend to precision.

Item 23: Students create models to compare the size of fractions. They communicate in a variety of ways to justify their understanding.

MP7	Look for and make use of structure.

Item 21: Students recognize that the numerators are the same and look at the denominators to draw comparisons.

The Common Core Review covers all the standards presented in the unit. Use it to assess your students' mastery of the unit's concepts and skills.

Depth of Knowledge

The depth of knowledge is a ranking of the content complexity of assessment items based on Webb's Depth of Knowledge (DOK) levels. The levels increase in complexity as shown below.

Level 1: Recall and Reproduction
Level 2: Basic Skills and Concepts
Level 3: Strategic Reasoning and Thinking
Level 4: Extended Thinking

Item	Standard	DOK
1	3.NF.1	1
2	3.NF.1	3
3	3.NF.2a	2
4	3.NF.2a	2
5	3.NF.2b	2
6	3.NF.2b	2
7	3.NF.3d	2
8	3.NF.3d	2
9	3.NF.3c	1
10	3.NF.3b	1
11	3.NF.2b	2
12	3.NF.2b	2
13	3.NF.1	2
14	3.NF.1	2
15	3.NF.1	2
16	3.NF.3c	3
17	3.NF.1	4
18	3.NF.3d	3
19	3.NF.3a	4
20	3.NF.1	3

UNIT 3 Common Core Review

For exercises 1 and 2, use these figures.

1. Circle each figure with a shaded part that can be named by a unit fraction.

2. Describe one figure that does NOT show a unit fraction. Explain. Possible answer: square or triangle; Possible explanation: A unit fraction shows 1 equal part of a whole. The square and the triangle each show parts that are not equal. So, the shaded part of the figure does not show a unit fraction.

Read the fraction. Partition the number line into equal parts. Locate the fraction on the number line and draw a point. Label the point.

3. $\frac{1}{4}$

4. $\frac{1}{2}$

Locate the fraction on the number line and draw a point. Label the point.

5. $\frac{3}{8}$

6. $\frac{2}{3}$

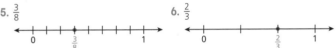

Compare. Write >, =, or <. Draw a model or number line to support your answer. Check students' drawings.

7. $\frac{5}{6}$ $\left(> \right)$ $\frac{3}{6}$

8. $\frac{3}{8}$ $\left(< \right)$ $\frac{3}{4}$

9. Which fraction is equivalent to 1?

a. $\frac{5}{4}$

(b.) $\frac{4}{4}$

c. $\frac{3}{4}$

d. $\frac{1}{4}$

10. Which fraction is equivalent to $\frac{1}{2}$?

a. $\frac{2}{8}$

b. $\frac{1}{3}$

(c.) $\frac{2}{4}$

d. $\frac{5}{6}$

For exercises 11 and 12, locate the fractions on the number line. Draw a point for each fraction. Label the points.

11. $\frac{3}{6}$

12. $\frac{6}{6}$

For exercises 13–16, use this problem.

Miguel and a friend order a pizza. The pizza has 8 equal slices. They eat $\frac{5}{8}$ of the pizza and take the rest home.

They take home 3 slices.

13. How many slices of pizza do Miguel and his friend eat?

They eat 5 slices of pizza.

They eat 5 slices.

14. Use two colors. Show how much of the pizza the two friends eat. Show how much they take home.

15. Write a fraction that shows the part of the pizza that Miguel and his friend take home. $\frac{3}{8}$

16. Write a fraction that represents the whole pizza. $\frac{8}{8}$

Solve the problems.

17. Eva makes a flag for her soccer team. She uses three different fabrics.

$\frac{1}{4}$ of the flag is striped; $\frac{1}{8}$ of the flag is red; $\frac{5}{8}$ of the flag is blue.

Make a drawing to show a possible flag that Eva made.
Flags will vary. Check students' drawings.

Unit 3 ■ Focus on Number and Operations—Fractions **207**

This chart correlates the Common Core Review items with the lessons in which the concepts and skills are presented.

Item	Lesson
1	16
2	17
3	18
4	18
5	18
6	18
7	22
8	23
9	21
10	20
11	18
12	18
13	17
14	17
15	17
16	21
17	17
18	23
19	19
20	17

Writing About Math

Direct students to respond to the Unit 3 Essential Question. (This can also be found on student page 141.)

Essential Question:
How are fractions and whole numbers alike?

Possible responses:
- Fractions can be used to represent any whole number.
- You can plot fractions on a number line.
- You can compare fractions.

Unit Assessment

- Unit 3 Common Core Review, *pp. 206–208*
- Unit 3 Performance Task (ONLINE)

Additional Assessment Options

- Performance Task 1, *pp. 209–214*
(ALSO ONLINE)

Optional Purchase:
- iProgress Monitor (ONLINE)
- Progress Monitor Student Benchmark Assessment Booklet

MP4 18. Kwame eats $\frac{4}{4}$ cup of soup. Jasmine eats $\frac{4}{8}$ cup of soup. Who eats more soup?

Answer Kwame eats more soup.

· **Justify your answer using words, drawings, or numbers.**
Possible justification: Kwame eats more soup because $\frac{4}{4} > \frac{4}{8}$. I can use a fraction model to show this.

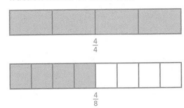

$\frac{4}{4}$

$\frac{4}{8}$

MP3 19. Skylar cuts a submarine sandwich into 6 equal slices. He gives 2 slices each to Lily and Ben. Skylar also takes 2 slices for himself. "We each get $\frac{1}{6}$ of the sandwich," he says. What is Skylar's error?

· **Show your work.**
Possible answer: Skylar counted each portion as $\frac{1}{6}$, since he cut 6 equal slices. However, each person got 2 of 6 slices, or $\frac{2}{6}$ of the sandwich. $\frac{2}{6}$ is not equivalent to $\frac{1}{6}$; it is equivalent to $\frac{1}{3}$.

Each person got $\frac{2}{6}$ or $\frac{1}{3}$ of the sandwich.

MP5 20. Angela has a ribbon that is 4 feet long. She uses 3 feet of the ribbon for a craft project. What fraction of the ribbon is left?

Answer $\frac{1}{4}$ of the ribbon is left.

· **Justify your answer using words, drawings, or numbers.**
Possible justification: I can partition a number line into 4 equal parts, then show that Angela uses 3 parts or $\frac{3}{4}$ of the ribbon. This means that $\frac{1}{4}$ of the ribbon is left.

Mathematical Practices	
MP3	**Construct viable arguments and critique the reasoning of others.**
Item 19: Students analyze a problem situation and share their reasoning with others.	
MP4	**Model with mathematics.**
Item 18: Students may use diagrams to explain the relationship of quantities.	
MP5	**Use appropriate tools strategically.**
Item 20: Students use an appropriate tool to solve a problem.	

Performance Task 1

3.OA.1, 3.OA.3, 3.OA.4, 3.OA.7, 3.OA.8,
3.NBT.1, 3.NBT.2, 3.NBT.3, 3.NF.1,
3.NF.2a, 3.NF.2b, 3.NF.3c, 3.NF.3d

Performance Tasks

Performance Tasks show your understanding of the Math that you have learned. You will be doing various Performance Tasks as you complete your work in this text, **Common Core Progress Mathematics**.

Beginning This Task

The next five pages provide you with the beginning of a Performance Task. You will be given 5 items to complete, and each item will have two or more parts. As you complete these items you will:

I   Demonstrate that you have mastered mathematical skills and concepts

II   Reason through a problem to a solution, and explain your reasoning

III   Use models and apply them to real-world situations.

Extending This Task

Your teacher may extend this Performance Task with additional items provided in our online resources at sadlierconnect.com.

Scoring This Task

Your response to each item will be assessed against a rubric, or scoring guide. Some items will be worth 1 or 2 points, and others will be worth more. In each item you will show your work or explain your reasoning.

Performance Task 1   **209**

ONLINE   Customize Performance Task 1

Performance Task 1 in *Common Core Progress Mathematics* also provides students with additional practice. You can use the online items of Performance Task 1 to customize the amount and kind of performance task practice based on your ongoing evaluation of your students. You may choose to challenge some students, to give extra experience with a particular kind of task for other students, or to extend exposure to performance assessments for the entire class.

Go to **sadlierconnect.com** to download the following resources for Performance Task 1.

• Additional Items

• Additional Teacher Support

• Additional Scoring Rubrics

Performance Task 1 Overview

Performance Task 1 in *Common Core Progress Mathematics* provides students with practice for the types of items that may be found on standardized performance assessments.

Various item formats, including short- and extended-response items and technology-enhanced items, are included in the tasks. All items connect mathematical content correlated to the mathematical practices.

Items in Performance Task 1 are based on three primary types of tasks.

Type I   Mastery of mathematical concepts, skills and procedures

Type II   Using and explaining mathematical reasoning

Type III   Modeling problem situations in a real-world context

Performance Task 1 begins with a collection of five self-contained items in the Student Book and continues with additional items online at **sadlierconnect.com**.

Introduce Performance Task 1   Read student page 209 with the class. Explain that Performance Task 1 may cover any of the math they have learned in Units 1–3. Orient students to each item and communicate helpful reminders that will enable students to approach each item successfully. Once students have completed each item, go over the correct responses with them.

Recommended Pacing   Administer Performance Task 1 on Student Book pages 210–214 over five 20-minute sessions.

Teacher Resources   For each task, the teacher materials include:

• Item types and purposes

• Correlations to Common Core State Standards for Mathematical Content and Practice and Depth of Knowledge (DOK) levels

• Suggested Administration procedure

• Scoring Rubric

Item 1: Rows of Radishes

Item	Type	Purpose
1.a.	III	Draw two arrays that represent 24.
1.b.	I	Write multiplication facts for the two arrays in item 1.a.
1.c.	II	Explain relationship of arrays and multiplication facts.

Item	CCSS	MP	DOK
1.a.	3.OA.3	4	Level 2
1.b.	3.OA.3	2	Level 1
1.c.	3.OA.3	3	Level 3

Administering Item 1 (Pacing: 20 minutes)

Ask a volunteer to read the introductory paragraph. Have others describe the situation in their own words.

Item 1.a. (8 minutes)

Read the directions and discuss what students need to do to complete this part of the task. Guide students to see that there are several arrays that can be drawn. Encourage them to use simple shapes that are easy to draw. To help students who have difficulty with the task, provide them with 24 counters so that they can easily experiment with different ways to arrange 24 in an array.

Item 1.b. (4 minutes)

Make sure students understand that they need to write the multiplication facts for the arrays they drew.

Item 1.c. (8 minutes)

Have students begin working independently on this item, but hold a short class discussion, if needed, to clarify the goal for this item.

Rows of Radishes

1. Ms. Galindo counts 24 tiny radish plants. The radish plants are in rows. Each row has the same number of plants.

   a. Draw two different arrays to show how the radish plants might be growing.
   Arrays may vary. Possible arrays shown:

   • • • • • •   • • • • • • • •
   • • • • • •   • • • • • • • •
   • • • • • •   • • • • • • • •
   • • • • • •

   Also accept arrays that show 1 × 24, 2 × 12, 6 × 4, 8 × 3, 12 × 2, and 24 × 1.

   b. Write a multiplication fact for each array.
   Multiplication facts must represent the arrays students drew for ex. 1.a.
   Possible multiplication facts:
   4 × 6 = 24   3 × 8 = 24

   c. Explain how each of your arrays relates to the multiplication fact.
   Possible explanation: For each multiplication fact, one factor is the same as the number of rows. The other factor is the same as the number of radishes in each row.

Scoring Rubric

Item	Points	Student Responses
1.a.	2	Correctly draws 2 arrays that represent 24.
	1	Correctly draws 1 array for 24.
	0	Does not draw an array.
1.b.	2	Correctly writes 2 multiplication facts for the arrays.
	1	Correctly writes 1 multiplication fact for an array.
	0	Does not write a correct multiplication fact.
1.c.	2	Shows clear understanding of the relationship between the arrays and the multiplication fact.
	1	Shows some understanding of the relationship between the arrays and the multiplication facts.
	0	Shows no understanding of the relationship between the arrays and the multiplication facts.

Planting a Corn Patch

2. Tony and Marco want to plant sweet corn in their corn patch. The corn patch is partitioned into 6 equal parts.

   a. Draw a diagram to show what the corn patch might look like.
   Diagrams may vary. Possible diagram:

   b. Tony and Marco plant sweet corn in 1 of the parts of the corn patch.

   Write a fraction that represents the part of the corn patch that they use.
   $\frac{1}{6}$

   c. Explain how the fraction you wrote represents 1 part of the corn patch.
   Possible explanation: There are 6 equal parts in the corn patch, so 6 is the denominator. Tony and Marco use 1 of the parts, so 1 is the numerator.

   d. Shade in the diagram in item 2.a. to model the fraction that represents the part of the corn patch that Tony and Marco use.
   Modeling may vary. Students might shade 1 part of the diagram, or they might record the fraction $\frac{1}{6}$ in 1 part.

Scoring Rubric

Item	Points	Student Responses
2.a.	2	Correctly draws a diagram for 6 equal parts.
	1	Draws a diagram but does not show 6 equal parts.
	0	Does not draw a diagram.
2.b.	2	Correctly writes the fraction.
	0	Does not write a fraction.
2.c.	2	Shows clear understanding of how $\frac{1}{6}$ represents 1 of 6 equal parts.
	1	Does not mention that the 6 parts are equal.
	0	Shows no understanding of how $\frac{1}{6}$ represents 1 of 6 euqal parts.
2.d.	2	Correctly models $\frac{1}{6}$.
	1	Models a fraction, but not $\frac{1}{6}$.
	0	Does not model a fraction.

Item 2: Planning a Corn Patch

Item	Type	Purpose
2.a.	III	Draw a diagram to represent 6 equal parts.
2.b.	III	Write a fraction to represent 1 of 6 equal parts.
2.c.	II	Explain why the fraction in item 2.b. represents 1 of 6 equal parts.
2.d.	II	Use the diagram in item 2.a. to model the fraction that represents 1 of 6 equal parts.

Item	CCSS	MP	DOK
2.a.	3.OA.2	1	Level 2
2.b.	3.OA.2	2	Level 2
2.c.	3.OA.2	3	Level 3
2.d.	3.OA.2	2	Level 2

Administering Item 2 (Pacing: 20 minutes)

Ask a volunteer to read the introductory paragraph. Have others describe the problem situation in their own words.

Item 2.a. (6 minutes)
Read the directions. Ask a volunteer to explain what needs to be done to complete this part of the task. Then let students work independently to draw their diagrams.

Item 2.b. (3 minutes)
Have students think about how many parts are in the whole. Then ask them to write how many parts are being used for sweet corn.

Item 2.c. (8 minutes)
Students should know that they are using 1 part out of 6 equal parts.

Item 2.d. (3 minutes)
Point out that there is more than one way to model the fraction.

Item 3: A Twist in the Garden Hose

Item	Type	Purpose
3.a.	I	Locate $\frac{1}{4}$ on the number line.
3.b.	II	Explain how to locate $\frac{1}{4}$ on the number line.
3.c.	II	Name a distance from 1 on the number line.
3.d.	II	Compare distances on a number line.

Item	CCSS	MP	DOK
3.a.	3.OA.3	2	Level 2
3.b.	3.OA.3	3	Level 3
3.c.	3.OA.3	2	Level 2
3.d.	3.OA.3	6	Level 3

Administering Item 3 (Pacing: 20 minutes)

Ask a volunteer to read the introductory paragraph. Have others describe the situation in their own words.

Item 3.a. (3 minutes)

Lead students to realize that the number line is divided into fourths.

Item 3.b. (7 minutes)

Help students understand that since there are 4 equal parts on the number line, the location of $\frac{1}{4}$ is at the end of the first equal part.

Item 3.c. (3 minutes)

Suggest that students count back from the nozzle by fourths.

Item 3.d. (7 minutes)

Discuss how students may find different ways to explain their thinking but that they should all have the same conclusion.

A Twist in the Garden Hose

3. Mr. Chan uses a garden hose to water his garden. There is a twist in the garden hose. The number line below represents the garden hose.

  a. The twist in the garden hose is located at $\frac{1}{4}$ the distance from the faucet to the nozzle of the garden hose.

  Write the fraction $\frac{1}{4}$ in the correct location on the number line.

  faucet ——————————————————— nozzle

  0 ————|—$\frac{1}{4}$—|————|————|————

  b. Explain how you decided where to locate the fraction on the number line.

  Possible explanation: The number line shows 4 equal parts from 0 to 1. The distance from 0 to the end of the first equal part is $\frac{1}{4}$ the distance from 0 to 1.

  c. How far from the nozzle is the twist located? Use a fraction to name the distance.
  $\frac{3}{4}$

  d. Mr. Chan says that the twist is closer to the faucet than to the nozzle. Is Mr. Chan correct?

  Explain your reasoning.

  Yes, Mr. Chan is correct. The faucet is located at 0 on the number line. The nozzle is located at 1, or $\frac{4}{4}$. $\frac{1}{4}$ is closer to 0 than to 1 on the number line.

Scoring Rubric

Item	Points	Student Responses
3.a.	2	Correctly locates $\frac{1}{4}$ on the number line.
	0	Does not locate any point.
3.b.	2	Shows clear understanding of how to locate a point on a number line.
	1	Shows some understanding of how to locate a point on a number line.
	0	Shows no understanding of how to locate a point on a number line.
3.c.	2	Correctly names a fraction for the distance.
	0	Does not name a fraction.
3.d.	2	Provides a clear explanation and uses given information as support.
	1	Provides an explanation but does not use the given information as support.
	0	Provides no explanation.

Performance Task 1

Boxing Up the Tomatoes

4. Tina and Stewart pick tomatoes. They put all of the tomatoes in boxes. Tina puts 6 tomatoes in each of 8 boxes. Stewart puts 4 tomatoes in each of 11 boxes.

   a. Write an equation to find the number of tomatoes Tina and Stewart put in boxes.

   Possible equation:
   $(8 \times 6) + (11 \times 4) = t$

   b. Use words to tell about the equation you wrote.

   Possible answer: The number of tomatoes Tina puts in boxes plus the number of tomatoes Stewart puts in boxes equals the total number of tomatoes.

   c. How many tomatoes do Tina and Stewart put in boxes?

   Solve the equation.
   $(8 \times 6) + (11 \times 4) = t$
   $48 + 44 = t$
   $92 = t$
   Tina and Stewart put 92 tomatoes in boxes.

   d. Use estimation to check if your answer is reasonable.

   Justify your reasoning.
   48 rounds to 50.
   44 rounds to 40.
   $50 + 40 = 90$
   The estimate is 90.
   The actual answer, 92, is close to my estimate 90. So my answer is reasonable.

Performance Task 1   213

Scoring Rubric

Item	Points	Student Responses
4.a.	2	Correctly writes an equation that can be used to solve the problem.
	1	Writes an incorrect equation.
	0	Does not write an equation.
4.b.	2	Completely describes reasoning used to write the equation.
	1	Partially describes reasoning used to write the equation.
	0	Does not describe reasoning.
4.c.	2	Solves the equation correctly.
	0	Does not solve the equation correctly.
4.d.	2	Uses estimation correctly and justifies reasoning.
	1	Estimate correctly but does not justify reasoning.
	0	Does not attempt to use estimation or to justify reasoning.

Item 4: Boxing Up the Tomatoes

Item	Type	Purpose
4.a.	III	Write an equation to solve the problem.
4.b.	II	Describe the thinking used to write the equation in item 4.a.
4.c.	I	Solve the equation.
4.d.	II	Use estimation to check.

Item	CCSS	MP	DOK
4.a.	3.OA.3	4	Level 2
4.b.	3.OA.3	6	Level 3
4.c.	3.OA.3	2	Level 2
4.d.	3.OA.3	2	Level 2

Administering Item 4 (Pacing: 20 minutes)

Ask a volunteer to read the introductory paragraph. Have others describe the situation in their own words.

Item 4.a. (4 minutes)

Ask students to write two expressions to represent each person's total tomatoes, then add the expressions to write an equation.

Item 4.b. (6 minutes)

Suggest that students think back to the discussion of item 4.a. as they describe how they wrote their equations.

Item 4.c. (5 minutes)

Make sure students remember to use the Order of Operations while completing this problem.

Item 4.d. (5 minutes)

Discuss estimation strategies and how to use rounding to check their answers.

Item 5: Picking and Piling Peppers

Item	Type	Purpose
5.a.	III	Write an equation that can be used to solve the problem.
5.b.	II	Solve the equation in item 5.a.
5.c.	II	Analyze the reasoning behind a statement.

Item	CCSS	MP	DOK
5.a.	3.OA.5	4	Level 2
5.b.	3.OA.5	2	Level 2
5.c.	3.OA.5	2	Level 3

Administering Item 5 (Pacing: 20 minutes)

Ask a volunteer to read the introductory paragraph. Have others describe the situation in their own words.

Item 5.a. (7 minutes)

Tell students to first find an equation for the amount of peppers Bill and Cynthia pick together. Then add the additional peppers.

Item 5.b. (7 minutes)

Remind students to complete the operations within parentheses first.

Item 5.c. (6 minutes)

Students should understand that there are 40 peppers in each of the 9 piles, and only 23 peppers in the last pile.

Picking and Piling Peppers

5. Cynthia and Bill pick peppers. They put all of the peppers in piles of 40 peppers each.

   a. Cynthia and Bill make 9 piles. Then Cynthia picks 23 more peppers.

      Write an equation to find the number of peppers Cynthia and Bill pick altogether.

      Possible equation:
      $(9 \times 40) + 23 = p$

   b. How many peppers do Cynthia and Bill pick altogether?

      Solve the equation.

      Possible solution:
      $(9 \times 40) + 23 = p$
      $360 + 23 = p$
      $383 = p$
      Cynthia and Bill pick 383 peppers.

   c. Cynthia uses the 23 more peppers she picks to make another pile. She says that now they have 10 equal piles of peppers. Why might Bill disagree? Explain your reasoning.

      Possible explanation: Bill might disagree because each pile does not have the same number of peppers, 40.

Scoring Rubric

Item	Points	Student Responses
5.a.	2	Correctly writes an equation that can be used to solve the problem.
	1	Writes an incorrect equation.
	0	Does not write an equation.
5.b.	2	Solves the equation correctly.
	0	Does not solve the equation correctly.
5.c.	2	Presents a reasonable argument and shows logical support.
	1	Presents an argument but does not provide support.
	0	Does not attempt to answer.

Progress Check

Look at how the Common Core standards you have learned and will learn connect.

It is very important for you to understand the standards from the prior grade level so that you will be able to develop an understanding of measurement and data in this unit and be prepared for next year. To practice your skills, go to sadlierconnect.com.

UNIT 4

GRADE 2	Before Unit 4	GRADE 3	After Unit 4	GRADE 4
I Can...		**Can I?**		**I Will...**
2.MD.7 Tell and write time to the nearest five minutes	☐	**3.MD.1** Tell and write time to the nearest minute	☐	
		Solve word problems by adding and subtracting time intervals in minutes	☐	
2.MD.1 Use appropriate tools to measure length	☐	**3.MD.2** Measure and estimate liquid volumes and masses	☐	**4.MD.2** Solve word problems involving distance, time, liquid volumes, masses, and money
2.MD.5 Solve problems involving lengths	☐	Solve one-step problems involving masses or volumes	☐	
2.MD.10 Draw a picture graph and a bar graph for the same data set	☐	**3.MD.3** Draw a scaled picture graph or a scaled bar graph to represent a data set	☐	
Solve problems using data shown in a bar graph	☐	Solve "how many more" and "how many less" problems using information in scaled bar graphs	☐	
2.MD.9 Show length measurements on a line plot	☐	**3.MD.4** Show length measurements in inches, half inches, and quarter inches on a line plot	☐	**4.MD.4** Display a set of measurements in fractions of a unit on a line plot
				Solve problems involving addi and subtraction of fractions by using information presented in line plots

Unit 4 ■ Focus on Measurement and Data

Student Page 215

Progress Check

Progress Check is a self-assessment tool that students can use to gauge their own progress. Research shows that when students take accountability for their learning, motivation increases.

Before students begin work in Unit 4, have them check any items they know they can do well. Explain that it is fine if they don't check any of the boxes; they will have the opportunity to learn and practice all the standards through the course of the unit.

Let them know that at the end of the unit they will review their checklists to check their progress. After students have completed the last lesson of the unit, before they begin Common Core Review, you will be prompted to have students revisit this page.

HOME ◆ CONNECT...

The Home Connect feature is a way to keep parents or other adult family members apprised of what their children are learning. The key learning objectives are listed, and some ideas for related activities and discussions are included.

Explain to students that they can share the Home Connect page at home with their families. Let students know there is an activity connected to their classroom learning that they can do with their families.

Encourage students and their parents to share their experiences using the suggestions on the Home Connect. You may wish to invite students to share this work with the class.

HOME ◆ CONNECT...

In this unit your child will continue to develop problem-solving skills using measurements and estimations as well as representing and interpreting data.

Scientists and mathematicians use measurements and data in their world. But families use them every day too. Support your child using the following Math vocabulary of units of measurement you use each day: **minute**, **hour, inch**, foot, centimeter, mile, meter, **gram, kilogram**, ounce, pound, quart, **liter**, and many more. When taking measurements, whether measuring **elapsed time, liquid volume, mass**, or length, you are collecting data. **Data** is information.

Once the data is collected, it can be represented in various ways. Children are already familiar with **line plots, picture graphs**, and **bar graphs**. Now they are given the opportunity to review and expand their knowledge of graphs as well as collect data and represent it in various formats.

On the Go: Make a plan to determine how much time a daily activity takes up in one week. Choose a daily activity such as watching TV or reading independently. Together, determine the elapsed time spent on the activity each day during the week and record the data. Then make a graph of the data and talk about what it shows.

In this unit your child will:

- Tell and write time to the nearest minute.
- Solve word problems by adding and subtracting time intervals in minutes.
- Measure and estimate liquid volumes and masses.
- Solve one-step problems involving liquid volumes and masses.
- Draw a scaled picture graph or a scaled bar graph to represent a data set.
- Solve "how many more" and "how many less" problems using information in scaled bar graphs.
- Show length measurements in inches, half inches, and quarter inches on a line plot.

NOTE: All of these learning goals for your child are based on the Grade 3 Common Core State Standards for Mathematics.

Ways to Help Your Child

Is it better for your child to begin homework before after-school activities, or after dinner? Does your child need some play time or down time? Talk with your child in order to set up some ground rules for managing time after school. Make the most of whatever time of day works best.

ONLINE
For more Home Connect activities, continue online at sadlierconnect.com

216   Unit 4 ■ Focus on Measurement and Data

Student Page 216

UNIT PLANNER

	Lesson	Standard(s)	Objective
24	Problem Solving: Time	3.MD.1	Solve problems involving time.
25	Problem Solving: Liquid Volumes and Masses	3.MD.2	Solve problems involving liquid volume and mass.
26	Draw Graphs to Represent Categorical Data	3.MD.3	Use data to create and analyze picture graphs and bar graphs.
27	Generate and Graph Measurement Data	3.MD.4	Use a line plot to represent data gathered from measuring the lengths of objects.

Essential Question	Words to Know
How can you solve problems involving time?	time, minute, elapsed time, time interval, hour
How can you solve problems involving liquid volume and mass?	liquid volume, liter (L), mass, gram (g), kilogram (kg)
How can I draw graphs to show data?	picture graph, data, key, bar graph, scale
How can I draw line plots to show measurement data?	line plot, half-inch, quarter-inch

Unit Assessment

- Unit 4 Common Core Review, *pp. 250–252*
- Unit 4 Performance Task ONLINE

Additional Assessment Options

Optional Purchase:
- iProgress Monitor ONLINE
- Progress Monitor Student Benchmark Assessment Booklet

ONLINE Digital Resources

- Home Connect Activities
- Unit Performance Tasks
- Additional Practice
- Fluency Practice
- Teacher Resources
- iProgress Monitor (optional purchase)

Go to SadlierConnect.com to access your Digital Resources.

For more detailed instructions see page T3.

LEARNING PROGRESSIONS

This page provides more in-depth detail on the development of the standards across the grade levels. See also the unit Progress Check page in the Student Edition for a roadmap of the Learning Progressions.

Grade 2

- Students measure the lengths of objects using appropriate tools. (2.MD.1)
- Students solve problems involving lengths given in the same units using addition and subtraction within 100 and equations. (2.MD.5)
- Students tell and write time to the nearest five minutes. (2.MD.7)
- Students generate measurement data by measuring objects to the nearest whole unit, and display the measurements on a line plot marked off in whole number units. (2.MD.9)
- Students draw a picture graph and a bar graph, using a single-unit scale, to represent a data set of up to four categories. They solve simple problems (put-together, take-apart, and compare) using information in a bar graph. (2.MD.10)
- Note: the vertical axes of bar graphs may be thought of as segments of number line diagrams that function as count scales. When drawing bar graphs on grid paper, students should place the tick marks representing the scale at intersections of grid lines. (2.MD.10)

Grade 3

- Students extend their understanding of time measurement to tell and write time to the nearest minute, and solve word problems involving addition and subtraction of time intervals in minutes. (3.MD.1)
- Students measure and estimate liquid volumes and masses of objects using the metric units gram (g), kilogram (kg), and liter (L). They add, subtract, multiply, or divide to solve one-step word problems involving masses or volumes given in the same units. (3.MD.2)
- Work with categorical data is extended to drawing and reading scaled picture graphs and bar graphs representing data sets with several categories. Students solve one- and two-step "how many more" and "how many less" problems based on data presented in scaled bar graphs. (3.MD.3)
- Students generate measurement data using rulers marked to halves and fourths of an inch and display the data on a line plot marked off in appropriate units. (3.MD.4)

Grade 4

- Students solve word problems involving distance, time, liquid volumes, masses of objects, and money using the four operations. Problems may involve simple fractions and decimals (4.MD.2)
- Work with plotting data sets of measurements is extended to halves, fourths, and eighths of units. Students solve problems involving addition and subtraction of fractions using data presented in line plots. (4.MD.4)

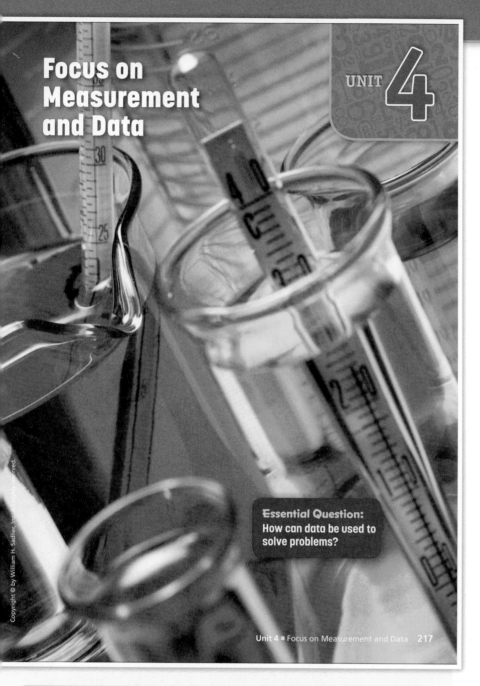

Focus on Measurement and Data

Essential Question:
How can data be used to solve problems?

Essential Question:
How can data be used to solve problems?

As students become involved with the Essential Question they will begin to see that data includes measurements as well as categorical information that they can represent in different ways that will help solve problems.

Conversation Starters

Have students discuss the photograph. Encourage students to examine the picture of the lab equipment by asking questions such as: *Where do you think this photo was taken? What are all of the pieces of lab equipment in the photo and what are they used for?*

Have students look at the containers. *Without measuring, what information can you gather by looking at the test tubes?* (You can gather information about the color of the substance.) *Are all of the test tubes the same size? Do they all have the same substance in them?*

Have students look at the tools in the picture. *What tools do you see? What do they measure?* (There is a beaker that measures the amount of the substance and a thermometer that measures the temperature.) *Why might you want to know the temperature of a substance?* (You may need to know if it is a safe temperature for a particular activity.)

Let students work in pairs to discuss what they have measured in the past and what kind of data they recorded. Students can also discuss how they analyzed the data.

Activity

Materials: test tubes (or cups), water, food coloring
Ask students to work in groups of four. Give each group four test tubes with a different colored water to look like the image. Each test tube should contain a different amount of water, too. If possible, give each group a different set of tubes so that the data for each group is different than the others.

Ask students to arrange the test tubes to show a pattern. Ask them to share with the class what data they used to arrange the test tubes and their results. Discuss as a class why you might need this data.

Common Core Focus:

3.MD.1 Tell and write time to the nearest minute and measure time intervals in minutes. Solve word problems involving addition and subtraction of time intervals in minutes.

OBJECTIVE
Solve problems involving time.

ESSENTIAL QUESTION

This lesson builds upon knowledge students already have about telling time to include time to the nearest minute. Students will also solve word problems involving intervals of time and elapsed time.

PREREQUISITE SKILLS

Use Item G on page 340 of the Foundational Skills Handbook to review reading time to the nearest five minutes.

FLUENCY PRACTICE

Fluency practice is available at **sadlierconnect.com**.

Concept Development

Understand: How to tell and write time

■ Discuss the similarities and differences between the digital and analog clocks.

■ Reading the time on an analog clock is often a stumbling block for students. The hour is read as the number the hour hand has just passed. The clock shows the hour hand has passed the 7 but has not reached the 8. The hour is 7.

■ Students may count by fives or multiples of fives to calculate the time to the nearest 5 minutes. Then they can count each additional minute to find the exact time.

✏ ▸ Have students share their answers. Challenge them to determine which kind of clock is more common in their home.

Lesson 24 Problem Solving: Time

Essential Question:
How can you solve problems involving time?
3.MD.1

Words to Know:
time
minute
elapsed time
time interval
hour

In this lesson you will learn how to tell and write time and measure intervals of time.

Understand: How to tell and write time

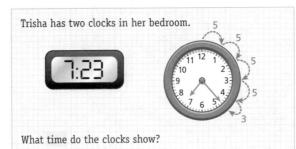

Trisha has two clocks in her bedroom.

What time do the clocks show?

Read the digital clock.   7:23

You can say, "Seven twenty-three." or "Twenty-three minutes after seven."

Read the clock with hands. Each mark shows 1 minute.

Look at the hour hand. The hour hand points at a little past 7.

Look at the minute hand.
5 + 5 + 5 + 5 = 20
20 + 3 = 23
The minute hand points at 23 minutes past the hour.
The clock shows 7:23.

▸ Both clocks show 7:23.

Remember!
The hour hand moves from one number to the next in 60 minutes. The minute hand moves from one number to the next in 5 minutes.

✏ ▸ Why is it important to be able to read both kinds of clocks?
Possible answer: Both kinds of clocks are everywhere, so even though it is easy to read a digital clock, you still need to read time from the hands on the other clocks.

Words to Know

time: a quantity that can be measured using years, months, days, hours, minutes, and/or seconds

minute (min): a unit of time; 60 minutes = 1 hour

elapsed time: the amount of time between two given times

time interval: a segment of time

hour (h): a unit of time; 1 hour = 60 minutes

Glossary can be found on pp. 347–350.

Understand: How to measure intervals of time

> Aaron swam from 8:45 A.M. to 9:35 A.M.
> How long did Aaron swim?

You need to find the amount of time Aaron swam. The difference from one time to another time is called elapsed time.

To find the elapsed time, look at the minute hand for 8:45. Count time intervals of 10 minutes to 9:35.
10 + 10 + 10 + 10 + 10 = 50

➤ Aaron swam for 50 minutes.

> A soccer team practiced from 3:00 P.M. to 4:30 P.M.
> How long did the team practice?

Use a number line.

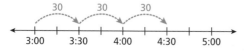

Count time intervals of 30 minutes.
30 + 30 + 30 = 90

Remember!
60 minutes is 1 hour.

1 hour   +   30   = 1 hour 30 minutes

➤ The team practiced for 90 minutes, or 1 hour 30 minutes.

✎ What other time intervals could you count to find how long the team practiced? 5 minutes, 10 minutes, 15 minutes

Understand: How to measure intervals of time

■ In this presentation, students learn how to measure intervals of time. To help them understand the relationship between the two times it may be helpful to use two different clocks, one for the start time and the other for the end time. Students can then compare the two clocks to help them determine the elapsed time.

■ Discuss with students that they are measuring intervals of time by counting equal sets of minutes.

■ For students struggling with the concept of time intervals, allow them to use clocks to work through the problems.

✎ Ask students to share the other time intervals they found. Discuss with students how their counting changes depending on which interval they are using.

Support English Language Learners

Provide English language learners practice using the time-telling terms *hour* and *minute*. Students will have likely used the terms to describe lengths of time (such as we go home in 4 hours or lunch is in 20 minutes), but they may not have made the connection to time on a clock.

Help transfer students' knowledge of these terms by using an analog clock. Show students how minutes and hours are represented on the clock. English language learners may also need support understanding the idea of repeating times (A.M. and P.M.). Repetition of telling time at various times of the day can be helpful so students understand how time is used in relation to activities they are doing.

Guided Instruction

Connect: Problem solving and elapsed time

Use this page to help students strengthen the relationship between telling time and problem solving. Students have used both skills previously, but are new to putting the two together.

■ Remind students that when using an interval of 10 minutes, they need to skip every other number on the face of the clock.

■ Encourage students to discuss the benefits of using a clock or a number line to solve elapsed time problems. When the elapsed time is greater than 1 hour, students may find using a number line more helpful as they keep track of multiple hours. When the elapsed time does not fall exactly on a 5-minute interval, students may find using a clock face that shows the individual minutes more useful.

Connect: Problem solving and elapsed time

Lunch starts at 12:05 P.M. and lasts for 50 minutes. When does lunch end?

Step 1

Start at 12:05.
Decide what time interval you will count.
Try 10 minutes.

Step 2

You can add time intervals by counting on.
Count ahead by time intervals of 10 minutes.
After 50 minutes, the minute hand points to 11.

➡ Lunch ends at 12:55.

A movie ends at 8 P.M. The movie lasts 2 hours 15 minutes. When does the movie start?

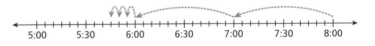

Step 1

You can subtract time intervals by counting back.
Start at 8:00.
Count back 2 hours. 8:00 → 7:00 → 6:00

Step 2

Count back 15 more minutes.
Count back by intervals of 5 minutes. 6:00 → 5:55 → 5:50 → 5:45

➡ The movie started at __5:45__ P.M.

Math-to-Math Connection

Time and Geography Discuss with students the idea that different places are in different time zones. Display a time zone map and talk about the difference between your location and other places. Discuss with students those places that are ahead and behind your time zone. Students may also find it interesting to think about what students in other times zones are currently doing while they are currently in class.

Write the time shown by each clock.

1.

5:18

2.
11:04

3.
3:40

Solve the problems.

4. Maria leaves for school at 7:25 A.M. She arrives at school at 7:50 A.M. How long does it take her to get to school?

___25___ minutes

5. Mr. Landon put a loaf of oatmeal bread in the oven at 2:30 P.M. He takes the bread out at 3:20 P.M. How long is the bread in the oven?

2:30   3:00   3:30

___50___ minutes

6. Henry works on a project for 40 minutes. If he started at 4:45 P.M., when did he finish?
_____5:25_____ P.M.

7. A cat wakes at 10:10 A.M. It slept for 1 hour 20 minutes. When did it go to sleep?
_____8:50_____ A.M.

☆ Think·Pair·Share

MP4 8. A dinosaur movie starts at 12:30 P.M. The movie lasts 1 hour 30 minutes. Luis counts by intervals of 30 minutes to find when the movie ends. Sara counts by intervals of 10 minutes. Do Luis and Sara find the same answer to the problem? Explain your thinking. Yes. Possible explanation: You can count by either interval to reach 1 hour 30 minutes.

Unit 4 ■ Focus on Measurement and Data   **221**

Mathematical Practices

Mathematical Practice Standards underline the teaching and understanding of all concepts and skills presented. The emphasis of specific practices is noted throughout the guided and independent practice of this lesson.

MP4	**Model with mathematics.**

Item 8: Students relate mathematics to everyday problems.

Observational Assessment

Use page 221 to assess whether students are able to tell time and solve problems involving elapsed time by using appropriate intervals. Watch for students who have difficulty finding elapsed times greater than 1 hour.

☆ Think·Pair·Share

Peer Collaboration Have students work with a partner. Ask one student to solve the problem using a number line and 30-minute intervals. Have the other student solve the problem using a clock face and 10-minute intervals. Students should compare their answers and discuss the following questions:

- *Why do both time intervals work?*

- *How many 30-minute intervals are there in 1 hour, 30 minutes? How many 10-minute intervals are there in 1 hour, 30 minutes?*

- *Are there any other time intervals you could use to get the same answer?*

- *How many 15-minute intervals are there in 1 hour 30 minutes? How many 5-minute intervals?*

Remind students that counting by intervals of time is one way to find the amount of elapsed time.

Return to the Essential Question

Reread the Lesson 24 Essential Question on page 218: *How can you solve problems involving time?*

Ask volunteers to use what they learned in this lesson to answer this question. (Possible response: I can use a clock face or number line to count time intervals to find the elapsed time in word problems.)

Independent Practice

Concept Application

Students may work independently on these pages in the classroom or at home. They may refer to the first four pages of the lesson to revisit the instruction or to see a worked-out example.

Common Errors and **Teaching Tips** may help you support student learning either in the classroom or as a follow-up for work done at home.

Common Errors

Item 7

Students may incorrectly choose the clock that shows 12:20. Remind students that the minute hand moves one tick mark for each minute. Suggest they count by intervals of 5 and then count on by ones to find the clock that shows the correct time.

Teaching Tips

Items 1–6

If students have difficulty naming the hour, have students circle the number the hour hand has just passed.

Items 2–3 and 5–6

Encourage students to determine the minutes past or before the hour by counting from any number on the clock face they know. For example, students are often comfortable with 6 representing 30 minutes. Suggest they begin with 30 minutes and count on or count back to find the exact time.

Independent Practice

Write the time shown by each clock.

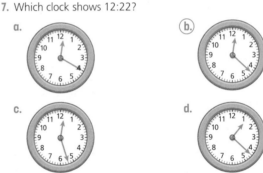

1. 7:15

2. 1:41

3. 10:37

4. 2:08

5. 4:28

6. 8:43

7. Which clock shows 12:22?

   a.

   b.

   c.

   d.

8. The clocks show when Nelson starts and finishes washing his mother's car. How long does it take Nelson to wash the car?

   Starts   Finishes

   Answer It takes Nelson 45 minutes to

   wash the car.

222   Unit 4 ■ Focus on Measurement and Data

Writing About Math

 ▸ **Write a Narrative** Ask students to write a paragraph that describes what they normally do on a Monday morning. Students should name the events and give an approximated time that they do these things. The paragraphs should be written to show a natural progression so that events are discussed in the order they do them. Remind students to include the elapsed time between each consecutive event they describe.

After students have written their paragraphs, have them work in small groups to compare and discuss the similarities and differences among their morning activities.

Independent Practice

Solve the problems.

MP2 **9.** Anna rides her bike to the library. The clocks show the time she leaves for the library and the time she arrives there. How long is Anna's ride.

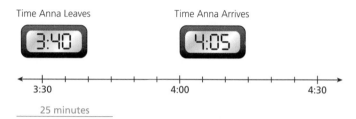

Time Anna Leaves

Time Anna Arrives

3:30   4:00   4:30

25 minutes

MP1 **10.** Mr. Cruz drives to the grocery store. He returns at 7:20 P.M. after being gone for 45 minutes. What time did Mr. Cruz leave for the store?

Time Mr. Cruz Leaves

Time Mr. Cruz Returns

Answer Mr. Cruz left at 6:35 P.M.

MP7 **11.** Jenna starts reading a story book at 6:10 P.M. She reads for 50 minutes. Then her mother tells her to set the dinner table. When does Jenna stop reading?

Answer Jenna stops reading at 7:00 P.M.

MP4 **12.** Ray and his dad go fishing. They leave the house at 5:45 A.M. They are gone for 7 hours 30 minutes. When do they come home?

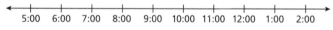

5:00 6:00 7:00 8:00 9:00 10:00 11:00 12:00 1:00 2:00

Answer They come home at 1:15 P.M.

Unit 4 ■ Focus on Measurement and Data   **223**

Common Errors

Item 12

Students may not understand the implication of 12:00 on the number line and incorrectly label their answers A.M. Review the meaning of A.M. and P.M. Tell students that the time between 12:00 in the afternoon and 12:00 at night is P.M. and the time between 12:00 at night and 12:00 in the afternoon is A.M. Have students write A.M. to label the hours on the number line before 12:00, and P.M. to label the hours after 12:00.

Teaching Tips

Item 9

This is the first time students are asked to use a digital clock to solve a word problem about time. For students who are struggling, have them transfer the time to an analog clock before they solve.

Item 12

Ask students to identify and label the starting time. The time halfway between 5:00 and 6:00 is 5:30. Halfway between 5:30 and 6:00 is 5:45, which is the beginning time.

Students may not know which interval to use to count the elapsed time. Suggest they use hour intervals to count the whole hours, then count on 30 minutes to find the end time.

Mathematical Practices		
MP1	**Make sense of problems and persevere in solving them.**	
Item 10: Students use pictures to help conceptualize and solve a problem.		
MP2	**Reason abstractly and quantitatively.**	
Item 9: Students consider the units involved to solve the problem.		
MP4	**Model with mathematics.**	
Item 12: Students use a number line to interpret the solution of a situation.		
MP7	**Look for and make use of structure.**	
Item 11: Students discern a pattern to solve a problem.		

Independent Practice

Teaching Tips

Items 13–14

Point out that these problems are not asking for an exact answer. They are asking for students to explain a strategy for how to find an exact answer.

Items 15–16

Some students might need to use analog clocks to solve these problems. If necessary, allow them to use one clock to show the start time, and another to show the end time in each problem.

Independent Practice

MP8 **13.** Basketball practice starts at 3:15 P.M. and lasts 1 hour 30 minutes. Explain how to find when basketball practice will end.
Possible answer: Draw a number line with intervals of 15 minutes. Start at 3:15. Count ahead four intervals for 1 hour. Then count ahead two intervals for 30 minutes.

MP7 **14.** Dan leaves the dentist office at 2:20 P.M. He was at the office for 50 minutes. How can Dan figure out when he arrived at the office?
Possible answer: He can draw a number line with intervals of 10 minutes. He can start at 2:20. Then he can count back 5 intervals for 50 minutes.

MP2 **15.** Sue practices her violin each day for 45 minutes. Today she starts practicing at 4:55 P.M. When does she finish?

✏ · **Show your work.**

Possible answer:

Answer Sue finishes at 5:40 P.M.

MP1 **16.** A plane arrives at an airport at 7:10 A.M. The flight lasted 2 hours 20 minutes. When did the plane take off?

✏ · **Show your work.**

Possible answer:

Answer The plane took off at 4:50 A.M.

224   Unit 4 ▪ Focus on Measurement and Data

Mathematical Practices

MP1	**Make sense of problems and persevere in solving them.**
Item 16:	Students use a number line to help conceptualize and solve a problem.
MP2	**Reason abstractly and quantitatively.**
Item 15:	Students create a coherent representation to solve a problem.
MP7	**Look for and make use of structure.**
Item 14:	Students evaluate a problem's structure to explain how to solve it.
MP8	**Look for and express regularity in repeated reasoning.**
Item 13:	Students explain the process of problem solving.

MORE ONLINE sadlierconnect.com

Independent Practice

MP5 **17.** Lucy walks to the bus stop, waits for the bus, and then takes the bus to school. She walks 10 minutes. She waits 5 minutes. And the bus trip lasts 25 minutes. If Lucy leaves her home at 7:15 A.M., when does she arrive at school?

✏ **Show your work.**
Possible answer: 10 + 5 + 25 = 40

Answer Lucy arrives at school at 7:55 A.M.

MP4 **18.** At Culver Elementary, the school day lasts 6 hours 30 minutes. The first bell rings at 8:00 A.M. When does the last bell ring?

Answer The last bell rings at 2:30 P.M.

✏ **Justify your answer using words, drawings, or numbers.**
Possible justification:

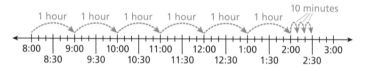

MP2 **19.** Marcy's mother takes a roast out of the oven at 7:35 P.M. The roast was in the oven for 1 hour 45 minutes. When did Marcy's mother put the roast in the oven?

Answer Marcy's mother put the roast in the oven at 5:50 P.M.

✏ **Justify your answer using words, drawings, or numbers.**
Possible justification:
I can subtract 1 hour 45 minutes mentally. Count back 1 hour from 7:35 to 6:35. Then count back 35 minutes to 6:00. And then count back 10 more minutes, from 6:00 to 5:50.

Unit 4 ■ Focus on Measurement and Data 225

Common Errors

Item 19
Students may count forward 1 hour 45 minutes rather than backward. Point out that the given time is the ending time. Students are asked to find the beginning time.

Teaching Tips

Item 17
Students may write an equation to find the total time first, or they may choose to show the intervals on the clock as 10 minutes, 5 minutes, and 25 minutes.

Item 18
Help students identify each tick mark on the number line as representing a 10-minute interval.

Mathematical Practices

MP2	**Reason abstractly and quantitatively.**

Item 19: Students consider units in problem solving.

MP4	**Model with mathematics.**

Item 18: Students use concrete tools to relate mathematics to real-world problems.

MP5	**Use appropriate tools strategically.**

Item 17: Students use a model to solve a word problem.

Common Core Focus:

3.MD.2 Measure and estimate liquid volumes and masses of objects using standard units of grams (g), kilograms (kg), and liters (l). Add, subtract, multiply, or divide to solve one-step word problems involving masses or volumes that are given in the same units.

OBJECTIVE

Solve problems involving liquid volume and mass.

ESSENTIAL QUESTION

Students will estimate and measure liquid volumes using liters, and measure masses using grams and kilograms.

PREREQUISITE SKILLS

Use Item H on page 340 of the Foundational Skills Handbook to review measuring length with an inch ruler.

FLUENCY PRACTICE

Fluency practice is available at **sadlierconnect.com**.

Concept Development

Understand: How to estimate liquid volume

■ Give students the opportunity to fill containers with water to visualize the size of a liter.

■ Tell students that a 1-liter bottle is a benchmark they can use to compare the liquid volume of containers.

■ Have students estimate how many times Fred could fill the pitcher using the 1-liter bottle.

Understand: How to solve problems involving liquid volume

■ Remind students that they can use a letter to represent an unknown.

✏ Students might find it helpful to draw a picture to model the problem.

Essential Question:
How can you solve problems involving liquid volume and mass?
3.MD.2

Words to Know:
liquid volume
liter (L)
mass
gram (g)
kilogram (kg)

In this lesson you will learn about liquid volume and mass.

Understand: How to estimate liquid volume

Liquid volume is the amount of liquid a container can hold.

> Fred filled a pitcher with juice.
>
> Which is the best estimate of the liquid volume of the pitcher?
>
> 1 L
>
> **less than 1 liter   1 liter   more than 1 liter**

Use a benchmark to get an idea of how much 1 liter is. A tall water bottle has a liquid volume of 1 liter. Compare the amount of juice in the pitcher with the amount of water that would fill a 1-liter bottle.

➡ The liquid volume of the pitcher is more than 1 liter.

Understand: How to solve problems involving liquid volume

> Teresa has a fish tank that holds 25 liters of water.
> She takes out 9 liters of water to clean the tank.
> How many liters of water are still in the tank?

Write a subtraction equation for the problem.
$25 - 9 = w$

Solve the subtraction equation.
$25 - 9 = 16$

➡ 16 liters of water are still in the tank.

✏ Write an addition equation you could use to solve the problem.
$9 + w = 25$

Words to Know

liquid volume: the amount of liquid a container can hold

liter (L): a metric unit of liquid volume

Example: A tall water bottle can hold about 1 liter of liquid.

Glossary can be found on pp. 347–350.

MORE ONLINE sadlierconnect.com

Lesson 25

Guided Instruction

Understand: How to estimate mass

Mass is the amount of matter an object contains.

Betty found a robin feather.

Which is the best estimate of the feather's mass?

about 1 gram   about 10 grams   about 100 grams

Use a benchmark. Look at the chart. Which of the benchmark objects has about the same mass as a feather? A pencil is too heavy, so use a paper clip. A paper clip has a mass of about 1 gram.

➡ The feather has a mass of about 1 gram.

Benchmarks	
Object	Mass
Paper clip	1 gram
Pencil	10 grams
Cell phone	100 grams
1-liter bottle of water	1000 grams

Understand: How to solve problems involving mass

At the aquarium, Henry filled 6 small paper bags with fish food flakes. He made this drawing of his balance to show how he measured the mass of 1 filled bag.

What is the mass of the fish flakes Henry used to fill the 6 small bags?

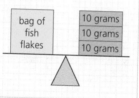

Start by using the drawing to find the mass of 1 bag.

The drawing shows that the mass of 1 bag of fish flakes is about 30 grams.

Hint: A bag has very little mass, so do not worry about including the mass of a bag.

Then use this information to write an equation.

$f = 6 \times 30$
$f = 180$

➡ Six bags of fish flakes have a mass of about 180 grams.

Understand: How to estimate mass

■ Help students understand that a 1-liter bottle of water can also be used as a benchmark for measuring mass. Explain that if a 1-liter bottle of water was placed on a balance, its mass would be about 1000 grams.

■ Give students the opportunity to compare the mass of several classroom objects. If a balance is not available, have students hold one object in each hand to determine which object feels heavier.

Understand: How to solve problems involving mass

■ Be sure students know that when a balance is level, it means that the masses of the objects on each side of the balance are equivalent.

■ Have students draw 6 bags and label each bag with a mass of 30 grams. Ask students what operation they can use to determine the total mass of 6 small bags of fish flakes.

Words to Know

mass: the measure of the amount of matter an object contains

gram (g): a metric unit of mass

Example: A paper clip has a mass of about 1 gram.

kilogram (kg): a metric unit of mass

Example: A textbook has a mass of about 1 kilogram.
1 kilogram = 1000 grams

Glossary can be found on pp. 347–350.

Guided Instruction

Connect: **Solving problems involving liquid volumes and masses** Use this page to help students strengthen their understanding of volume and mass.

■ In the first problem, point out that all three types of liquid are measured with the same unit, liters. Remind students that they can only add measurements with the same unit.

■ A common misconception students make is to think that a larger object always has more mass than a smaller object. Use the benchmark table to compare the masses of a math book and a brick. Even though a textbook is larger than a brick, a brick has more mass. Explain that mass is not just dependent on size; students must also consider the material that makes up the object.

■ After students have worked through the second problem, have them look at the benchmark table on page 227. Have them identify the object that has a mass of 1 kilogram. Remind them that 1 kilogram = 1000 grams. Tell students that both a gram and a kilogram can be used to measure mass. However, a kilogram is typically used to measure the mass of heavy objects.

Guided Instruction

Connect: **Solving problems involving liquid volumes and masses**

The Fielder family is having a party. Mr. Fielder makes a large batch of punch. He mixes together 5 liters of lemon-lime soda, 2 liters of orange juice, and 4 liters of grape juice. How much punch does Mr. Fielder make in all?

Step 1

Use a drawing to write an equation.

$5 + 2 + 4 = p$

liters of punch in all		
5 liters	2 liters	4 liters

Step 2

Solve the equation.

$5 + 2 + 4 = 11$

➡ Mr. Fielder makes 11 liters of punch in all.

A kilogram is a unit used to measure mass. 1 kg = 1000 g

Tina has a softball bat. Help Tina find the best estimate of the mass of the bat.

about 1   about 3   about 5
kilogram   kilograms   kilograms

Step 1

Use a benchmark.
Look at the chart.
Which of the benchmark objects has about the same mass as a bat?
A brick is too heavy, so it is a math book.

Benchmarks	
Object	Mass
Math book	1 kilogram
Brick	3 kilograms
Medium size cat	5 kilograms

Step 2

A math book has a mass of about 1 kilogram.

➡ The bat has a mass of about __1__ kilogram.

Support English Language Learners

Write the word *benchmark* on the board. Have English language learners pronounce the word along with you. Then, write the word *common* on the board. Point out that common objects, such as a paper clip and a pencil are often used as benchmarks. Display a paper clip, a pencil, a cell phone, and a 1-liter bottle of water. Have students hold the objects to compare their masses by how heavy they feel. Refer students to the benchmark chart on page 227 and read the benchmark masses aloud. Tell students that these benchmarks are used to estimate the mass of objects. Have students make a drawing of the common benchmarks and their masses. They should write the word *Benchmarks* as a title. If time permits, present other benchmarks for students to manipulate and draw, such as a feather (1 g), a textbook (1 kg), or a brick (3 kg).

Guided Practice

Circle the best estimate of the liquid volume.

1.

1 L

1 liter   10 liters   (50 liters)

2.

1 L

1 liter   (10 liters)   20 liters

Circle the best estimate of the mass.

3.

1
kilogram   (10
kilograms)   100
kilograms

4.

(1 gram)   25 grams   50 grams

Solve each problem.

5. Ms. Lewis makes 6 mini bran muffins. Each muffin has a mass of 20 grams. What is the total mass of the bran muffins?

   _120_ grams

6. Jerry's two fish tanks have liquid volumes of 90 liters and 38 liters. How many fewer liters of water does the smaller tank hold than the larger tank?

   _52_ liters

✸ Think•Pair•Share

MP1 7. Abu wants to estimate the mass of two nickels. He knows that the mass of a pencil is about 10 grams and the mass of a cell phone is about 100 grams. He estimates that the two nickels have a mass of about 100 grams. What mistake did Abu make? Explain.
Possible explanation: The two nickels's mass is closer to the mass of two pencils than to the mass of a cell phone. He may have thought that the two nickels's mass had to be greater than the mass of a pencil.

Unit 4 ■ Focus on Measurement and Data   **229**

Observational Assessment

Use page 229 to assess whether students are able to estimate the volumes and masses of common objects. Tell students to look back at the benchmarks on pages 227 and 228 for help, if needed.

✸ Think•Pair•Share

Peer Collaboration Have students work in pairs to discuss the problem and come to an agreement on an explanation. As students work, ask questions such as:

- *What is your estimate for one nickel?*

- *What operation can you use to estimate the mass of two nickels?*

Return to the Essential Question

Reread the Lesson 25 Essential Question on page 226: *How can you solve problems involving liquid volume and mass?*

Ask volunteers to use what they learned in this lesson to answer this question. (Possible response: I can use a benchmark to estimate the volume or mass of an object. I can add, subtract, multiply, and divide measurements if they are measured in the same unit.)

Mathematical Practices

Mathematical Practice Standards underline the teaching and understanding of all concepts and skills presented. The emphasis of specific practices is noted throughout the guided and independent practice of this lesson.

MP1	Make sense of problems and persevere in solving them.

Item 7: Students use reasoning to estimate the mass of two objects by comparing the mass to two different benchmarks.

Independent Practice

Concept Application

Students may work independently on these pages in the classroom or at home. They may refer to the first four pages of the lesson to revisit the instruction or to see a worked-out example.

Common Errors and **Teaching Tips** may help you support student learning either in the classroom or as a follow-up for work done at home.

Teaching Tips

Items 1–4

Remind students that the benchmark for liquid volume is a 1-liter bottle. Students should think about how many 1-liter bottles of water it would take to fill each object.

Items 5–8

Students should eliminate unreasonable answer choices. Then, compare the remaining answer choices to the benchmarks for mass given in the lesson.

Independent Practice

Draw a line connecting each object with the best estimate of its liquid volume.

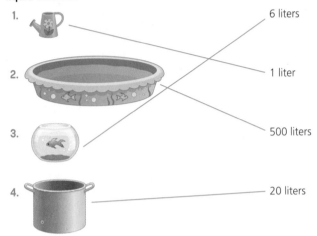

1.   6 liters

2.   1 liter

3.   500 liters

4.   20 liters

Circle the best estimate of the mass of each object.

5.

   (a.) 15 grams   b. 150 grams

   c. 500 grams   d. 1000 grams

6.

   a. 1 kilogram   b. 2 kilograms

   (c.) 10 kilograms   d. 50 kilograms

7.

   a. 5 grams   (b.) 5 kilograms

   c. 50 kilograms   d. 500 kilograms

8.

   (a.) 1 gram   b. 20 grams

   c. 40 grams   d. 100 grams

230   Unit 4 ■ Focus on Measurement and Data

Math-to-Science Connection

Density   Density is a physical property of matter. The density of a material is its mass per unit volume. Students can compare densities by comparing the difference in the mass of two different objects of the same size. For example, a marble would feel much heavier than a ball of clay that was the same size. Ask students for ideas of small objects that might feel heavier than they might expect.

Solve the problems.

9. In science class, Ms. Franklin wants to combine two liquids. How big of a container does she need?

__12__-liter container

10. Ed takes 9 packages to the post office. Each package has the same mass. What is the mass of the packages?

__27__ kilograms

11. BriAnna has a bag of pebbles. She puts an equal amount of pebbles into each of 5 flowerpots. If she uses all the pebbles, how much does she put in each pot?

PEBBLES
450 g

__90__ grams of pebbles

12. Steve fills a bucket with water. He pours 12 liters of the water into a trough for his horse. How much water is left in the bucket?

18 L

__6__ liters of water

Circle the correct answer.

13. Mr. Neil buys a piece of cheese that has a mass of 1000 grams. After he slices off some cheese, the piece has a mass of 680 grams. How much cheese does he slice off?

　(a.) 320 grams　　b. 480 grams

　c. 620 grams　　d. 1680 grams

14. Samantha has 8 tomato plants. She waters them with a can that holds 4 liters. If she gives each plant a full can of water, how much water does she use?

　a. 15 liters　　b. 24 liters

　(c.) 32 liters　　d. 36 liters

Unit 4 ■ Focus on Measurement and Data　**231**

Common Errors

Item 14

None of the incorrect answer choices are a result of choosing the wrong operation. If a student answers incorrectly, then the student made a multiplication error or made no attempt to solve the word problem and guessed. Suggest that students check their computation.

Teaching Tips

Item 9

Make sure students read the marked scale correctly.

Item 11

There are no examples of division word problems in the Guided Instruction of this lesson. Make sure students understand that they should consider all four operations when solving a problem.

Talking About Math

Collaborative Conversations Have students work in small groups to discuss how they can use benchmarks to estimate measurements. Using the benchmarks given in the lesson as a guide, have students think of their own benchmarks for mass and volume. Students should include illustrations of the objects they choose to use as benchmarks.

After groups have completed their list, have them share their benchmarks with the class. Decide as a class which benchmarks are most useful to estimate measurements and display a chart of the students' benchmarks in the classroom.

Independent Practice

Common Errors

Item 18
Students may perform the division correctly, but use the wrong unit. Have students check the units in their answers to make sure they match the units in the question.

Teaching Tips

Item 15
Point out that students need to use the calculated mass from part a to answer part b correctly.

Independent Practice

Solve the problems.

MP4 **15.** Trent made a drawing to show how he measured the mass of 1 plum.

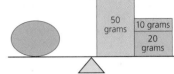

    a. About what is the mass of 1 plum?

    The mass of 1 plum is about 80 grams.

    b. About what would the mass of 6 plums be?

    The mass of 6 plums would be about 480 grams.

MP2 **16.** Ms. Rivera has two goldfish ponds. The first pond holds 190 liters of water. The second pond holds 28 fewer liters than the first pond. How can she find the liquid volume of the second pond?
Possible answer: She can subtract. She knows the second pond holds less water, so she should subtract 28 liters from 190 liters.

MP1 **17.** Helen buys a fish tank. She puts in 65 liters of water on Monday. She adds 42 liters of water on Tuesday and 83 liters of water on Wednesday to fill the tank. What is the liquid volume of the tank?

    Show your work.
Possible answer: 65 + 42 + 83 = 190

    Answer The liquid volume of the tank is 190 liters.

MP2 **18.** Dave has a sack of concrete. The mass of the concrete is 24 kilograms. When he pours equal amounts of concrete into some buckets, he empties the sack. Each bucket has 3 kilograms of concrete. How many buckets does he use?

    Show your work.
Possible answer: 24 ÷ 3 = 8

    Answer Dave uses 8 buckets.

232 Unit 4 ■ Focus on Measurement and Data

Mathematical Practices

MP1	Make sense of problems and persevere in solving them.
Item 17: Students analyze a problem and determine a method to solve.	
MP2	Reason abstractly and quantitatively.
Item 16: Students determine which operation to use to solve.	
Item 18: Students attend to the meaning of quantities to solve a problem.	
MP4	Model with mathematics.
Item 15: Students analyze a balance to determine an object's mass.	

Independent Practice

MP6 19. A box contains 80 crackers. Each cracker has a mass of 5 grams.
What is the total mass of the crackers?

　　　Show your work.
Possible answer: 80 × 5 = 400

Answer The total mass of the crackers is 400 grams.

MP1 20. Ms. Thomson puts 480 liters of water in a wading pool. Her children
and their friends play in the pool. Now the pool has 393 liters of
water. How much water do the children and their friends splash out?

Answer The children and their friends splash out 87 liters of water.

　　　Justify your answer using words, drawings, or numbers.
Possible justification: 480 − 393 = 87
I knew I had to subtract because there was less water after the children
and their friends played.

MP2 21. Sam makes a regular veggie burger and a super veggie burger.
He uses mustard from a 250-gram jar in the veggie burgers. The
regular veggie burger has a mass of 140 grams. The super veggie
burger has a mass of 235 grams. What is the total mass of the
veggie burgers?

Answer The total mass of the veggie burgers is 375 grams.

　　　Justify your answer using words, drawings, or numbers.
Possible justification: 140 + 235 = 375
The total mass has to be the sum of the two masses of the
veggie burgers. The mass of the jar of mustard is not needed.

Common Errors

Item 21

Students may use all of the numbers
given in the problem. Point out that
there is extra information. Make sure
students understand that the total mass
of the veggie burgers includes the mass
of the regular veggie burger and the
mass of the super veggie burger.

Mathematical Practices	
MP1	**Make sense of problems and persevere in solving them.**
Item 20: Students interpret a problem to determine that they need to subtract to determine the displacement of volume.	
MP2	**Reason abstractly and quantitatively.**
Item 21: Students attend to the meaning of quantities to identify extra information that is not needed to solve the problem.	
MP6	**Attend to precision.**
Item 19: Students write a multiplication equation to find the total mass.	

Common Core Focus:

3.MD.3 Draw a scaled picture graph and a scaled bar graph to represent a data set with several categories. Solve one- and two-step "how many more" and "how many less" problems using information presented in scaled bar graphs.

OBJECTIVE
Use data to create and analyze picture graphs and bar graphs.

ESSENTIAL QUESTION
Have students discuss what they already know about graphs. Share ideas about collecting data, making graphs, and using them to solve problems.

PREREQUISITE SKILLS
Use Item I on page 341 of the Foundational Skills Handbook to review making bar graphs to represent data.

FLUENCY PRACTICE
Fluency practice is available at **sadlierconnect.com**.

Concept Development

Understand: How to draw picture graphs

■ When creating a picture graph, students should choose a symbol that is easy to draw. Discuss what symbols would be good to use and why. Simple symbols are easier to draw and will look consistent.

■ Keys help scale data sets down to a manageable size. Ask students why a key is necessary and how to choose an appropriate scale.

✏ A tally chart and corresponding graph need to reflect the same data set. By looking at the key, students can correctly calculate how many students like oranges the best.

Essential Question:
How can I draw graphs to show data?
3.MD.3

Words to Know:
picture graph
data
key
bar graph
scale

In this lesson you will learn about picture graphs and bar graphs.

Understand: How to draw picture graphs

A picture graph shows data, or information.

The data in the tally chart to the right show the favorite fruits of students in a third-grade class. How many students chose peaches as their favorite fruit?

Favorite Fruit	
Peaches	卌 卌
Strawberries	卌 I
Bananas	IIII
Oranges	卌 III

➡ Ten students chose peaches as their favorite fruit.

You can use the data from the tally chart to make a picture graph. Each picture or symbol represents a number of data.

Look at the row for Peaches in the tally chart.
Ten students chose peaches as their favorite fruit.

Look at the row for Peaches in the picture graph.
There are 5 🍶 symbols. Look at the key. The key tells what each symbol represents. Each 🍶 symbol represents 2 students.
    $5 \times 2 = 10$

Favorite Fruit	
Peaches	🍶 🍶 🍶 🍶 🍶
Strawberries	🍶 🍶 🍶
Bananas	🍶 🍶
Oranges	🍶 🍶 🍶 🍶
Key: 🍶 = 2 students	

✏ Explain why the picture graph shows the data for oranges correctly. The tally chart shows that 8 students chose oranges. The picture graph has 4 symbols in the oranges row, so 4 × 2, so it shows that 4 × 2 students chose oranges, and that is the same as 8 students.

Words to Know

picture graph: a display of data, or information, that uses symbols or pictures

data: facts or information

key: tells what each symbol in a picture graph stands for

Example: Data is shown in this **picture graph**. The **key** is typically placed in the last row of a picture graph.

Favorite Fruit	
Peaches	🍶 🍶 🍶 🍶 🍶
Strawberries	🍶 🍶 🍶
Bananas	🍶 🍶
Oranges	🍶 🍶 🍶 🍶
Key: 🍶 = 2 students	

Glossary can be found on pp. 347–350.

Understand: How to draw bar graphs

A bar graph is another way to represent data.

The tally chart shows how students in a third-grade class get to school. How many students ride their bikes to school?	Ways to Get to School	
	Bus	卌 卌 ‖
	Car	‖
	Bike	卌 ‖‖
	Walk	卌 ‖

➡ Eight students ride their bikes to school.

You can use the data from the tally chart to make a bar graph.

Each bar represents a row of data from the tally chart. The length of the bar shows the number of students.

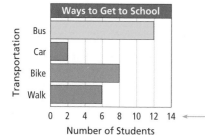

The scale tells how many for the length of a bar.

Look at the bike data in the tally chart. Eight students ride their bikes to school.

Look at the bike bar in the bar graph. Read the scale below the end of the bar. The end of the bar is at 8.

✏ How can you tell whether the car data in the bar graph is the same as the car data in the tally chart? The tally chart shows that 2 students come to school by car and the bar graph also shows the same thing.

Unit 4 ■ Focus on Measurement and Data **235**

Words to Know

bar graph: a display of data, or information, that uses either vertical or horizontal bars

scale: On a bar graph, it tells how many are represented by the length of a bar.

Example:

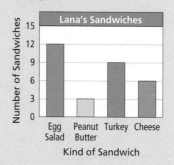

Glossary can be found on pp. 347–350.

Understand: How to draw bar graphs

■ Discuss the ways picture graphs and bar graphs are similar and how they are different. They both have labels, titles, and represent data. A picture graph represents data with pictures; a bar graph represents data with bars.

■ Discuss why the bars on the bar graph are different colors. Point out that the bars for each category are different colors in order to make them easier to differentiate.

■ Students should use the vertical lines on the bar graph to ensure proper measurement of the bars.

■ Share ideas about why graphs can be a helpful tool when examining data. Graphs make information easier to analyze, compare, and visualize. Graphs are used for many reasons in real-life situations, such as showing election statistics. Showing pictures or bars makes it easy and fast to quickly see who is winning or losing, and by how much, without even looking at actual facts or numbers.

✏ ➡ Graphs need to represent the exact data set collected. The tally chart and corresponding graph show the same information, but in different ways. Checking that the information matches up will encourage students to pay attention to the bar graph scale. Students may mistake the car transportation bar as representing only 1 student, but tally marks are more easily seen as 2 because each tally mark represents one student.

Guided Instruction

Connect: What you know about graphs to solve problems

■ Comparing data can involve multiple steps and operations, such as addition and subtraction. Encouraging students to look for key words like "how many more" and "how many fewer" will give them a clue about what operation is needed.

■ Remind students that comparing two categories on a graph is one of many ways to analyze a graph. Ask other questions about this graph, such as what is the total number of sandwiches Lana ate last month.

■ Comparing two categories in a graph provides a good opportunity for students to practice writing equations. Using letters to represent unknowns builds algebraic concepts and makes it easier for students to rewrite the equation with the opposite operation.

✏ Remind students to use a letter to represent the unknown in this problem. This process can be helpful because some students may find it easier to add than subtract.

Guided Instruction

Connect: What you know about graphs to solve problems

The bar graph shows the kinds of sandwiches Lana ate for lunch last month.

How many more egg salad sandwiches did Lana eat than cheese sandwiches?

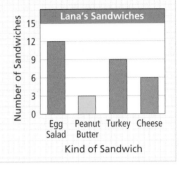

Step 1

Find the number of egg salad sandwiches.
Read the scale on the left side of the graph.
The end of the egg salad bar is at 12.
Lana ate 12 egg salad sandwiches.

Step 2

Find the number of cheese sandwiches.
Read the scale to find the number Lisa ate.
The end of the cheese bar is at 6.
Lana ate 6 cheese sandwiches.

Step 3

Write and solve a subtraction equation.
$12 - 6 = n$
$12 - 6 = \underline{\;6\;}$

➤ Lana ate 6 more egg salad sandwiches than cheese sandwiches.

✏ Write an addition equation you can use to solve the problem.
$n + 6 = 12$

236   Unit 4 ■ Focus on Measurement and Data

Support English Language Learners

Write the word *data* on the board. Say the word and have the students repeat after you. Explain that data is a group of facts. Ask students to give examples of data by ensuring that they say *data* in their example. It is okay for students to use examples of data from their book.

Write the word *graph* on the board, say the word, and have the students repeat. Tell students that a graph is a drawing that shows facts, or data. Have students point to the graph on page 236. Ask them what type of data, or facts, are shown on the graph. Ensure that students use *data* and *graph* when describing their examples. Repeat this process until students are comfortable using these terms.

Lesson 26

Guided Practice

Use data from the tally chart.

Plants in Will's Garden	
Melon	IIII
Tomato	ЖТ III
Squash	ЖТ ЖТ
Carrot	ЖТ ЖТ II

Plants in Will's Garden	
Melon	● ●
Tomato	● ● ● ●
Squash	● ● ● ● ●
Carrot	● ● ● ● ● ●

Key: ● = 2 plants

1. Draw ● symbols in the picture graph to represent Will's tomato plants.

2. Draw ● symbols in the picture graph to represent Will's carrot plants.

Use the bar graph to answer exercises 3–5.

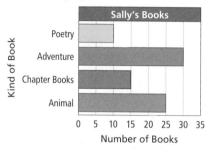

3. How many fewer poetry books does Sally have than animal books?

___15 books___

4. How many more adventure books does Sally have than animal books?

___5 books___

♥♥ Think•Pair•Share

MP2 **5.** Sally gets 10 more Chapter Books. Explain how she should change the bar graph. Possible explanation: She should make the Chapter Books bar longer so that the end of the bar is at 25.

Mathematical Practices

Mathematical Practice Standards underline the teaching and understanding of all concepts and skills presented. The emphasis of specific practices is noted throughout the guided and independent practice of this lesson.

MP2 **Reason abstractly and quantitatively.**

Item 5: Students analyze a bar graph and use additional data to change the graph appropriately.

Observational Assessment

Use page 237 to assess whether students understand how to create picture graphs and bar graphs and solve problems using them. Students should look for and interpret words like "how many more" and "how many fewer" to help determine appropriate strategies and operations to use when comparing.

♥♥ Think•Pair•Share

Peer Collaboration Ask pairs to share their strategies with each other, then the class. While they are in pairs, circulate and ask questions. Asking these same questions when they are presenting in front of the class will give all students an opportunity to share effectively:

• *What will change on Sally's graph? How many bars should she change?*

• *What categories are affected because of this change?*

• *Does the scale on the bottom need to change? Why or why not?*

• *What is one new observation you can make about the kinds of books Sally read?*

To summarize, the bar for Chapter Books should get longer by ten. The rest of the graph should remain the same. This new data will change how the graph is analyzed, but not the basic structure. Now she has just as many chapter books as animal books.

Return to the Essential Question

Reread the Lesson 26 Essential Question on page 234: *How can I draw graphs to show data?*

Ask volunteers to use what they learned in this lesson to answer this question. (Possible response: Creating graphs allows me to present data in a way that is easy to understand. Using pictures or bars, I can quickly compare categories or make generalizations about data.)

Independent Practice

Concept Application

Students may work independently on these pages in the classroom or at home. They may refer to the first four pages of this lesson to revisit the instruction or to see a worked-out example.

Common Errors and **Teaching Tips** may help you support student learning either in the classroom or as a follow-up for work done at home.

Common Errors

Items 2–3

Some students may try to draw 9 triangles instead of 3 for the Green category or 3 triangles for the Orange category instead of 1. Remind students to pay attention to the key.

Item 4

Help students understand that the question is about the length of the distance between each number of the bottom scale, not the distance between each bar.

Teaching Tips

Items 1–6

The data in tally charts and graphs often reflect each other in length. This is a quick way for students to check their work, as the length of a row of tallies, and the length of a bar or row of pictures will be proportional. For instance, there are more tallies for Mindy than for Tom, so the bar will also be longer for Mindy.

Independent Practice

Use the tally chart and picture graph.

Students' Favorite Colors	
Green	ⅢⅢ			
Red	ⅢⅢ ⅢⅢ ||
Blue	ⅢⅢ	
Orange	|||

Students' Favorite Colors	
Green	▲ ▲ ▲
Red	▲ ▲ ▲ ▲
Blue	▲ ▲
Orange	▲

Key: ▲ = 3 students

1. How many students are represented by each ▲ symbol in the picture graph?

   __3__ students

2. Draw ▲ symbols in the picture graph to represent students whose favorite color is green.

3. Draw ▲ symbols in the picture graph to represent students whose favorite color is orange.

Use the tally chart and bar graph.

Baseball Hits	
Mindy	ⅢⅢ ⅢⅢ ⅢⅢ ⅢⅢ ||||
Ed	ⅢⅢ ⅢⅢ ⅢⅢ ⅢⅢ
Tom	ⅢⅢ |||
Lisa	ⅢⅢ ⅢⅢ ⅢⅢ	

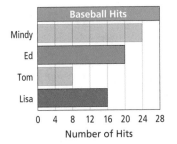

4. What does each distance between two vertical lines in the bar graph represent?

   _____4 hits_____

5. Draw the bar for Mindy. Bar goes to 24; check students' work.

6. Draw the bar for Tom. Bar goes to 8; check students' work.

Math-to-Math Connection

Collect and Display Data Creating and analyzing a graph requires many steps. Have students come up with their own topic, collect data, create a graph, and describe it. This will help students see the importance of categories, labels, scales, keys, and data presentation.

Encourage students to pick a topic of interest to them, such as favorite snacks, and survey their classmates. Students will choose to create a picture graph or a bar graph and determine an appropriate scale or key, determine appropriate labels and where to put them, and interpret the data as bars or pictures. Evaluating their graphs and presenting them to the class allows students to communicate their findings.

Lesson 26

Independent Practice

Use the bar graph to answer exercises 7–12.

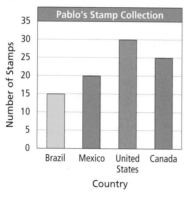

Pablo's Stamp Collection

Circle the correct answer.

7. How many more stamps from Canada does Pablo have than stamps from Brazil?

a. 2 stamps   b. 5 stamps

c. 10 stamps   d. 12 stamps

8. How many fewer stamps from Brazil does Pablo have than stamps from the United States?

a. 15 stamps   b. 10 stamps

c. 5 stamps   d. 3 stamps

9. How many more stamps from Brazil and Mexico does Pablo have than stamps from the United States?

a. 4 stamps   b. 5 stamps

c. 10 stamps   d. 15 stamps

10. How many fewer stamps from Mexico does Pablo have than stamps from the United States and Canada?

a. 15 stamps   b. 20 stamps

c. 35 stamps   d. 40 stamps

11. How many more stamps from Mexico and Canada does Pablo have than stamps from the United States?

a. 30 stamps   b. 25 stamps

c. 20 stamps   d. 15 stamps

12. How many fewer stamps from Canada does Pablo have than stamps from Mexico and Brazil?

a. 0 stamps   b. 5 stamps

c. 10 stamps   d. 20 stamps

Unit 4 ■ Focus on Measurement and Data **239**

Common Errors

Items 7–12

Some students may struggle with how to begin to answer each question. Remind students to cue into key words like "fewer" and "more" to help them interpret each question.

Teaching Tips

Items 7–12

Use this opportunity to discuss test-taking skills. Students should always read every answer option, cross out wrong answers, and check their work.

Encourage students to always write equations when using addition or subtraction to compare categories. This builds algebraic reasoning and helps students solve problems successfully.

Writing About Math

▸ **Write Persuasive Text** Have students imagine they are discussing bar graphs with their friend Greg. Greg thinks that the categories and labels can go anywhere, and the scale can be anything. Students will write down all the reasons that these things do matter and how they have an impact on how data is represented on a graph. Students should explain the reasons why these aspects of a graph allow us to correctly show data, which makes us able to make generalizations and solve problems correctly. Encourage students to provide specific examples of how these aspects can be used incorrectly and how it would affect the data shown.

Ask volunteers to read their ideas to the class and record them on the board.

Independent Practice

Common Errors

Item 16

Students may not multiply the number of apples Ms. Brown gave to her children by the number of days to determine how many apples she gave away. Repeated addition or subtraction can be used to remove the apples she gives away one day at a time.

Teaching Tips

Items 13–16

Students can solve these problems using different strategies. Some students may skip count, use repeated addition, or draw a picture to problem solve. Encourage students to always include appropriate equations in their work.

Item 16

Ask students how 1 apple would be shown on the graph. Share ideas about how a symbol can represent a number that is not part of the key. Half of a diamond would correctly represent 1 because the whole diamond equals 2.

Lesson 26   **Draw Graphs to Represent Categorical Data**

Independent Practice

Use the picture graph to answer exercises 13–16.

⟩ **Show your work.**

Ms. Brown's Fruit	
Bananas	◆◆
Pears	◆◆◆
Apples	◆◆◆◆◆
Mangos	◆
Key: ◆ = 2 fruits	

MP4 **13.** How many more bananas than mangos does Ms. Brown have?

Possible answer:
$2 \times 2 = 4$ bananas
$1 \times 2 = 2$ mangos
$4 - 2 = 2$
Answer Ms. Brown has 2 more bananas than mangos.

MP2 **14.** How many fewer bananas than apples does Ms. Brown have?

Possible answer:
$2 \times 2 = 4$ bananas
$5 \times 2 = 10$ apples
$4 + n = 10$
$n = 6$
Answer Ms. Brown has 6 fewer bananas than apples.

MP1 **15.** Ms. Brown gives 4 pears to her neighbor. How many pears does Ms. Brown have left?

Possible answer:
$3 \times 2 = 6$ pears
$6 - 4 = 2$

Answer Ms. Brown has 2 pears left.

MP6 **16.** Ms. Brown has 3 children. She gives each child an apple each day. How many apples does she have after 3 days?

Possible answer:
$5 \times 2 = 10$ apples
$3 \times 3 = 9$
$10 - 9 = 1$
Answer Ms. Brown has 1 apple left after 3 days.

Mathematical Practices

MP1	**Make sense of problems and persevere in solving them.**
Item 15: Students solve a real-world problem by analyzing data.	
MP2	**Reason abstractly and quantitatively.**
Item 14: Students recognize the word "fewer" to use an appropriate operation.	
MP4	**Model with mathematics.**
Item 13: Students use a graph to compare and interpret data.	
MP6	**Attend to precision.**
Item 16: Students formulate full explanations with multiple steps and operations.	

Independent Practice

Use the bar graph to answer exercises 17–19.

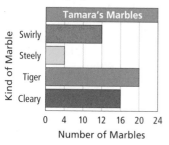

MP2 **17.** How many fewer swirly and steely marbles does Tamara have than tiger and cleary marbles?

Show your work. Possible answer:

$$
\begin{array}{r} 12 \\ +\ 4 \\ \hline 16 \end{array}
\qquad
\begin{array}{r} 20 \\ +16 \\ \hline 36 \end{array}
\qquad
\begin{array}{r} 36 \\ -16 \\ \hline 20 \end{array}
$$

Answer Tamara has 20 fewer swirly and steely marbles than tiger and cleary marbles.

MP7 **18.** Does Tamara have more than 40 marbles in all?

Answer Tamara has more than 40 marbles in all.

Justify your answer using words, drawings, or numbers.
Possible justifications: She has 20 tiger marbles and 16 cleary marbles, so that is 36. The four steely marbles make 40, so with the swirly marbles, there is more than 40. I can add 12 + 4 + 20 + 16 to get 52 and 52 is greater than 40.

MP3 **19.** Tamara wants to change the scale on her bar graph. She decides to make the distance between vertical lines represent 3 marbles. Is that a good choice?

Answer No, it is not a good choice.

Justify your answer using words, drawings, or numbers.
Possible justification: She could draw a bar to show 12 swirly marbles. But it would be hard to show the other marbles. For the other marbles, you can't multiply a number by 3 and get 4 or 20 or 16.

Common Errors

Item 18

Students may overlook the word "more" and, instead, determine if Tamara has 40 marbles in all. Suggest that students reread the problem to make sure they have not missed any information.

Teaching Tips

Item 18

When finding the totals, students do not need to continue adding categories once they reach a sum of 40. They should recognize that adding the value of another bar will result in a sum that is greater than 40.

Item 19

To focus students on the idea of an effective scale, ask them what is similar about the bars in all the bar graphs throughout the lesson (all the bars line up with the vertical or horizontal lines on the scale). Help students see why it would be more difficult to read a graph where the lines did not correspond with the bars.

Mathematical Practices

MP2	Reason abstractly and quantitatively.
Item 17:	Students determine appropriate operations to use to interpret data.
MP3	Construct viable arguments and critique the reasoning of others.
Item 19:	Students analyze a problem, solve it, and explain their reasoning.
MP7	Look for and make use of structure.
Item 18:	Students evaluate a graph's structure to problem solve.

Common Core Focus:

3.MD.4 Generate measurement data by measuring lengths using rulers marked with halves and fourths of an inch. Show the data by making a line plot, where the horizontal scale is marked off in appropriate units—whole numbers, halves, or quarters.

OBJECTIVE

Use a line plot to represent data gathered from measuring the length of objects.

ESSENTIAL QUESTION

Explain to students that they will learn how to draw and use line plots. This will allow them to organize measurement information in a way that makes it easier to understand.

PREREQUISITE SKILLS

Use Item J on page 341 of the Foundational Skills Handbook to review using a line plot to represent measurement data.

FLUENCY PRACTICE

Fluency practice is available at **sadlierconnect.com**.

Concept Development

Understand: How to draw line plots

■ Students must understand the necessary components of a line plot, how to draw a line plot, and how to organize measurement data on the line plot. For this lesson, students may need inch rulers, preferably ones that show $\frac{1}{4}$, $\frac{1}{2}$, and $\frac{3}{4}$ inches.

■ Have students discuss the components of the tally chart, and interpret the information.

✎ Have students read their questions aloud. Ask volunteers to answer the questions using the data provided.

Lesson 27 — Generate and Graph Measurement Data

Essential Question:
How can I draw line plots to show measurement data?
3.MD.4

Words to Know:
line plot
half-inch
quarter-inch

Guided Instruction

In this lesson you will learn about line plots.

Understand: How to draw line plots

Anya gathers data by pulling some carrots from her garden. She measures the length of each carrot. She records the data in a tally chart.

For homework she has to use the tally chart to make a line plot of the data. Then she has to write a question about her data.

What question can she write?

Lengths of Carrots (in.)	
Length (in.)	Tally
6			
$6\frac{1}{2}$		
7				
$7\frac{1}{2}$	||||
8		

To make a line plot, she draws a number line that includes all her data. She uses half-inch intervals on the scale.

She draws an X for each carrot length above that number.

Carrot Lengths (in.) ← A line plot needs a title.

When you need more than 1 X for a number, put the Xs in a stack.

Anya decides to ask a question about carrots that are less than $7\frac{1}{2}$ inches long.

➤ She can write this question: How many carrots are less than $7\frac{1}{2}$ inches long?

To answer, use the line plot to count the Xs to the left of $7\frac{1}{2}$ inches. There are 6 carrots less than $7\frac{1}{2}$ inches long.

✎ What are some other questions Anya could write?
Possible answers: How many carrots does Anya pull? How many carrots are 8 inches long? How much longer is the longest carrot than the shortest carrot?

Words to Know

line plot: a graph that uses a number line and symbols to represent data

Example:

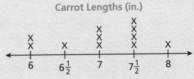

Carrot Lengths (in.)

half-inch: a customary unit of length

quarter-inch: a customary unit of length

Glossary can be found on pp. 347–350.

Connect: Drawing line plots to show measurement data

Dan measures the lengths of his toy cars. He records the data in a chart.	Lengths of Toy Cars (in.)		
	$2\frac{1}{4}$	3	$2\frac{1}{2}$
Use the chart to make a line plot of the measurement data.	$2\frac{3}{4}$	$3\frac{1}{4}$	3
	$2\frac{1}{2}$	$2\frac{1}{2}$	3
Find how many toy cars are 3 inches or longer.	$2\frac{3}{4}$	$3\frac{1}{2}$	$2\frac{1}{2}$

Step 1

Draw a number line. Show inches, half-inches, and quarter-inches on the scale.

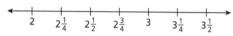

Step 2

Draw an X for each toy car above its length. Write a title for the line plot.

Lengths of Toy Cars (in.)

To find how many toy cars are 3 inches or longer, look at the line plot.

Count the Xs above 3 inches. __3__ Xs

Count the Xs to the right of 3 inches. __2__ Xs

3 + 2 = __5__

▶ There are 5 toy cars that are 3 inches or longer.

Connect: Drawing line plots to show measurement data Use this page to help students strengthen their understanding of how to create line plots and organize measurement data using line plots.

■ Remind students that measurements to the nearest quarter-inch are shown on the line plot scale. Also, remind students that the increments on the scale are equally placed. Explain that the scale is used to display and compare the data, not measure it, so the tick marks do not have to be a quarter-inch apart.

■ Make the connection that each X represents the measurement of one unique toy car. If there is more than one car with the same measurement, another X is placed on the stack for that measurement. In other words, the number of Xs in each stack represents the number of cars of equivalent measure.

Support English Language Learners

Write *half-inch* and *quarter-inch* on the board. Point out that the last part of each term is the same: *inch*. Use a ruler to display an inch.

Have students draw pictures, use physical models, or tell the meaning of *half* and *quarter*. Students may be familiar with *half* such as half an hour or half an apple. Students may be most familiar with *quarter* in terms of money. Show students a quarter and explain that it takes four of these coins to equal 1 whole dollar.

Draw students' attention back to the ruler. Have them identify one inch. Ask them to apply what they have learned about the terms *half* and *quarter* to find a *half-inch* mark and a *quarter-inch* mark.

Guided Practice

Observational Assessment

Use pages 244–245 to assess whether students are able to measure and represent data to the nearest quarter-inch on a line plot. Note those students that have difficulty labeling the scale on the line plot. Help them to determine the size of the intervals.

Guided Practice

Use the chart to complete the line plot of the measurement data.

Earthworm Lengths (in.)

5	4	$4\frac{1}{2}$
$5\frac{1}{2}$	3	4
$3\frac{1}{2}$	$5\frac{1}{2}$	$5\frac{1}{2}$
4	5	$3\frac{1}{2}$

Earthworm Lengths (in.)

1. Complete the scale of the number line.

2. Draw an X for each earthworm that is 4 inches long.

3. Draw an X for each earthworm that is $4\frac{1}{2}$ inches long.

4. Draw an X for each earthworm that is 5 inches long.

5. Draw an X for each earthworm that is $5\frac{1}{2}$ inches long.

6. Write a title for the line plot.

7. How many earthworms are less than 5 inches long?

    __7__ earthworms

8. How many earthworms are more than 5 inches long?

    __3__ earthworms

Math-to-Science Connection

Data Collection A strong understanding of measurement and data collection is essential in understanding a wide variety of scientific ideas. As a class, decide on some measurement data to gather, such as hand span, foot length, or height. Have students work together to record the measurements to the nearest quarter-inch for the entire class. To ensure accuracy, each measurement should be taken three separate times. The two most similar measurements can be assumed to be the most accurate. Have students work together to draw a line plot and record the scale at equal intervals along the number line. After each student has plotted his/her data on the line plot, encourage students to write and share questions based on the data.

MORE ONLINE sadlierconnect.com   Lesson 27

9. Measure each line segment. Record each length in the chart.

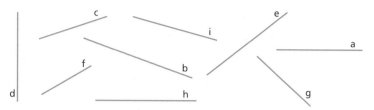

Line Segment Lengths (in.)

a: $1\frac{1}{2}$	b: 2	c: $1\frac{1}{4}$
d: $1\frac{1}{2}$	e: $1\frac{3}{4}$	f: 1
g: $1\frac{1}{4}$	h: $1\frac{3}{4}$	i: $1\frac{1}{2}$

Use your chart to make a line plot of your measurement data.

10. Complete the scale of the number line.

11. Draw an X for each line segment above its measurement.

12. Write a title for your line plot.

Line Segment Lengths (in.)

```
                    X
            X       X
    X       X       X       X
    X       X       X       X       X
 ───┼───────┼───────┼───────┼───────┼───►
    1      1¼      1½      1¾       2
```

13. Which length has the most line segments? ___$1\frac{1}{2}$ in.___

👑 **Think·Pair·Share**

MP4 **14.** Why is it not necessary to make a tally chart first when you make a line plot?
Possible answer: Because you draw an X for each measurement or piece of data, the measurements or data do not need to be in order. As you draw an X for each one, you are making sure you record all the data.

Mathematical Practices

Mathematical Practice Standards underline the teaching and understanding of all concepts and skills presented. The emphasis of specific practices is noted throughout the guided and independent practice of this lesson.

MP4	**Model with mathematics.**

Item 14: Students interpret the solution in the context of a situation.

👑 **Think·Pair·Share**

Peer Collaboration Ask students to discuss their responses with a partner, referring to the following questions as a guideline:

• *How is information displayed in a tally chart and a line plot similar and different?*

• *When might it be easier to first use a tally chart and then transfer the information to a line plot?*

• *When might it be easier to use a line plot without using a tally chart first?*

To summarize, tell students that a tally chart and a line plot tell you the same information. A tally chart is a useful tool to use to record data while you are gathering it. If the data is already provided to you, a tally chart is not necessary. The same information is just displayed two different ways.

Return to the Essential Question

Reread the Lesson 27 Essential Question on page 242: *How can I draw line plots to show measurement data?*

Ask volunteers to use what they learned in this lesson to answer this question. (Possible response: I can use a line plot to organize the measurements that have been taken. I can number a scale on a line plot and draw an X for each measurement to keep track of how many objects have that measurement.)

Invite as many volunteers as possible to express ideas about using a line plot to display measurement data.

Independent Practice

Concept Application

Students may work independently on these pages in the classroom or at home. They may refer to the first four pages of the lesson to revisit the instruction or to see a worked-out example.

Common Errors and **Teaching Tips** may help you support student learning either in the classroom or as a follow-up for work done at home.

Teaching Tips

Item 1

Remind students that a scale on a line plot is divided into equal increments.

Items 4–7

Remind students to use the data in the line plot to solve these problems.

Independent Practice

Ines and Marco find a frog in the garden. They measure the lengths of its hops. They record the data in a chart.

Use the chart to make a line plot of the measurement data.

Frog Hops (in.)		
8	7	$8\frac{1}{2}$
$8\frac{1}{2}$	9	7
8	$9\frac{1}{2}$	$8\frac{1}{2}$
$9\frac{1}{2}$	$8\frac{1}{2}$	8

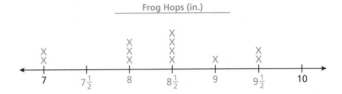

1. Complete the scale of the number line.

2. Draw an X for each hop above its measurement.

3. Write a title for the line plot.

Circle the correct answer.

4. How many of the frog's hops are longer than 9 inches?

   a. 1 hop   (b.) 2 hops

   c. 3 hops   d. 4 hops

5. How many of the frog's hops are 8 inches or shorter?

   a. 2 hops   b. 4 hops

   (c.) 5 hops   d. 10 hops

6. Which frog hop length occurs most often?

   a. $7\frac{1}{2}$ inches   (b.) $8\frac{1}{2}$ inches

   c. $9\frac{1}{2}$ inches   d. 10 inches

7. Which lengths, in inches, had no frog hops?

   a. 7 and $7\frac{1}{2}$ b. 8 and 9

   c. 9 and $9\frac{1}{2}$ (d.) $7\frac{1}{2}$ and 10

Writing About Math

▸ **Research to Build and Present Knowledge** Ask students to use a line plot to organize the data taken from their own measurements. Explain to students that scientists present analyses of results from measurements taken in paragraph form. Encourage students to write a paragraph summarizing the information provided by the line plot.

Independent Practice

8. Heidi cut some little boards to make a model barn. Measure each board. Record each length in the chart.

Board Lengths (in.)

a: 4	b: $4\frac{1}{4}$	c: $3\frac{1}{4}$
d: $4\frac{3}{4}$	e: 5	f: $3\frac{1}{2}$

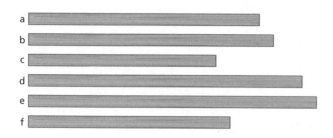

Use your chart to make a line plot of the measurement data.

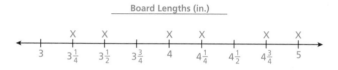

Board Lengths (in.)

$$\text{X} \quad \text{X} \qquad \text{X} \quad \text{X} \qquad \text{X} \quad \text{X}$$
$$3 \quad 3\frac{1}{4} \quad 3\frac{1}{2} \quad 3\frac{3}{4} \quad 4 \quad 4\frac{1}{4} \quad 4\frac{1}{2} \quad 4\frac{3}{4} \quad 5$$

9. Write a scale for the number line.

10. Draw an X for each board above its measurement.

11. Write a title for your line plot.

Circle the correct answer.

12. How many boards are $4\frac{1}{2}$ inches long?

   (a.) 0 boards   b. 1 board

   c. 2 boards   d. 3 boards

13. How many boards are at least $4\frac{1}{4}$ inches long?

   a. 2 boards   (b.) 3 boards

   c. 4 boards   d. 5 boards

Unit 4 ▪ Focus on Measurement and Data   **247**

Common Errors

Item 10

Students commonly forget to make an entry or two when completing a line plot. Remind students that the number of Xs on the line plot should be equal to the number of measurements taken.

Teaching Tips

Item 8

It is important for students to make accurate measurements. Remind students to place the 0 tick mark at one end of the object and carefully measure each board to the nearest quarter-inch.

Item 13

Remind students to read the problem carefully. The phrase *at least* means the total number of boards that are $4\frac{1}{4}$ inches long or longer.

Digital Connection

Online Measurement Games Use a search engine to search for online games involving measurement and making line plots. Save the links to the games you find for students to play on classroom computers. Another option is to project the games you find on an interactive whiteboard and play with the entire class.

Independent Practice

Teaching Tips

Item 14

Remind students that even though a line plot uses a number line, the scale does not need to start at 0. Students need only to make sure the greatest and least values in the data table are included in the range of the number line.

Item 16

Point out that the term $1\frac{1}{2}$ *inches or shorter* includes lengths of $1\frac{1}{2}$ inches.

Independent Practice

MP3 **14.** Stan measures 9 pieces of celery. He records his data in a chart. He wants to make a line plot of the data. What scale should he use? Explain.

Celery Lengths (in.)		
$7\frac{1}{2}$	$7\frac{1}{2}$	6
$6\frac{1}{2}$	8	$6\frac{1}{2}$
8	7	$6\frac{1}{2}$

Possible explanation: He should start at 6 inches because that's the shortest length. He should show half-inches because some of the measurements have half-inches. The scale should go to 8 inches, the longest length.

MP1 **15.** Stan measures 3 more pieces of celery. The lengths are $7\frac{3}{4}$ inches, $6\frac{1}{4}$ inches, and 7 inches. How should he change his scale to show the new celery pieces?
Possible answer: He should make the scale show quarter-inches because two of the new measurements have quarter-inches.

Use the line plot to answer exercises 16 and 17.

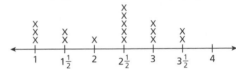

Lengths of Chicken Footsteps (in.)

MP6 **16.** How many chicken footsteps are $1\frac{1}{2}$ inches or shorter?

🖊 **Show your work.** Possible answer:
$$3 + 2 = 5$$

Answer Five chicken footsteps are $1\frac{1}{2}$ inches or shorter.

MP7 **17.** How many chicken footsteps are measured in all?

🖊 **Show your work.** Possible answer:
$$3 + 2 + 1 + 5 + 3 + 2$$
$$5 \;+ 1 + 5 + \;5 = 16$$

Answer Sixteen chicken footsteps are measured in all.

248   Unit 4 ▪ Focus on Measurement and Data

Mathematical Practices

MP1	**Make sense of problems and persevere in solving them.**
Item 15:	Students evaluate progress and change course if needed.
MP3	**Construct viable arguments and critique the reasoning of others.**
Item 14:	Students use previous results in constructing arguments.
MP6	**Attend to precision.**
Item 16:	Students communicate with precision.
MP7	**Look for and make use of structure.**
Item 17:	Students evaluate the structure of a problem.

Independent Practice

MP4 **18.** Nancy measures the widths of her favorite books. She records her data in a chart. How many of the books are wider than $5\frac{1}{2}$ inches?

Book Widths (in.)		
$4\frac{1}{2}$	6	$5\frac{1}{2}$
4	7	$5\frac{1}{2}$
$4\frac{1}{2}$	$5\frac{1}{2}$	6

■ **Show your work.** Possible answer:

Book Widths (in.)

Answer Three books are wider than $5\frac{1}{2}$ inches.

Use the chart of measurement data to answer questions 19 and 20.

Guppy Lengths (in.)		
$2\frac{1}{4}$	2	$1\frac{1}{2}$
2	$1\frac{1}{4}$	$2\frac{1}{2}$
1	$1\frac{1}{4}$	2
$1\frac{1}{4}$	$1\frac{1}{2}$	$2\frac{1}{4}$

MP3 **19.** Edgar wants to make a line plot of the guppy lengths. "There are 12 measurements," he says. "I should make the scale go from 1 to 12." Is he right?

Answer No, Edgar is not right.

■ **Justify your answer using words, drawings, or numbers.**

Possible justification: The scale does not include a mark for each measurement. It should start at 1 inch, which is the shortest measurement. It should end at $2\frac{1}{2}$ inches, which is the longest measurement.

MP5 **20.** How many of the guppies are less than 2 inches long?

Answer Six guppies are less than 2 inches long.

■ **Justify your answer using words, drawings, or numbers.**

Possible justification:

Guppy Lengths (in.)

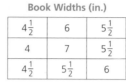

Unit 4 ■ Focus on Measurement and Data   **249**

Teaching Tips

Item 18
Point out that this problem asks only about books with a width greater than $5\frac{1}{2}$ inches.

Return to the

Remind students to return to the Progress Check self-assessment, page 215, to check off additional items they have mastered during the unit.

Mathematical Practices

MP3	**Construct viable arguments and critique the reasoning of others.**
Item 19:	Students analyze a problem situation.
MP4	**Model with mathematics.**
Item 18:	Students interpret the solution in the context of a situation.
MP5	**Use appropriate tools strategically.**
Item 20:	Students decide on an appropriate tool to use to solve a problem.

The Common Core Review covers all the standards presented in the unit. Use it to assess your students' mastery of the unit's concepts and skills.

Depth of Knowledge

The depth of knowledge is a ranking of the content complexity of assessment items based on Webb's Depth of Knowledge (DOK) levels. The levels increase in complexity as shown below.

Level 1: Recall and Reproduction
Level 2: Basic Skills and Concepts
Level 3: Strategic Reasoning and Thinking
Level 4: Extended Thinking

Item	Standard	DOK
1	3.MD.1	1
2	3.MD.1	1
3	3.MD.1	1
4	3.MD.3	2
5	3.MD.3	2
6	3.MD.3	2
7	3.MD.2	2
8	3.MD.2	2
9	3.MD.2	2
10	3.MD.2	2
11	3.MD.4	2
12	3.MD.4	2
13	3.MD.4	2
14	3.MD.4	1
15	3.MD.4	2
16	3.MD.4	2
17	3.MD.4	2
18	3.MD.4	2
19	3.MD.1	4
20	3.MD.3	3

UNIT 4 Common Core Review

Write the time shown by each clock.

1.

3:12

2.

5:45

3.

12:36

Dionne surveyed 70 students about their favorite color. The pictograph shows her data. Use the pictograph for exercises 4–8.

4. In Dionne's survey, 10 students chose green as their favorite color. Complete the pictograph. Students should draw two squares in the row labeled Green.

5. Which color was chosen by 15 students?

purple

6. How many more students chose red than purple? 5 students

Favorite Colors	
Color	Number of Students
Blue	■ ■ ■ ■
Green	■ ■
Purple	■ ■ ■
Red	■ ■ ■ ■
Yellow	■
Key: ■ = 5 students	

Circle the best estimate of the liquid volume.

7.

Milk

1 liter   (4 liters)   16 liters

8.

2 liters   20 liters   (200 liters)

Circle the best estimate of the mass.

9.

15 kilograms   150 kilograms   (1500 kilograms)

10.

(1 gram)   10 grams   100 grams

250 Unit 4 ■ Focus on Measurement and Data

UNIT 4 Common Core Review

For exercises 11–16, use the table of Leaf Lengths.

MP6 11. Jill collected 12 leaves for a science project. She measured the length of each leaf to the nearest $\frac{1}{4}$ inch and recorded the lengths in the chart. Jill will use the chart to make a line plot of the measurement data. What scale should Jill use for the line plot? Explain. Jill should use a $\frac{1}{4}$-inch scale. The lengths between 3 inches and 5 inches show $\frac{1}{4}$-inch amounts.

Leaf Lengths (in.)

$3\frac{3}{4}$	$4\frac{1}{2}$	$3\frac{1}{4}$	$3\frac{3}{4}$
$3\frac{1}{4}$	$3\frac{3}{4}$	$4\frac{1}{2}$	5
$3\frac{3}{4}$	3	$3\frac{1}{4}$	$3\frac{3}{4}$

12. Record the scale on the number line below. Check students' work.

13. Draw an X for each leaf above its measurement on the number line.
Check students' line plots.

14. Write a title for the line plot. Leaf Lengths (in.)

Leaf Lengths (in.)

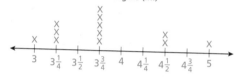

15. How many leaves have a length longer than 3 inches and shorter than 4 inches? __8__ leaves

16. Jacob measured the same 12 leaves to the nearest inch. What scale should Jacob use for his line plot?
Jacob should use a 1-inch scale.

For exercises 17 and 18, use the line plot above. Circle the correct answer.

17. Which leaf length occurs most often?
   a. 3 in.
   b. $3\frac{1}{4}$ in.
   (c.) $3\frac{3}{4}$ in.
   d. $4\frac{1}{2}$ in.

18. How many leaves are longer than 4 inches?
   a. 12
   b. 8
   c. 5
   (d.) 3

This chart correlates the Common Core Review items with the lessons in which the concepts and skills are presented.

Item	Lesson
1	24
2	24
3	24
4	26
5	26
6	26
7	25
8	25
9	25
10	25
11	27
12	27
13	27
14	27
15	27
16	27
17	27
18	27
19	24
20	26

Mathematical Practices

MP6	Attend to precision.

Item 11: Students use measurement units appropriately.

Writing About Math

✏️ Direct students to respond to the Unit 4 Essential Question. (This can also be found on student page 217.)

Essential Question:
How can data be used to solve problems?

Possible responses:
- Data can be displayed in different ways so it is easier to understand.
- Data can be used to make comparisons and draw conclusions.
- Data can be used to support reasoning and justify solutions.

Unit Assessment

- Unit 4 Common Core Review, *pp. 250–252*
- Unit 4 Performance Task (ONLINE)

Additional Assessment Options

Optional Purchase:

- iProgress Monitor (ONLINE)
- Progress Monitor Student Benchmark Assessment Booklet

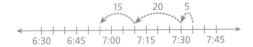
Solve the problems.

MP5 **19.** Ian needs to leave for school at 7:35 each morning It takes him 5 minutes to get dressed, 20 minutes to eat, and 15 minutes to walk his dog. What time should Ian wake up?

Answer Ian should wake up at 6:55 in the morning.

✏️ **Justify your answer using words, drawings or numbers.**
Students' work may vary. Possible justification:

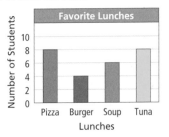

MP3 **20.** Kimora surveyed her classmates to find their favorite lunches. She made the bar graph to show her data.

Favorite Lunches	
Pizza	JHT III
Burger	IIII
Soup	JHT I
Tuna	JHT I

Favorite Lunches (bar graph)
Number of Students (y-axis: 0, 2, 4, 6, 8, 10)
Lunches (x-axis: Pizza, Burger, Soup, Tuna)

Compare the tally chart and the bar graph. What error did Kimora make on the bar graph? How can she correct it?

Answer Kimora's tally chart shows that 6 students chose tuna as their favorite lunch, but her bar graph shows that 8 students chose tuna. To correct her error, Kimora should change the bar for tuna to show 6 students.

Mathematical Practices

MP3	Construct viable arguments and critique the reasoning of others.

Item 20: Students construct arguments by using tables and graphs.

MP5	Use appropriate tools strategically.

Item 19: Students use available tools to solve a problem.

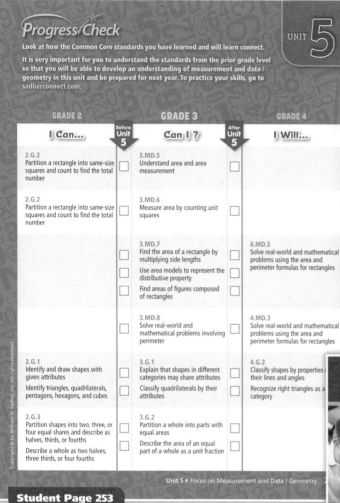

Progress Check

Look at how the Common Core standards you have learned and will learn connect.

It is very important for you to understand the standards from the prior grade level so that you will be able to develop an understanding of measurement and data / geometry in this unit and be prepared for next year. To practice your skills, go to sadlierconnect.com.

UNIT 5

GRADE 2 — I Can...	Before Unit 5	GRADE 3 — Can I ?	After Unit 5	GRADE 4 — I Will...
2.G.2 Partition a rectangle into same-size squares and count to find the total number	☐	**3.MD.5** Understand area and area measurement	☐	
2.G.2 Partition a rectangle into same-size squares and count to find the total number	☐	**3.MD.6** Measure area by counting unit squares	☐	
		3.MD.7 Find the area of a rectangle by multiplying side lengths	☐	**4.MD.3** Solve real-world and mathematical problems using the area and perimeter formulas for rectangles
		Use area models to represent the distributive property	☐	
		Find areas of figures composed of rectangles	☐	
		3.MD.8 Solve real-world and mathematical problems involving perimeter	☐	**4.MD.3** Solve real-world and mathematical problems using the area and perimeter formulas for rectangles
2.G.1 Identify and draw shapes with given attributes	☐	**3.G.1** Explain that shapes in different categories may share attributes	☐	**4.G.2** Classify shapes by properties of their lines and angles
Identify triangles, quadrilaterals, pentagons, hexagons, and cubes		Classify quadrilaterals by their attributes	☐	Recognize right triangles as a category
2.G.3 Partition shapes into two, three, or four equal shares and describe as halves, thirds, or fourths	☐	**3.G.2** Partition a whole into parts with equal areas	☐	
Describe a whole as two halves, three thirds, or four fourths	☐	Describe the area of an equal part of a whole as a unit fraction	☐	

Unit 5 ■ Focus on Measurement and Data / Geometry

Student Page 253

Progress Check

Progress Check is a self-assessment tool that students can use to gauge their own progress. Research shows that when students take accountability for their learning, motivation increases.

Before students begin work in Unit 5, have them check any items they know they can do well. Explain that it is fine if they don't check any of the boxes; they will have the opportunity to learn and practice all the standards through the course of the unit.

Let them know that at the end of the unit they will review their checklists to check their progress. After students have completed the last lesson of the unit, before they begin Common Core Review, you will be prompted to have students revisit this page.

HOME ◆ CONNECT...

In this unit your child will:

- Find areas of rectangles using tiling, multiplication, and decomposition.
- Find perimeters of polygons.
- Compare perimeters and areas.
- Recognize and name quadrilaterals according to their attributes.
- Partition shapes into parts with equal areas.

NOTE: All of these learning goals for your child are based on the Grade 3 Common Core State Standards for Mathematics.

Shapes are all around us. Some shapes, or **polygons**, are named by the number of sides and the number of **vertices** they have. A **vertex** is where two sides of a **plane**, or flat, figure meet. Working with geometric figures, your child will learn practical skills used to measure these figures. Support your child by using the following Math vocabulary:

- A **quadrilateral** is a polygon with four sides and include squares and rectangles. **Rhombuses** are quadrilaterals with all four sides the same length.
- The **area** of a figure is the number of **square units** needed to cover the figure without gaps or overlaps.
- Some of the units used to find areas are **square inch, square foot, square centimeter,** and **square meter.**
- Your child will use various strategies to find areas include **tiling**, covering the figure with square units; multiplying measurements of the figure; and **decomposing**, or breaking the figure into smaller parts and adding the areas of the parts.
- The **perimeter** of a figure is the sum of the lengths of the figure's sides.

Activity: Bring a measuring tape or yardstick with you when you are out running errands. Ask your child to take measurements to find the perimeter and area of items in the world around them, for example, items in the grocery store; the table in a restaurant; a waiting room.

Ways to Help Your Child

A great way to experience math with your child is to play games! Many old-fashioned card games and board games use mathematics and will help your child practice the math skills learned all year. Digital games are also readily available and can be fun to play as a family, too.

ONLINE
For more Home Connect activities, continue online at sadlierconnect.com

254 Unit 5 ■ Focus on Measurement and Data/Geometry

Student Page 254

HOME ◆ CONNECT...

The Home Connect feature is a way to keep parents or other adult family members apprised of what their children are learning. The key learning objectives are listed, and some ideas for related activities and discussions are included.

Explain to students that they can share the Home Connect page at home with their families. Let students know there is an activity connected to their classroom learning that they can do with their families.

Encourage students and their parents to share their experiences using the suggestions on the Home Connect. You may wish to invite students to share this work with the class.

UNIT PLANNER

Lesson		Standard(s)	Objective
28	Understand Concepts of Area Measurement	3.MD.5a 3.MD.5b 3.MD.6	Measure the area of plane figures.
29	Find Areas of Rectangles: Tile and Multiply	3.MD.7a 3.MD.7b	Use tiling and multiplication to find the area of a rectangle.
30	Find Areas of Rectangles: Use the Distributive Property	3.MD.7c	Use the Distributive Property to find the area of a rectangle.
31	Find Areas: Decompose Figures into Rectangles	3.MD.7d	Decompose a figure into non-overlapping rectangles in order to find the area.
32	Problem Solving: Measurement	3.MD.2 3.MD.7 3.OA.3	Use drawings to solve problems with measurements.
33	Problem Solving: Perimeter	3.MD.8	Solve problems about the perimeters of polygons.
34	Problem Solving: Compare Perimeter and Area	3.MD.8	Solve problems by comparing the areas and perimeters of different rectangles..
35	Understand Shapes and Attributes	3.G.1	Use attributes to identify shapes.
36	Partition Shapes to Make Equal Areas	3.G.2	Understand how to partition shapes into parts with equal areas.

Essential Question	Words to Know
How can you measure the area of plane figures?	plane figure, unit square, area, square inch, square foot, square centimeter, square meter
How can you use tiling and multiplication to find the area of a rectangle?	tiling
How can you use area models to show the Distributive Property?	
How can you find the area of a figure by decomposing it into rectangles?	decompose
How can you make drawings to solve problems with measurements?	
How can you solve problems about the perimeters of polygons?	closed figure, polygon, perimeter, quadrilateral
How can you compare different rectangles with the same perimeter or the same area?	
How do you use attributes to identify shapes?	vertex (vertices), angle, right angle, rhombus
How do you partition shapes to make equal areas?	

Unit Assessment

- Unit 5 Common Core Review, *pp. 328–330*
- Unit 5 Performance Task `ONLINE`

Additional Assessment Options

- Performance Task 2, *pp. 331–336*
  `ALSO ONLINE`

Optional Purchase:
- iProgress Monitor `ONLINE`
- Progress Monitor Student Benchmark Assessment Booklet

`ONLINE` Digital Resources

- Home Connect Activities
- Unit Performance Tasks
- Additional Practice
- Fluency Practice
- Teacher Resources
- iProgress Monitor (optional purchase)

Go to SadlierConnect.com to access your Digital Resources.

For more detailed instructions see page T3.

LEARNING PROGRESSIONS

This page provides more in-depth detail on the development of the standards across the grade levels. See also the unit Progress Check page in the Student Edition for a roadmap of the Learning Progressions.

Grade 2

- Students identify and draw shapes with specified attributes, such as a given number of angles or sides. (2.G.1)
- Students identify triangles, quadrilaterals, pentagons, hexagons, and cubes. (2.G.1)
- Students partition rectangles into rows and columns of same-size squares and count to find the total number of squares. (2.G.2)
- Students partition shapes into two, three, or four equal shares and describe them as halves, thirds, and fourths. (2.G.3)

Grade 3

- Students understand area as an attribute of two-dimensional figures and understand the concept of a unit square. (3.MD.5)
- Students measure area by counting unit squares. (3.MD.6)
- Students show that the area found by tiling a rectangle with unit squares is the same as would be found by multiplying the side lengths. They go on to multiply whole-number side lengths to find areas of rectangles in mathematical and real-world contexts, and represent whole-number products as rectangular areas. (3.MD.7b)
- Students use area models to represent the Distributive Property. (3.MD.7c)
- Students recognize area as additive and use this understanding to find the area of rectilinear figures by decomposing them into rectangles. (3.MD.7d)
- Students solve problems involving perimeter, including finding the perimeter, finding an unknown side length, and drawing rectangles with the same perimeter and different areas or the same area and different perimeters. (3.MD.8)
- Students understand that shapes in different categories may share attributes and that the shared attributes may define a larger category. Students recognize rhombuses, rectangles, and squares as types of quadrilaterals, and can draw examples of quadrilaterals that don't belong to any of these subcategories. (3.G.1)
- Students partition shapes into equally sized parts and express the area of each part as a unit fraction. (3.G.2)

Grade 4

- Students apply the area and perimeter formulas for rectangles to solve real-world and mathematical problems, including finding the missing length or width given the area and the width or length. (4.MD.3)
- Students classify shapes by properties of their lines and angles. They identify right triangles and recognize them as a category. (4.G.2)

Focus on Measurement and Data / Geometry

UNIT 5

Essential Question:
How can you find the area and perimeter of geometric shapes?

Unit 5 ■ Focus on Measurement and Data / Geometry   255

Essential Question:
How can you find the area and perimeter of geometric shapes?

As students become involved with the Essential Question they will use tiling, multiplication, and the Distributive Property to find the areas of rectangles and other shapes that are decomposed into rectangles. They will compare perimeter and area to develop a fundamental understanding of these measurement concepts.

Conversation Starters

Have students discuss the photograph. Ask questions such as: *What do you see in this photo? Where might these tables be? From where was the photo taken?*

Have students look at one of the tables. *What objects do you see? Can you group any of these objects as the same shape? What shape is that?* (I see placemats, tables, chairs, and plates. The placemats and tables are rectangles. The plates are circles.)

Lead students to look at the flooring. *How would you describe the flooring? What shape do you see?* (The flooring is made from gray and white tiles. The tiles are squares.) *What does it mean that these squares are tiled?* (The squares fill the floor without overlaps or leaving gaps.)

Let students work in pairs to discuss how they could measure the floor in this picture. Lead them to see that they can find the number of tiles needed to cover the floor by counting each tile.

Activity

Materials: grid paper, colored pencils

Ask students to work in pairs. Tell students that rooms may have different shapes and sizes, but the floor of any room can be tiled. Have each pair of students draw an outline on grid paper by tracing chosen lines on the grid. They can be as creative as they like as long as their edges coincide with gridlines. Then, they should color a tiling pattern to be the floor of their space.

Ask students to show their floors to the class. They should include the count for the number of tiles it would take to cover their floor. They should also describe how they determined their tiling pattern.

Common Core Focus:

3.MD.5a A square with side length 1 unit, called "a unit square," is said to have "one square unit" of area, and can be used to measure area; **3.MD.5b** A plane figure which can be covered without gaps or overlaps by *n* unit squares is said to have an area of *n* square units; **3.MD.6** Measure areas by counting unit squares (square cm, square m, square in, square ft, and improvised units).

OBJECTIVE
Measure the area of plane figures.

ESSENTIAL QUESTION
Have students discuss experiences they have had with measurement—what they measured and the tools and units they used. These conversations can help prepare students for measuring area.

FLUENCY PRACTICE
Fluency practice is available at **sadlierconnect.com**.

Concept Development

Understand: The meaning of area

■ It is important for students to recognize area as an attribute of plane figures. Developing an understanding of area will lay the foundation for finding area by multiplying the lengths of the sides of a rectangle.

■ Discuss that area can be measured by tiling a two-dimensional surface with a fixed two-dimensional unit, such as a square.

■ Have students pay attention to the unit square provided and understand that sometimes the squares are not shown as an exact representation. Discuss why a small unit square might be used to portray a meter or a foot. Point out that once the unit square is determined, the squares are simply counted to find the area.

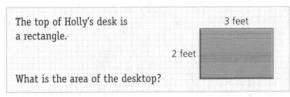

Lesson 28 — Understand Concepts of Area Measurement

Essential Question:
How can you measure the area of plane figures?
3.MD.5a, 3.MD.5b, 3.MD.6

Words to Know:
plane figure
unit square
area
square inch
square foot
square centimeter
square meter

Guided Instruction

In this lesson you will learn about area.

Understand: The meaning of area

The top of Holly's desk is a rectangle.

What is the area of the desktop?

3 feet

2 feet

A plane figure is flat. A rectangle is a plane figure. A unit square is a square with sides that are 1 unit long.

Unit squares

1 inch   1 foot

1 inch   1 foot
1-inch square   1-foot square

> A unit square can be a square with side lengths that represent any unit of measure.

The area of a plane figure is the number of unit squares needed to cover the figure without gaps or overlaps.

The 1-inch square has an area of 1 square inch, which can be written as *square in*. The 1-foot square has an area of 1 square foot, which can be written as *square ft*.

Look at Holly's desktop. You can use unit squares that measure 1 square foot each to cover the desktop. Count the number of unit squares that cover the desktop.

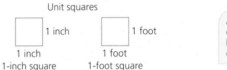

3 feet

2 feet

6 unit squares cover the desktop.

➡ The area of the desktop is 6 square feet.

Words to Know

plane figure: a two-dimensional figure

unit square: a square with side lengths of 1 unit

area: the number of unit squares needed to cover the figure without gaps or overlaps

square inch: the area of a square whose side lengths measure 1 inch; can be written as *square in*.

Glossary can be found on pp. 347–350.

Connect: Measuring the area of figures

Ted drew a figure on grid paper.

What is the area of the figure?

Step 1

Determine the unit square.

Each square in the grid has sides that are 1 centimeter long.

1 centimeter
1 centimeter

Each centimeter square in the grid has an area of 1 square centimeter, which can be written as *square cm*.

Step 2

Count the centimeter squares that cover Ted's figure.

_5_ centimeter squares cover the figure.

➡ The area of the figure is 5 square centimeters.

▬ Draw two different figures, each with an area of 5 square centimeters.
Possible answers:

Unit 5 ■ Focus on Measurement and Data/Geometry   **257**

Connect: Measuring the area of figures

Use this page to help students strengthen their understanding of unit squares and measuring area.

■ Ensure that students understand the importance of writing the unit in their answers. If no specific unit is given in the problem, then students should still label their answer with *unit* or *units*. Provide a real-world example to clarify this point. For example, have students imagine ordering food at a deli counter by asking for 6. The deli attendant will not know what kind of food or how much food is being ordered unless there is a specific unit with the number.

■ Students should use grid paper to work through the area problem on this page. Students can label the squares as they count them to keep track of which ones have been counted. Using this strategy will ensure that every unit square is counted only once.

■ Point out the importance of unit squares not overlapping or having gaps. To effectively measure all the space the surface covers, every part must be measured.

✏ This problem encourages students to focus on the space covering the surface of a figure, no matter what the shape is. To reinforce this idea, have students compare drawings and determine how many different figures with an area of 5 square units can be made. Make a class list of all the possibilities.

Words to Know

square foot: the area of a square whose side lengths measure 1 foot; can be written as *square ft*

square centimeter: the area of a square whose side lengths measure 1 centimeter; can be written as *square cm*

square meter: the area of a square whose side lengths measure 1 meter; can be written as *square m*

Glossary can be found on pp. 347–350.

Guided Practice

Observational Assessment

Use pages 258–259 to assess whether students understand how to find area using unit squares. Comparing different figures and using different units builds a deep understanding of this concept.

■ Students will need centimeter and inch rulers for exercises 1 and 2. Students will also need a sheet of square centimeters and a sheet of square inches to cut out and use to measure area. Remind students that there can be no gaps or overlaps when they cover each figure to measure the area.

■ Use exercises 1 and 2 to portray the reasoning behind why we use unit squares to measure area. Each unit square is actually 1 centimeter or 1 inch in two directions, vertically and horizontally. Unit squares are two-dimensional rulers, and can be placed side by side and counted to measure area, much like a ruler functions when measuring in one dimension.

■ Explain to students that the diagrams in exercises 4–6 are not actual size. Tell students to look at the key in each exercise to determine the unit that each square represents.

Guided Practice

Find the area of each figure. Use a ruler.

1.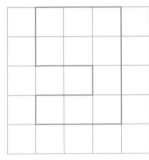

   __1__ square centimeter

2.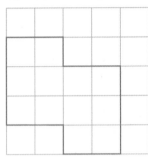

   __1__ square inch

Find the area of each figure. Use the key.

3. Key: 1 square = 1 square cm

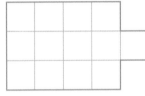

   __10__ square cm

4. Key: 1 square = 1 square inch

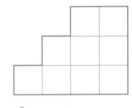

   __12__ square in.

5. Key: 1 square = 1 square meter

   __13__ square meters

6. Key: 1 square = 1 square foot

   __9__ square feet

Support English Language Learners

Write the word *plane* on the board. Say the word and have students repeat after you. Have students give you examples of planes. Most likely, they will describe airplanes. Tell students that in math, the use of the word *plane* is different. Tell them a *plane figure* is a flat shape. Point to flat surfaces in the classroom and have students identify them as plane figures. Have students look through the pages of this lesson and observe the various plane figures on the pages. Provide students with rulers and paper. Have them draw plane figures on a sheet of paper, using the figures in the lesson as a model.

Lesson 28

Guided Practice

Cut out centimeter squares. Use them to find the area of each figure.

7.

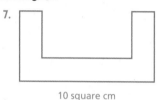

_____ 10 square cm

8.

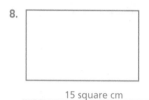

_____ 15 square cm

Cut out inch squares. Use them to find the area of each figure.

9.

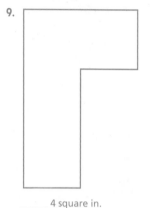

_____ 4 square in.

10.

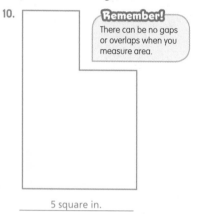

Remember!
There can be no gaps or overlaps when you measure area.

_____ 5 square in.

☻♔☻ Think•Pair•Share

MP3 **11.** Uma says the area of the square is 1 square unit.
Peter says the area of the square is 4 square units.
Can both students be right? Explain your reasoning.
Possible answer: Yes. Uma could be measuring the area
with a unit square that is the same size as the square.
Peter could be using a smaller unit square.

Unit 5 ■ Focus on Measurement and Data/Geometry **259**

☻♔☻ Think•Pair•Share

Peer Collaboration Ask pairs to share their strategies with each other, then the class. Ask questions such as:

- *What needs to be true about the unit for both Uma and Peter to be correct?*

- *If you think that both Uma and Peter could be right, how can you change the square to justify your answer?*

- *Can both students be right if they are both measuring with centimeters? Inches?*

To summarize, if the square was split equally into four smaller unit squares, both students could be correct. In order for both students to be correct, they need to be measuring in different unit squares.

Return to the Essential Question

Reread the Lesson 28 Essential Question on page 256: *How can you measure the area of plane figures?*

Ask volunteers to use what they learned in this lesson to answer this question. (Possible response: Unit squares can be used to measure area, as long as they completely cover the surface of a figure without overlapping and without gaps.)

Mathematical Practices

Mathematical Practice Standards underline the teaching and understanding of all concepts and skills presented. The emphasis of specific practices is noted throughout the guided and independent practice of this lesson.

MP3	**Construct viable arguments and critique the reasoning of others.**

Item 11: Students analyze the problem and explain their reasoning.

Independent Practice

Concept Application

Students may work independently on these pages in the classroom or at home. They may refer to the first four pages of this lesson to revisit the instruction or to see a worked-out example.

Common Errors and **Teaching Tips** may help you support student learning either in the classroom or as a follow-up for work done at home.

Common Errors

Items 4–7

Some students may try to measure these unit squares with a ruler. Remind students to look at the key when determining the unit. Explain that the grid and squares represent the units indicated, but are not actual size.

Teaching Tips

Item 1–7

Ask students which figures are calculating the true area (exercises 1–3) and which are scaled down models (exercises 4–7). Thinking critically about these models and their purpose allows for real-world applications and deep understanding.

Independent Practice

Find the area of each figure. Determine the unit square. Use a ruler.

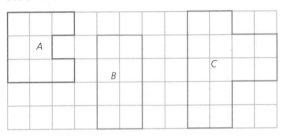

1. Figure *A*

   8 square cm

2. Figure *B*

   8 square cm

3. Figure *C*

   14 square cm

Find the area of each figure. Use the key.

4. Key: 1 square = 1 square foot

   7 square feet

5. Key: 1 square = 1 square inch

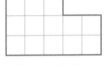

   13 square inches

6. Key: 1 square = 1 square meter

   6 square meters

7. Key: 1 square = 1 square centimeter

   16 square centimeters

Writing About Math

▪ **Write an Explanatory Text** Have students imagine that they are helping to retile their kitchen floor. They need to calculate how many tiles they need to buy to cover the surface of the floor, but they only have one test tile to help them measure the area of the floor. Have students write an explanation of their process in order to tell the salesperson how many tiles they will need.

This is a description of how to find area using a square unit, and not necessarily a problem to solve. Students should explore how to find the unit of measurement, how to correctly use a unit square to measure, and any issues they might encounter.

Lesson 28

Independent Practice

Cut out centimeter squares. Use them to find the area of each figure.

8.
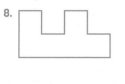

_____ 6 square cm _____

9.
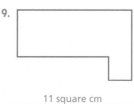

_____ 11 square cm _____

Cut out inch squares. Use them to find the area of each figure.

10.
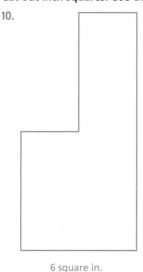

_____ 6 square in. _____

11.
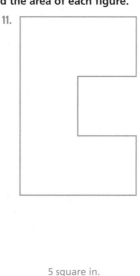

_____ 5 square in. _____

Teaching Tips

Items 8–11

Students will need a sheet of square centimeters and a sheet of square inches to cut out and use to measure area. Help students cut out the squares. Remind them that there can be no gaps or overlaps when they cover the figures to measure the areas. Also, remind students to always write the units in their answer.

Unit 5 ■ Focus on Measurement and Data/Geometry **261**

Math-to-Real-World Connection

Design and Area Measuring area is an important part of real-world crafting and design. To practice finding the area of any plane figure, have students use graph paper to create their own tee-shirt design.

Students can create any design they like using whole unit squares and up to three colors. Before students begin, explain that after they are done, they will have to determine how much paint they will need for each color on their design by determining the area covered by each color. Once students have finished their design and area calculations, allow them to share their designs with a partner or the class. Check student calculations for evidence of understanding.

Independent Practice

Common Errors

Item 12

Students may draw unit squares that have not been measured or that do not have straight edges. Remind students that area is a measurement and therefore the tools used need to reflect precision.

Teaching Tips

Item 13

Encourage students to find an effective unit for this situation. Discuss why the unit is appropriate and how it can help Roberta solve her problem quickly.

Independent Practice

MP7   **12.** Draw two types of unit squares. How are they alike? How are they different?

Possible answer: 1-centimeter square, 1-inch square. They are both squares and they both have sides that measure 1 unit, but the units are different, so their sides are different lengths.

MP6   **13.** Roberta wants to find the area of her bedroom window. She asks you for help. What would you tell her?

Possible answer: I would tell her to draw a 1-foot square on a large piece of paper and cut it out. Then she could see how many of the squares would cover the window. That would be the area in square feet.

MP4   **14.** Mike is building a tree house. The floor will have an area of 18 square feet. Draw an outline of a floor Mike could use.

Students' figures should contain 18 squares. Possible figure shown.

Key: 1 square = 1 square foot

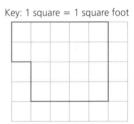

MP5   **15.** Gina is making a poster for a school fair. She wants to draw a figure with an area of 13 square inches. Draw a figure that Gina could use.

Students' figures should contain 13 squares. Possible figure shown.

Key: 1 square = 1 square inch

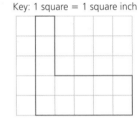

Mathematical Practices

MP4	**Model with mathematics.**
Item 14:	Students use concrete tools to show area.
MP5	**Use appropriate tools strategically.**
Item 15:	Students use square units to design a figure with a specific area.
MP6	**Attend to precision.**
Item 13:	Students communicate their reasoning for finding area.
MP7	**Look for and make use of structure.**
Item 12:	Students compare and contrast two different unit squares.

Lesson 28

Independent Practice

MP4 **16.** Mr. Davis is planning his summer garden. He decides to make a pumpkin patch with an area of 14 square meters. Draw an outline of a pumpkin patch Mr. Davis could make.

Key: 1 square = 1 square meter

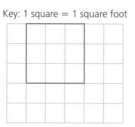

Students' figures should contain 14 squares. Possible figure shown.

MP4 **17.** Amanda uses chalk to draw a picture on a sidewalk. She draws a square with sides that are each 3 feet long. What is the area of the square?

Key: 1 square = 1 square foot

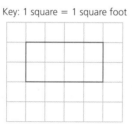

Answer The area of the square is 9 square feet.

▭ **Justify your answer using words, drawings, or numbers.**

Possible justification: I drew a square with sides that are each 3 feet long. Then I counted the small squares to find the area in square feet.

MP6 **18.** Richard measures the top of his desk. The desktop is a rectangle with side lengths 4 feet and 2 feet. "My desktop has an area of 6 square feet," he says. Is Richard right?

Key: 1 square = 1 square foot

Answer No, Richard is not right.

▭ **Justify your answer using words, drawings, or numbers.**

Possible justification: I drew a rectangle with side lengths 4 feet and 2 feet. Then I counted the unit squares. It has an area of 8 square feet.

Unit 5 ▪ Focus on Measurement and Data/Geometry **263**

Common Errors

Item 17

Students may draw a figure with an area of 3, instead of drawing a square with each side 3 units in length. Suggest that students reread the problem to correctly identify the shape of the figure and the length of each side.

Item 18

Students may add the side lengths instead of finding the area. Have them draw the shape of the desk, then use unit squares to find the area.

Teaching Tips

Item 16

Students can compare their drawings to see how they are alike and how they are different. Even though they look different, they should all have the same area.

Mathematical Practices

MP4	Model with mathematics.

Item 16: Students interpret area within the context of a real-world situation.

Item 17: Students use grid paper to draw unit squares to explain how to find area of a square.

MP6	Attend to precision.

Item 18: Students use measurement units appropriately and communicate clear explanations.

Common Core Focus:

3.MD.7a Find the area of a rectangle with whole-number side lengths by tiling it, and show that the area is the same as would be found by multiplying the side lengths;

3.MD.7b Multiply side lengths to find areas of rectangles with whole-number side lengths in the context of solving real world and mathematical problems, and represent whole-number products as rectangular areas in mathematical reasoning.

OBJECTIVE

Use tiling and multiplication to find the area of a rectangle.

ESSENTIAL QUESTION

In this lesson, students will extend their understanding of area to finding the area by tiling and by multiplying the side lengths. Students should be able to represent the products as rectangular areas by the end of the lesson.

FLUENCY PRACTICE

Fluency practice is available at **sadlierconnect.com**.

Concept Development

Understand: Finding the area of a rectangle

■ Have students compare and contrast tiling and multiplying to find the area of a rectangle.

■ Students should recognize that the factors in the multiplication equation are the labeled side lengths in the workbench diagram.

Lesson 29 — Find Areas of Rectangles: Tile and Multiply

Essential Question:
How can you use tiling and multiplication to find the area of a rectangle?
3.MD.7a, 3.MD.7b

Words to Know:
tiling

Guided Instruction

In this lesson you will learn about the areas of rectangles.

Understand: Finding the area of a rectangle

Jamal measures the sides of the top of his workbench.

What is the area of the top of the workbench?

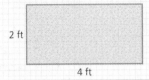

2 ft

4 ft

Method 1 Tiling

Tile the top of the workbench. To tile, cover the area with unit squares that represent 1-foot squares.
Count the unit squares that cover the top of the workbench.

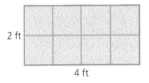

2 ft

4 ft

Eight unit squares cover the top of the workbench.
The sides are measured in feet, so the area will be in square feet.

➡ The area of the top of the workbench is 8 square feet.

Method 2 Multiplying

Each unit square has an area of 1 square foot. There are 2 rows of unit squares. Each row has an area of 4 square feet.

Multiply the side lengths of the top of the workbench.
$2 \times 4 = 8$

➡ The area of the top of the workbench is 8 square feet.

Tiling and multiplying give the same answer.
You can use either method to find the area of a rectangle.

Words to Know

tile (tiling): a method of determining area by joining unit squares along their edges to cover a figure

Glossary can be found on pp. 347–350.

Lesson 29

Guided Instruction

Connect: Solving problems about the area of rectangles.

Ms. Walker has a picture of her dog.

What is the area of the picture?

3 in.

5 in.

Method 1 Tiling

Tile with unit squares to find the area.
Count the unit squares that will cover the picture.

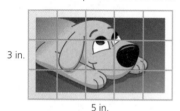

3 in.

5 in.

15 unit squares cover the picture.
The sides are measured in inches, so the area will be in square inches.
Each square represents an area of 1 square inch.

➡ The area of the picture is 15 square inches.

Method 2 Multiplying

Multiply the side lengths of the picture to find the area.

3 × 5 = __15__

➡ The area of the picture is 15 square inches.

Multiplying and tiling give the same answer.

✏ Write another multiplication sentence you could use to find the

area of the picture. __5 × 3 = 15__

Connect: **Solving problems about the area of rectangles.** Use this page to help students strengthen their understanding of how tiling and multiplying side lengths are related.

■ The first method, tiling, can be used as a stepping-stone to the second method—finding the area of a rectangle by multiplying side lengths.

■ Help students make the connection that once they have tiled a rectangle with unit squares, they can now find the side lengths. This means they can multiply the side lengths instead of counting each unit square.

✏ Have a volunteer share the multiplication sentence he or she wrote. Guide students to make a connection between multiplying side lengths to find area and the Commutative Property of Multiplication.

Support English Language Learners

Students need to be able to identify the side lengths of a rectangle using unit squares and to express the area in square units. For English language learners, the terms *unit squares* and *square units* may be confusing.

To help clarify, have students pick up a unit square tile (1 in. × 1 in.) and have them say the term *unit square*. Tell students that they can pick up and hold unit squares because they are objects. Give students 4 in. x 6 in. blank index cards. Have them cover the index card with the unit square tiles. Students should count the unit squares on the card (24). Write *24 square units* on the board. Have students say *square units*. Tell students that they cannot hold 24 square units; it is a measurement. But, they can hold 24 unit squares, because unit squares are objects. Encourage them to hold all 24 unit squares.

Guided Practice

Observational Assessment

Use pages 266–267 to assess whether students are able to use tiling and multiplication of side lengths to find the area of a rectangle. Watch for students who mistakenly multiply parallel sides instead of the length and width. This mistake may lead to a different area than tiling. Remind students to multiply only the side lengths labeled.

Guided Practice

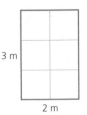

1. Use tiling to find the area of the rectangle.

   __6__ meter squares cover the rectangle.

   Area: __6__ square meters

   3 m

   2 m

2. Use multiplication to find the area of the rectangle.

   __3__ × __2__ = __6__

   Area: __6__ square meters

**Use tiling to find the area of each rectangle.
Then use multiplication to check your answer.**

3.
   1 cm

   4 cm

   __4__ centimeter squares cover the rectangle.

   __1__ × __4__ = __4__

   Area: __4__ square centimeters

4.
   3 ft

   3 ft

   __9__ foot squares cover the rectangle.

   __3__ × __3__ = __9__

   Area: __9__ square feet

5.
   2 in.

   5 in.

   __10__ inch squares cover the rectangle.

   __2__ × __5__ = __10__

   Area: __10__ square inches

6.
   4 m

   6 m

   __24__ meter squares cover the rectangle.

   __4__ × __6__ = __24__

   Area: __24__ square meters

Math-to-Real-World Connection

Area in the Workplace Finding the area of a rectangle is a common skill students will use in their daily lives as they grow up, especially if they want to build or decorate. As a class, discuss different situations for which one would need to find the area of a rectangle. If students need help brainstorming, have them consider the problems on pages 264 and 265. Ask students why someone would need to know the area of the top of a workbench or the area of a picture. Have students identify professions that would need to find the area of a rectangle.

Multiply to solve each problem.

7. Tina measures one of her animal stickers. What is the area of the sticker?

   The area of the sticker is 35 square cm.

5 cm

7 cm

8. Mr. Smith's class makes a square wall mural of a fish pond. What is the area of the mural?

   The area of the mural is 16 square m.

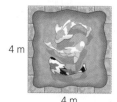

4 m

4 m

9. Waldron hits a baseball. The ball breaks his bedroom window. What is the area of the original window?

   The area of the original window is 12 square ft.

2 ft

6 ft

10. The Berners are getting a new kitchen floor. The floor is a rectangle. One side length is 6 feet. The other side length is 10 feet. What is the area of the floor?

    The area of the floor is 60 square ft.

11. Charles has a music box. The top of the box is a rectangle. One side measures 7 inches. The other side measures 8 inches. What is the area of the music box top?

    The area of the music box top is 56 square in.

👥 Think·Pair·Share

MP3 12. Maria draws two rectangles with different side lengths. She says that both rectangles have the same area: 20 square centimeters. Can she be right? Explain your reasoning.

Yes. Possible explanation: Each rectangle must have side lengths that have a product of 20. One rectangle could have side lengths of 5 cm and 4 cm. The other could have side lengths of 10 cm and 2 cm.

Unit 5 ■ Focus on Measurement and Data/Geometry **267**

👥 Think·Pair·Share

Peer Collaboration Have pairs of students draw or create models of rectangles that have an area of 20 square units. Discuss as a class all of the different possible rectangles and their dimensions. Encourage students' thinking by asking:

- *Which multiplications have a product of 20?*

- *What property of multiplication could help you find the side lengths of two rectangles?*

- *How could you find the side lengths if you weren't able to draw or create a model?*

Return to the Essential Question

Reread the Lesson 29 Essential Question on page 264: *How can you use tiling and multiplication to find the area of a rectangle?*

Ask volunteers to use what they learned in this lesson to answer this question. (Possible response: I can use tiling to cover a rectangle and count the number of unit squares to find the area. Then, I can count the number of unit squares that make up the side lengths and multiply the side lengths to find the area and check my answer.)

Mathematical Practices

Mathematical Practice Standards underline the teaching and understanding of all concepts and skills presented. The emphasis of specific practices is noted throughout the guided and independent practice of this lesson.

MP3	**Construct viable arguments and critique the reasoning of others.**

Item 12: Students construct an argument about the area of rectangles to explain whether another's reasoning is correct.

Independent Practice

Concept Application

Students may work independently on these pages in the classroom or at home. They may refer to the first four pages of the lesson to revisit the instruction or to see a worked-out example.

Common Errors and **Teaching Tips** may help you support student learning either in the classroom or as a follow-up for work done at home.

Common Errors

Items 1–5

Some students may try to skip the tiling method and go straight to multiplication. Make sure students are using both methods to ensure their counting and multiplications are correct. If needed, have students make a mark on each tile as they count it. Explain that using both methods help them verify that they haven't made a mistake if their answers match.

Teaching Tips

Items 1–5

Remind students that the unit squares represent the units indicated on the figure and that they are only actual size for item 4.

Independent Practice

Use tiling to find the area of each rectangle. Then use multiplication to check your answer.

1.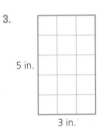

3 m, 4 m

_12_ meter squares cover the rectangle.

_3_ × _4_ = _12_

Area: _12_ square meters

2.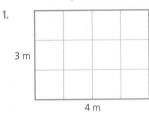

1 ft, 5 ft

_5_ foot squares cover the rectangle.

_1_ × _5_ = _5_

Area: _5_ square feet

3.

5 in., 3 in.

_15_ inch squares cover the rectangle.

_5_ × _3_ = _15_

Area: _15_ square inches

4.

4 cm, 2 cm

_8_ centimeter squares cover the rectangle.

_4_ × _2_ = _8_

Area: _8_ square centimeters

5.

3 ft, 7 ft

_21_ foot squares cover the rectangle.

_3_ × _7_ = _21_

Area: _21_ square feet

Talking About Math

Discuss Have students talk about their opinion on whether tiling, multiplying, or a combination of both strategies is most helpful to them when finding the area of a rectangle. Students should list reasons supporting their points of view. Encourage them to use linking words to connect their opinions and reasons. Remind students that these are opinions, so there are no right or wrong answers.

MORE ONLINE sadlierconnect.com

Lesson 29

Independent Practice

Multiply to solve each problem.

6. Sarah buys a rug for her cat.
What is the area of the rug?

The area of the rug is 36 square ft.

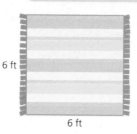

6 ft

6 ft

7. Gilberto measures a cookie sheet.
What is the area of the cookie sheet?

The area of the cookie sheet is 80 square in.

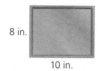

8 in.

10 in.

Circle the letter with the correct answer for exercises 8–11.

8. Andrea makes a birthday card
for her dad. The card is a rectangle.
One side length is 8 inches. The
other side length is 6 inches. What
is the area of the card?

a. 14 square in.   b. 24 square in.

c. 28 square in.   d. 48 square in.

9. Stanley is making a table. The
table's top is a rectangle. One
side measures 3 feet. The other
side measures 8 feet. What is
the area of the top of the table?

a. 11 square ft   b. 22 square ft

c. 24 square ft   d. 36 square ft

10. Ellen measures her family's
driveway. The driveway is a
rectangle. One side is 10 meters
long. The other side is 5 meters
long. What is the area of the
driveway?

a. 30 square m   b. 50 square m

c. 60 square m   d. 65 square m

11. José puts together a dinosaur
picture puzzle. The puzzle is a
rectangle. One side measures
9 centimeters. The other side
measures 8 centimeters. What
is the area of the puzzle?

a. 17 square cm   b. 34 square cm

c. 72 square cm   d. 81 square cm

Unit 5 ■ Focus on Measurement and Data/Geometry   **269**

Teaching Tips

Item 6

Explain to students that the area
does not include the fringe on the
rug. Students should use the given
measurements to find the area.

Items 8–11

The amount of text could be
overwhelming to some students. Have
students underline or highlight the
important information in each problem,
such as the question, the side lengths,
and the shape of the object.

Digital Connection

Virtual Dig Site Use the Internet to locate photographs of
archaeological dig sites that have been mapped using a rope grid. Share
the photographs with students and explain how these roped grids are
like tiling. They help archaeologists record information about the site,
including length and width.

Have groups of students create their own virtual archaeological dig sites
using presentation software. Begin by creating a rectangle and place
pictures of objects in the rectangle. Then, have students use a drawing
tool to place unit squares on top of the rectangle, creating a grid to help
them describe and catalog their dig site.

Independent Practice

Teaching Tips

Item 12

Remind students that *better* is a word that indicates an opinion. They should provide their opinion, but there is no right or wrong answer. Encourage students to think about the similarities and differences between the two methods and to give specific reasons to support their choice.

Independent Practice

MP7 **12.** Paula uses tiling to find the area of a rectangle. Zoe multiplies to find the area of the same rectangle. Which method is better?
Possible answer: They both give the correct answer, so neither is better. But I think multiplying is quicker than tiling.

MP6 **13.** Steve wants to find the area of a poster board that is 3 feet long. He asks you for help. What would you tell him?
Possible answer: I would tell him to measure the other side length of the poster board. He should measure in feet. Then he can multiply the two side lengths. The product would be the area of the poster board in square feet.

Solve the problems.

MP4 **14.** Mr. Baker paints a picture. The picture is a rectangle. One side of the picture is 7 inches long. The other side is 4 inches long. What is the area of the picture?

▸ **Show your work.**
Possible answer:

7 in.

4 in.

Answer The area of the picture is 28 square inches.

MP1 **15.** Jen has a postcard that shows her town one hundred years ago. The card is a rectangle. One side measures 6 centimeters. The other side measures 9 centimeters. What is the area of the card?

▸ **Show your work.**
Possible answer: $6 \times 9 = 54$. 54 square centimeters.

Answer The area of the card is 54 square centimeters.

Mathematical Practices	
MP1	**Make sense of problems and persevere in solving them.**
Item 15:	Students analyze a word problem, plan a solution, and solve it.
MP4	**Model with mathematics.**
Item 14:	Students relate mathematics to an everyday problem.
MP6	**Attend to precision.**
Item 13:	Students formulate explanations for finding area.
MP7	**Look for and make use of structure.**
Item 12:	Students compare tiling and multiplying to find area.

MP2 **16.** The floor of a school hallway is a rectangle. One side length is 4 meters. The other side length is 20 meters. What is the area of the hallway floor?

▸ **Show your work.**
Possible answer: 4 × 20 = 80

Answer The area of the hallway floor is 80 square meters.

MP7 **17.** Eric's favorite rug is a rectangle. The area of the rug is 60 square feet. If one side of the rug measures 10 feet, what is the length of the other side?

Answer The other side's length is 6 feet.

▸ **Justify your answer using words, drawings, or numbers.**
Possible justification:
  side length × side length = area
  So, 10 × ? = 60
  10 × 6 = 60

MP1 **18.** Mark's closet floor is a rectangle. One side length is 3 feet. The other side length is 6 feet. His sister's closet is bigger. One side is the same length as a side of Mark's closet floor. The other side is 3 feet longer than a side of Mark's closet floor. What is the area of the floor in Mark's sister's closet?

Answer The area of the floor in Mark's sister's closet is 36 square feet or 27 square feet.

▸ **Justify your answer using words, drawings, or numbers.**
Possible justification: It depends on which side is longer.
  Mark's closet: 3 × 6
  Sister's closet: (3 + 3) × 6 = 36
    Or: 3 × (6 + 3) = 27

Common Errors

Item 17

Students may try to multiply 60 by 10 to find the unknown length. Remind students to read the question carefully and think about what it is asking them to find. Have students use drawings, in addition to words or numbers, to check and justify their answers.

Teaching Tips

Item 18

This problem has more than one correct answer. After students find one answer, have volunteers share their results. Discuss as a class why both 36 square feet and 27 square feet are correct answers.

Mathematical Practices	
MP1	**Make sense of problems and persevere in solving them.**
Item 18: Students analyze a word problem, then solve and check solutions.	
MP2	**Reason abstractly and quantitatively.**
Item 16: Students pay attention to the mathematical language of a word problem to solve it using correct units.	
MP7	**Look for and make use of structure.**
Item 17: Students use the structure of information to solve for an unknown side length.	

Common Core Focus:

3.MD.7c Use tiling to show in a concrete case that the area of a rectangle with whole-number side lengths a and $b + c$ is the sum of $a \times b$ and $a \times c$. Use area models to represent the distributive property in mathematical reasoning.

OBJECTIVE

Use the Distributive Property to find the area of a rectangle.

ESSENTIAL QUESTION

Students have previously learned about the Distributive Property. In this lesson, they will learn how to apply this understanding to find the area of rectangles.

FLUENCY PRACTICE

Fluency practice is available at **sadlierconnect.com**.

Concept Development

Understand: Using tiling to show the Distributive Property

■ Students expand their understanding of area of rectangles to include the Distributive Property. This lesson provides students with a variety of strategies and tools for finding area of rectangles.

■ Point out that the next to last expressions in Method 1 and Method 2 are equated to show the Distributive Property: $4 \times (6 + 2) = (4 \times 6) + (4 \times 2)$.

■ Students might highlight each expression in the two methods using different colors, then, use the same colors to highlight the expressions within the final equation at the bottom of the page.

■ If students are ready for a challenge, have them solve the examples in this lesson without tiling. If students are struggling, have them continue to tile.

Lesson
30 Find Areas of Rectangles: Use the Distributive Property

Essential Question: How can you use area models to show the Distributive Property? 3.MD.7c

Guided Instruction

In this lesson you will learn to use area models to show the Distributive Property.

Understand: Using tiling to show the Distributive Property

Sue invites guests for dinner. She opens the extension of her dining table.

What is the area of the full table?

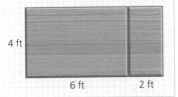

4 ft

6 ft   2 ft

Method 1

Tile the table with unit squares. Find one side length of the full table. Find the other side length of the full table. Multiply to find the area.

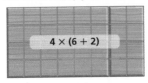

$4 \times (6 + 2)$

One side length of the table is 4. The other side length of the table is $6 + 2$.

$$4 \times (6 + 2)$$
$$= 4 \times \quad 8 = 32$$

➤ The area of the full table is 32 square feet.

Method 2

Tile the table with unit squares. Find the area of the original table. Find the area of the extension. Add the two areas.

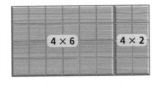

4×6 4×2

The area of the original table is 4×6.
The area of the extension is 4×2.

$$(4 \times 6) + (4 \times 2)$$
$$= \quad 24 \quad + \quad 8 = 32$$

➤ The area of the full table is 32 square feet.

The two methods show the Distributive Property.
$4 \times (6 + 2) = (4 \times 6) + (4 \times 2)$

Support English Language Learners

Two terms used often in this lesson are *tile* and *tiling*. Write the word *tile* on the board. Tell students that *tile* can be a noun or a verb.

Show students a stack of floor or wall tiles. Tell students these are tiles and in this case, tile is a noun—an object. Then, tell students you will *tile* with the *tiles*. In this case, *tile* is used first as a verb and then as a noun. Place the tiles in a rectangular arrangement on the floor. As you do so, tell students you are *tiling* with the *tiles*. Give students some small tiles. Have students say, "I have some tiles." Then, have them arrange tiles in a rectangular shape on their desktop, as they say, "I am tiling with tiles."

Lesson 30

Guided Instruction

Understand: Using area models to represent the Distributive Property

> Lenny wants to solve the multiplication problem 4×9. Mary says, "You can use the Distributive Property. Since $9 = 5 + 4$, multiply 4×5 and 4×4 and then add the products."
>
> Use an area model to show why Mary's method works.

Draw an area model.
One side length is 4.
The other side length is 9.

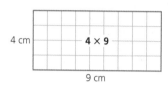

4 cm   **4 × 9**

9 cm

You can use any unit of length for your area model.

Since $9 = 5 + 4$, you can break the rectangle into these two rectangles.

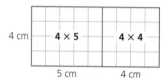

4 cm   **4 × 5**   **4 × 4**

5 cm   4 cm

Find the area of the first rectangle.
Find the area of the second rectangle.
Add the two areas.

$$
\begin{aligned}
4 \times 9 &= 4 \times (5 + 4) \\
&= (4 \times 5) + (4 \times 4) \\
&= \quad 20 \quad + \quad 16 \\
&= 36
\end{aligned}
$$

So, $4 \times 9 = 36$

➤ The area models above show that the Distributive Property works, since $4 \times 9 = (4 \times 5) + (4 \times 4)$.

Understand: Using area models to represent the Distributive Property

■ This presentation builds students' understanding of how to use the Distributive Property and why it works. Help students follow the step-by-step process of breaking down the multiplication to simplify it.

■ The first step is to draw and label the whole rectangle. Then, draw a line to divide the rectangle into two parts depending on how one of the factors is split into two. Remind students to label the side lengths of the smaller rectangles.

■ Ask students why the rectangle is divided with a vertical line instead of a horizontal line. Then, ask if a horizontal line could be used to break the rectangle into two parts. Once students respond, ask what possible multiplication the area model might represent. Students should be able to identify that 4 would be broken apart instead of 9. One model might show $(2 \times 9) + (2 \times 9)$.

Math-to-Real-World Connection

Area and Home Remodeling Discuss with students how a contractor would use an area model before he or she did a flooring project. Ask students to pick a room in their home and pretend that they are hiring someone to put down a new floor. Students need to figure out how much flooring they would need to buy. Ask students to provide drawings of the room and explanations about how much material they would buy. Encourage students to present their findings to the class.

Guided Instruction

Connect: **Solving area problems using the Distributive Property** Use this page to help students strengthen their understanding of using the Distributive Property to find area.

■ Before students begin working through the presentation, ask them to read the problem and verbalize a plan to solve the problem.

■ Emphasize the connection between the model and the equation for the Distributive Property. A common error students make is not writing the Distributive Property correctly by confusing the placement of the multiplication and addition symbols. Thinking about an area model will help students remember how to structure the multiplication correctly.

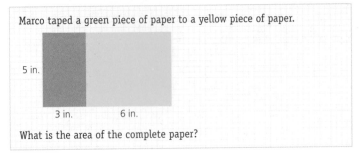

Lesson 30   Find Areas of Rectangles: Use the Distributive Property

Guided Instruction

Connect: **Solving area problems using the Distributive Property**

Marco taped a green piece of paper to a yellow piece of paper.

5 in.

3 in.   6 in.

What is the area of the complete paper?

Use the Distributive Property to find the area.

Step 1

Tile the figure with unit squares.
Find the area of the green paper.
Find the area of the yellow paper.

The area of the green paper is 5 × 3.
The area of the yellow paper is 5 × 6.

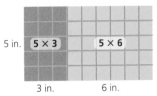

5 in.   5 × 3   5 × 6

3 in.   6 in.

Step 2

Add the two areas.

$$5 \times (3 + 6) = (5 \times 3) + (5 \times 6)$$
$$= \ \ 15 \ \ + \ \ 30$$
$$= \ \underline{45}$$

➤ The area of the complete paper is 45 square inches.

274 Unit 5 ■ Focus on Measurement and Data/Geometry

Math-to-Real-World Connection

Fish Farming and Area Fish farm managers not only need to be knowledgeable about the organisms they raise, they must also know how to make area calculations. Fish farmers calculate the area of the tank or pond where they stock fish and plants. The farmer must know how many organisms can safely live in the area. One way fish farmers find the area is to use stakes placed in straight lines and measure between the stakes with a measuring tape. Once measurements are made, they can use an area formula based on the shape of the tank or pond they are measuring. Staking and measuring are often done several times to ensure accuracy. A more reliable method of determining the area is using a surveyor's transit level to determine distance. Aerial photos are also used to generate an estimate of the area.

Lesson 30

Guided Practice

The rectangles are tiled with unit squares.
Use the Distributive Property to find the total area.

1.

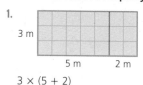

3 m

5 m   2 m

$3 \times (5 + 2)$

$= (\underline{3} \times \underline{5}) + (\underline{3} \times \underline{2})$

$= \underline{15} + \underline{6}$

$= \underline{21}$

$\underline{21}$ square meters

2.

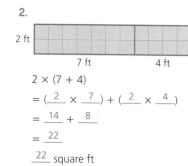

2 ft

7 ft   4 ft

$2 \times (7 + 4)$

$= (\underline{2} \times \underline{7}) + (\underline{2} \times \underline{4})$

$= \underline{14} + \underline{8}$

$= \underline{22}$

$\underline{22}$ square ft

Draw an area model to represent each problem.
Use your area model to solve the problem.

3. $5 \times (2 + 6)$

Accept any correct area model. Possible answers shown.

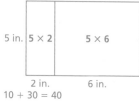

5 in. | 5×2 | 5×6

2 in.   6 in.

$10 + 30 = 40$

$5 \times (2 + 6) = \underline{40}$

4. $6 \times (4 + 3)$

6 cm | 6×4 | 6×3

4 cm   3 cm

$24 + 18 = 42$

$6 \times (4 + 3) = \underline{42}$

☆ Think•Pair•Share

MP7 **5.** Bob and Rick are trying to find the
area of the rectangle.
Bob writes $3 \times (6 + 3)$.
Rick writes $3 \times (4 + 5)$.
Explain why both students are right.
Possible explanation: They are both using the Distributive Property. They just
wrote the second side length as the sum of different addends.

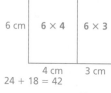

3 in.

9 in.

Unit 5 ■ Focus on Measurement and Data/Geometry **275**

Observational Assessment

Use page 275 to assess whether
students are able to use the Distributive
Property to find the area of a rectangle.
Be sure students are able to solve for
area and draw a model correctly.

In exercises 3 and 4, explain that the
area models can have any units of
length, since they are only models to
help solve the problem and a specific
unit is not suggested.

☆ Think•Pair•Share

Peer Collaboration Have students
work individually to come to a
conclusion as to why both Bob and Rick
are correct. Once students arrive at their
conclusions, divide the class into pairs
to discuss explanations. As students
provide a rationale for their thinking,
suggest that they discuss the following:

- *How did Bob break apart 9?*

- *How did Rick break apart 9?*

- *Why are Bob's answers and Rick's
  answers the same?*

- *Is there another way to solve the
  problem that would result in the
  same answer? Explain.*

Return to the Essential Question

Reread the Lesson 30 Essential
Question on page 272: *How can
you use area models to show the
Distributive Property?*

Ask volunteers to use what they learned
in this lesson to answer this question.
(Possible response: I can break apart one
of the factors and break apart the area
model into two rectangles. Then I can
find the area of both rectangles and add
the areas.)

Mathematical Practices

Mathematical Practice Standards underline the teaching and
understanding of all concepts and skills presented. The emphasis of
specific practices is noted throughout the guided and independent practice
of this lesson.

MP7 **Look for and make use of structure.**

Item 5: Students explain how two different methods for solving a
problem both result in the same answer.

Independent Practice

Concept Application

Students may work independently on these pages in the classroom or at home. They may refer to the first four pages of the lesson to revisit the instruction or to see a worked-out example.

Common Errors and **Teaching Tips** may help you support student learning either in the classroom or as a follow-up for work done at home.

Common Errors

Item 5

Students may choose a as it contains the correct numbers but uses addition in the parenthesis instead of multiplication, and multiplication instead of addition between the expressions.

Teaching Tips

Items 1–4

If needed, have students use grid paper and unit squares/tiles to replicate and tile the given rectangles. It can be helpful for students to be able to take the tiles off and count to find the area, or to separate tiles to illustrate the Distributive Property.

Independent Practice

The rectangles are tiled with unit squares.
Use the Distributive Property to find the total area.

1.
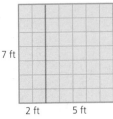
7 ft

2 ft   5 ft

$7 \times (2 + 5)$
$= (\underline{7} \times \underline{2}) + (\underline{7} \times \underline{5})$
$= \underline{14} + \underline{35} = \underline{49}$
$\underline{49}$ square feet

2.
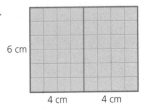
6 cm

4 cm   4 cm

$6 \times (4 + 4)$
$= (\underline{6} \times \underline{4}) + (\underline{6} \times \underline{4})$
$= \underline{24} + \underline{24} = \underline{48}$
$\underline{48}$ square centimeters

3.
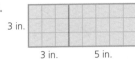
3 in.

3 in.   5 in.

$3 \times (3 + 5)$
$= (\underline{3} \times \underline{3}) + (\underline{3} \times \underline{5})$
$= \underline{9} + \underline{15} = \underline{24}$
$\underline{24}$ square inches

4.
4 cm

6 cm   4 cm

$4 \times (6 + 4)$
$= (\underline{4} \times \underline{6}) + (\underline{4} \times \underline{4})$
$= \underline{24} + \underline{16} = \underline{40}$
$\underline{40}$ square meters

5. Which answer represents the area model?

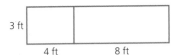
3 ft

4 ft   8 ft

a. $(3 + 4) \times (3 + 8)$ ⓑ $(3 \times 4) + (3 \times 8)$

c. $3 + 4 \times 8$ d. $(3 \times 4) \times (3 \times 8)$

276   Unit 5 ■ Focus on Measurement and Data/Geometry

Writing About Math

⬛ ▸ **Write an Explanatory Text** Break students up into small groups. Have each group write a paragraph explaining how to use the Distributive Property and an area model to find the area of a rectangle. Students should include illustrations and an example. After they have completed their paragraphs, have groups share their explanations with the rest of the class.

**Draw an area model to represent each problem.
Use your area model to solve the problem.**
Accept any correct area model. Possible answers shown.

6. 3 × (2 + 6)

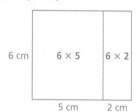

6 + 18 = 24
<u>24</u>

7. 4 × (5 + 7)

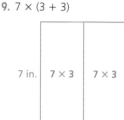

20 + 28 = 48
<u>48</u>

8. 6 × (5 + 2)

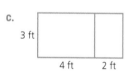

30 + 12 = 42
<u>42</u>

9. 7 × (3 + 3)

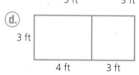

21 + 21 = 42
<u>42</u>

10. Which area model represents 3 × (4 + 3)?

a.

b.

c.

(d.)

Common Errors

Item 10

Students may choose c instead of d because the numbers used in c are very close to the correct numbers. Tell students that the lengths of the two smaller rectangles in c (4 ft and 2 ft) must match the addends in the expression 3 × (4 + 3).

Teaching Tips

Items 6–9

It can be helpful for students to actually tile the rectangles to find the area. Using tiles may help visual and tactile learners better understand the concept of area.

Digital Connection

Drawing Area Models Have students use a word processing program or drawing program to make area models. Give each student the dimensions of the area model they create. Once students create their area models, ask them to break up the area models into smaller area models. Ask students to explain how they broke up their models. Finally, have students utilize the word processing program or drawing program again to create the two smaller area models.

Independent Practice

Teaching Tips

Item 12

Some students may have a hard time understanding how multiple answers can be correct. Use unit square tiles to show how the areas can be the same.

Items 13–14

For these problems, students are asked to show their work. Pay special attention to the way they set up their area models and how they record the calculations.

Independent Practice

MP1 11. Compare the two area models. How are they alike? How are they different?
Possible answer: They both represent 4 × 6. But they represent the second side length as different addends or lengths.

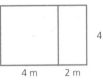
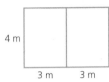

MP6 12. Heather wants to use the Distributive Property to find 8 × 12. She draws an area model. One side length is 8 inches. What could Heather use for the other side length? Explain.
Possible answer: She can use any two addends with a sum of 12 for the second factor. So she can draw side lengths such as 2 + 10 or 4 + 8.

Solve the problems.

MP7 13. Andy grows red roses and white roses in his garden. Use the Distributive Property to find the total area of Andy's rose garden.

▭ **Show your work.**
Possible answer:
(7 × 4) + (7 × 5)
= 28 + 35
= 63

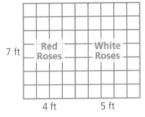

Answer The total area of the rose garden is 63 square feet.

MP4 14. Ines wants to find the area of her backyard. The yard is a rectangle. She measures the yard in meters. Then she writes 6 × (8 + 4). Draw an area model for the backyard. Use your model to find the area of the yard. Accept any correct area model.
Possible answer:

▭ **Show your work.**

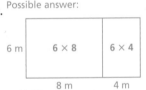

6 × 8 = 48
6 × 4 = 24

```
  4 8
+ 2 4
-----
  7 2
```

Answer The area of the yard is 72 square meters.

Mathematical Practices

MP1	**Make sense of problems and persevere in solving them.**
Item 11: Students use pictures to compare two area models.	
MP4	**Model with mathematics.**
Item 14: Students draw an area model to solve a real-world problem.	
MP6	**Attend to precision.**
Item 12: Students formulate an appropriate explanation.	
MP7	**Look for and make use of structure.**
Item 13: Students use the Distributive Property to find area.	

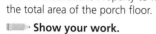

Lesson 30

Independent Practice

MP4 **15.** The Wilsons' porch floor is a rectangle. Part is brick, and part is concrete. Use the Distributive Property to find the total area of the porch floor.

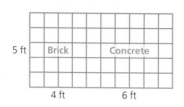

▬▬▸ **Show your work.**
Possible answer:
$(5 \times 4) + (5 \times 6)$
$= 20 + 30$
$= 50$

Answer The total area of the porch floor is 50 square feet.

MP8 **16.** Kendra tapes red, blue, and yellow paper strips together to make a flag. Each strip has one side 8 inches long. The red strip has a side 3 inches long, the blue strip has a side 4 inches long, and the yellow strip has a side 5 inches long. What is the area of the flag that Kendra makes?

Answer The area of the flag is 96 square inches.

▬▬▸ **Justify your answer using words, drawings, or numbers.**
Possible justification:

$24 + 32 + 40 = 96$

MP3 **17.** Jed wants to know the product for 4×11. He decides to use the Distributive Property. He draws this area model. "The product is 48," says Jed. Is Jed right?

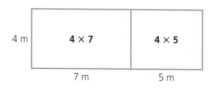

Answer No, Jed is not right.

▬▬▸ **Justify your answer using words, drawings, or numbers.**
Possible justification: Jed rewrites the second factor incorrectly. $7 + 5 \neq 11$. He should change the addends to something like $6 + 5$. Then he would get $(4 \times 6) + (4 \times 5)$, which is $24 + 20$, or 44.

Teaching Tips

Item 16
Pay special attention to students' drawings. Encourage students to explain how their drawings are related to the Distributive Property.

Item 17
Tell students to look carefully at Jed's drawing. Remind them that the sum of the second factors must equal 11. Also, the sum of the lengths of the longer side of each smaller rectangle must equal 11. Suggest that students correct Jed's drawing to make sure it makes sense.

Mathematical Practices	
MP3	**Construct viable arguments and critique the reasoning of others.**
Item 17: Students critique a given answer and justify their thinking.	
MP4	**Model with mathematics.**
Item 15: Students use a model to explain operations.	
MP8	**Look for and express regularity in repeated reasoning.**
Item 16: Students find the area of a rectangle and share their reasoning.	

Common Core Focus:

3.MD.7d Recognize area as additive. Find areas of rectilinear figures by decomposing them into non-overlapping rectangles and adding the areas of the non-overlapping parts, applying this technique to solve real world problems.

OBJECTIVE

Decompose a figure into non-overlapping rectangles in order to find the area.

ESSENTIAL QUESTION

Decomposing a figure into separate rectangles can help students determine the area of a figure. Introduce the lesson by reviewing the properties of a rectangle and how to determine the area of a single rectangle.

FLUENCY PRACTICE

Fluency practice is available at **sadlierconnect.com**.

Concept Development

Understand: Decomposing figures into rectangles to find their areas

■ Students are expected to understand how to find areas of rectangles, as well as recognize that areas are additive. To accomplish this task, students need to be able to decompose figures into rectangles.

■ Most students can determine the area of a rectangle by multiplying side lengths. Use this knowledge when working with students to break a figure down into non-overlapping rectangles.

✏️ ▸ Have students draw a line to decompose the figure. Challenge students to decompose the figure into three rectangles: $(2 \times 3) + (2 \times 2) + (2 \times 2)$. Students should verify that the area of the figure is the same no matter how they decompose it.

Essential Question:
How can you find the area of a figure by decomposing it into rectangles?
3.MD.7d

Words to Know:
decompose

Guided Instruction

In this lesson you will learn to decompose a figure into rectangles so that you can find the area.

Understand: Decomposing figures into rectangles to find their areas

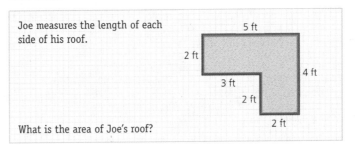

Joe measures the length of each side of his roof.

5 ft
2 ft
3 ft
4 ft
2 ft
2 ft

What is the area of Joe's roof?

Decompose, or break down, Joe's desktop into two rectangles that do not overlap.

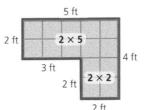

5 ft
2 ft
2 × 5
3 ft
4 ft
2 × 2
2 ft
2 ft

Remember!
To find the area of a rectangle, you can count unit squares, or you can multiply side lengths.

Find the area of one rectangle. ——▸ $2 \times 5 = 10$ square feet
Find the area of the other rectangle. ——▸ $2 \times 2 = 4$ square feet
Add the two areas. ——▸ $10 + 4 = 14$ square feet

▸ The area of Joe's roof is 14 square feet.

✏️ ▸ Show another way to decompose the figure into two rectangles.
Possible answer: $(2 \times 3) + (4 \times 2)$
Accept any correct decomposition.

280 Unit 5 ■ Focus on Measurement and Data/Geometry

Words to Know

decompose: breaking apart a plane figure into simpler plane figures to find the area of the entire figure

Glossary can be found on pp. 347–350.

MORE ONLINE sadlierconnect.com

Connect: What you know about area and decomposing figures

Sherry planted her garden with beans and carrots.

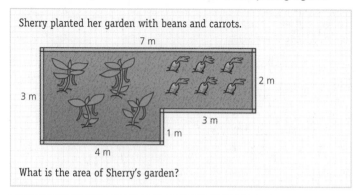

7 m

2 m

3 m

3 m

1 m

4 m

What is the area of Sherry's garden?

Step 1

Decompose the figure into two rectangles.

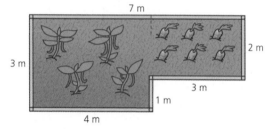

7 m

2 m

3 m

3 m

1 m

4 m

Step 2

Find the area of the bean rectangle. → 3 × 4 = 12 square meters
Find the area of the carrot rectangle. → 2 × 3 = 6 square meters

Step 3

Add the two areas.

12 + 6 = __18__ square meters

▶ The area of Sherry's garden is 18 square meters.

Connect: What you know about area and decomposing figures Use this page to help students strengthen their understanding of how to find the area of a figure by decomposing it into rectangles.

■ In this presentation, students examine how to decompose a figure that represents a real-world object into non-overlapping rectangles, and determine the area of each rectangle.

■ Have students draw a vertical line between the beans and the carrots to decompose the figure and identify the length and width of the rectangles they created.

■ Ask students if there is another way to decompose the figure. Students should see a (2 × 7) rectangle and a (1 × 4) rectangle. Have students use these rectangles to calculate the area of the figure.

■ Challenge students to find the area of the figure by finding the area of the large rectangle that is 3 × 7, and subtracting the area of the missing piece that is 1 × 3: 21 − 3 = 18 square meters.

Support English Language Learners

Distribute rectangular or square shapes to students. Have them connect the shapes to make one large figure. Then, write the term *decomposing* on the board, say the term, and have students repeat. Tell students to separate one shape from the large figure they made. Tell them that they *decomposed* the figure by taking the figure apart. Have students remove another shape and use the sentence frame: *I decomposed the shape by breaking it into _____ and _____*. Repeat this process until students are comfortable with the term *decompose*.

Guided Practice

Observational Assessment

Use pages 282–283 to assess whether students are able to decompose a figure into non-overlapping rectangles. Look for evidence that students know how to decompose a figure and that they understand that the area of each part can be added to find the total area of the figure.

For exercises 9–11, have the class share the different ways they decomposed the figure so others can see that there is more than one way. Be sure students understand that the total area does not change.

Guided Practice

For exercises 1–4, uses the figure at the right.

1. Decompose the figure into two rectangles.
   Accept either decomposition of the figure.

2. Find the area of one rectangle.

   $\underline{6} \times \underline{3} = \underline{18}$ square in.
   or 3 × 3 = 9

3. Find the area of the other rectangle.

   $\underline{3} \times \underline{2} = \underline{6}$ square in.
   or 3 × 5 = 15

4. What is the area of the figure?

   $\underline{18} + \underline{6} = \underline{24}$ square in.
   or 9 + 15 = 24

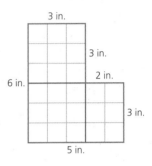

3 in.   3 in.   2 in.   6 in.   3 in.   5 in.

For exercises 5–8, use the figure at the right.

5. Decompose the figure into two rectangles.
   Accept either decomposition of the figure.

6. Find the area of one rectangle.

   $\underline{8}$ square cm
   or, 4 × 8 = 32

7. Find the area of the other rectangle.

   $\underline{30}$ square cm
   or, 1 × 6 = 6

8. What is the area of the figure?

   $\underline{38}$ square cm

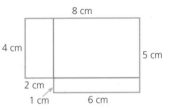

8 cm   4 cm   5 cm   2 cm   1 cm   6 cm

For exercises 9–11, use the figure at the right.

9. Decompose the figure into rectangles.
   Accept decomposition into two, three, or four rectangles.

10. Find the area of each rectangle.
    Two rectangles: 6 × 6 = 36 and 2 × 2 = 4
    Three rectangles: 6 × 2 = 12; 8 × 2 = 16; 6 × 2 = 12
    Four rectangles: 6 × 2 = 12; 6 × 2 = 12;
    6 × 2 = 12; 2 × 2 = 4

11. What is the area of the figure?
    Two rectangles: (6 × 6) + (2 × 2) = 36 + 4 = 40
    Three rectangles: (6 × 2) + (8 × 2) + (6 × 2) = 12 + 16 + 12 = 40
    Four rectangles: (6 × 2) + (6 × 2) + (6 × 2) + (2 × 2) = 12 + 12 + 12 + 4 = 40

    $\underline{40}$ square cm

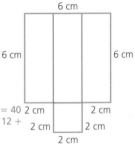

6 cm   6 cm   6 cm   2 cm   2 cm   2 cm   2 cm   2 cm

Math-to-Real-World Connection

Architecture A strong understanding of how to break down rectilinear figures into non-overlapping rectangles may be necessary in many real-world situations involving measurement. Connect the use of this skill to measuring a room for carpet, measuring a plot of land for a patio, measuring land for a garden, or measuring a countertop. Encourage students to measure an area of a field or a flowerbed on the school grounds. Have them record their findings and determine the area. Finally, have students explain their findings to the class.

MORE ONLINE sadlierconnect.com

Lesson 31

Guided Practice

12. Larry measures the floor of his kitchen. What is the area of the kitchen floor?

Accept any correct decomposition of the figure. (4 × 3) + (2 × 4) or (2 × 3) + (2 × 7) = 20 or (3 × 2) + (3 × 2) + (4 × 2)

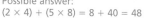
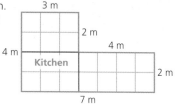

The area of the kitchen floor is 20 square meters.

13. Ms. Kim has a front porch. What is the area of the floor of the porch?

Accept any correct decomposition. Possible answer: (2 × 4) + (5 × 8) = 8 + 40 = 48

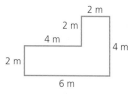

The area of the floor of the porch is 48 square feet.

☝ Think·Pair·Share

MP7 **14.** Brian wants to find the area of the figure. He cannot decide which way to decompose it. Does it matter? Explain your reasoning.

It doesn't matter. Possible explanation: The total area stays the same. He will find the areas of different rectangles, but they will add to the same total area.

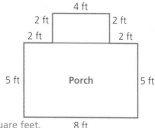

☝ Think·Pair·Share

Peer Collaboration Ask each student to decompose the figure on their own and then choose a partner and share their answers and methods. Tell students that they should find two different ways to decompose the figure. Ask:

- *Did you and your partner decompose the figure in the same way? Tell about your ways.*

- *What are the lengths and widths of the rectangles you drew?*

- *Did the total area change? Tell why or why not.*

In summary, the total area of the figure does not change regardless of the way the figure is decomposed.

Return to the Essential Question

Reread the Lesson 31 Essential Question on page 280: *How can you find the area of a figure by decomposing it into rectangles?*

Ask volunteers to use what they learned in this lesson to answer this question. (Possible response: I can decompose a figure into non-overlapping rectangles, compute the area of each, and then add to find the total area.)

Mathematical Practices

Mathematical Practice Standards underline the teaching and understanding of all concepts and skills presented. The emphasis of specific practices is noted throughout the guided and independent practice of this lesson.

| MP7 | **Look for and make use of structure.** |

Item 14: Students discuss geometric shapes in terms of their similarities and differences.

Independent Practice

Concept Application

Students may work independently on these pages in the classroom or at home. They may refer to the first four pages of the lesson to revisit the instruction or to see a worked-out example.

Common Errors and **Teaching Tips** may help you support student learning either in the classroom or as a follow-up for work done at home.

Teaching Tips

Items 5–8

Students are asked to show how they decomposed the figure. This figure is not broken down into square units, so students will need to pay special attention to decomposing accurately. Remind students that the shapes of the decomposed figures should be rectangles.

Independent Practice

For exercises 1–4, use the figure at the right.

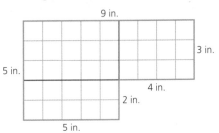

1. Decompose the figure into two rectangles. Accept either decomposition of the figure.
2. Find the area of one rectangle.

    _5_ × _5_ = _25_ square in.
    or 3 × 9 = 27
3. Find the area of the other rectangle.

    _3_ × _4_ = _12_ square in.
    or 2 × 5 = 10
4. What is the area of the figure?

    _25_ + _12_ = _37_ square in.
    or 27 + 10 = 37

For exercises 5–8, use the figure at the right

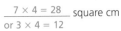 **Show your work.**

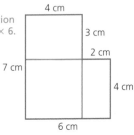

5. Decompose the figure into two rectangles. Accept either decomposition of the figure: 7 × 4 and 4 × 2 or 3 × 4 and 4 × 6.
6. Find the area of one rectangle.

    _7 × 4 = 28_ square cm
    or 3 × 4 = 12
7. Find the area of the other rectangle.

    _4 × 2 = 8_ square cm
    or 4 × 6 = 24
8. What is the area of the figure?

    _28 + 8 = 36_ square cm
    or 12 + 24 = 36

Writing About Math

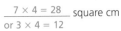 **Write an Explanatory Text** Ask students to write a paragraph explaining how to find the area of a figure that is not a simple rectangle. Look for evidence that students can explain each step thoroughly and in order. You may want the whole class to brainstorm the steps involved, and create a flow chart on the board that students can use to help them write. Guide them to use drawings as needed.

9. Zach built a tree fort in his backyard. He measures the floor of his fort. What is the area of the fort's floor?

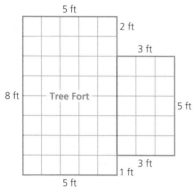

The area of the fort's floor is 55 square ft. $(8 \times 5) + (5 \times 3) = 40 + 15 = 55$ Accept any correct decomposition.

Circle the letter of the correct answer.

10. Dawn measures the floor of her bedroom and closet. What is the total area of the bedroom and closet floor?

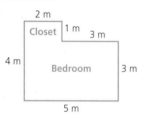

a. 15 square m   (b.) 17 square m

c. 18 square m   d. 20 square m

11. Bill digs a vegetable garden. What is the area of the garden?

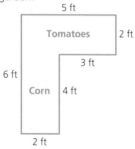

(a.) 18 square ft   b. 19 square ft

c. 20 square ft   d. 30 square ft

Teaching Tips

Item 9

Some students may have difficulty determining the measurements of the side lengths of the rectangles they draw. Remind students that opposite sides of a rectangle have equal lengths and you only need to know the measure of two adjacent sides to find the area.

Items 10–11

To find the total areas, most students will decompose the figures by the areas that represent different sections: the closet area and the bedroom area, and the corn section and tomato section. Challenge students to identify another way to decompose the figures.

Digital Connection

Interactive Whiteboard Draw a composite figure that can be decomposed into non-overlapping rectangles in several ways. Have students take turns drawing lines on the figure to show the decomposition and finding the total area. Students should identify the length and width of each rectangle in the figure. Repeat this activity with several different figures. You may also encourage students to create their own figures, then challenge the class to decompose the figure and determine the total area.

Independent Practice

Teaching Tips

Item 12

Students may be uncertain about how to decompose a figure that is already a rectangle. Demonstrate that a rectangle can be broken down into smaller rectangles. Be sure students know how to find the side lengths of the decomposed rectangles. Suggest that students draw a line to show how the large rectangle has been decomposed.

Item 13

Students should draw the 1 × 5 rectangle first and then determine the side lengths of the other rectangle. Remind students that rectangles may not overlap. Point out that the total length of the right side of the figure is 3 cm before it is decomposed.

Independent Practice

MP2 12. Samantha wants to find the area of the hallway floor but she does not want to multiply 3 × 14. How could she use decomposition to find the area?

> 3 ft | Hallway
> 14 ft

Possible answer: She could decompose the rectangle into two smaller rectangles and then add their areas mentally. She could use (3 × 10) + (3 × 4), which is 42 square feet.

MP3 13. Daniel decomposed the figure to find its area. He wrote 3 × 3 for the area of one rectangle. He wrote 1 × 5 for the area of the other rectangle. Daniel says the area of the figure is 14 square centimeters. What mistake did he make? Explain.

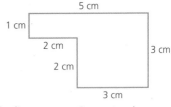

Possible explanation: He decomposed the figure wrong. One rectangle includes part of the other rectangle, so his area is too big.

Solve the problems.

MP4 14. Sean measures the floor of his hamster's house. What is the area of the floor?

✏ **Show your work.**
Possible answer:
2 × 4 = 8
3 × 10 = 30
8 + 30 = 38
Accept any correct decomposition.

> 4 in.
> 2 in.   2 in.
> 2 in.   4 in.
> 3 in.   3 in.
> 10 in.
> Hamster House

Answer The area of the floor is 38 square inches.

Mathematical Practices

MP2	Reason abstractly and quantitatively.

Item 12: Students consider the units in a problem as they determine how to decompose a figure.

MP3	Construct viable arguments and critique the reasoning of others.

Item 13: Students explain an approach to a problem and analyze where mistakes occurred.

MP4	Model with mathematics.

Item 14: Students relate mathematics to real-world problems.

Independent Practice

MP1 **15.** Tim is making a walkway from his mailbox to his house. What is the area of the walkway?

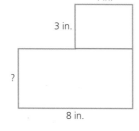
8 ft
3 ft
5 ft
5 ft
4 ft
5 ft
3 ft
7 ft
Walkway

> **Show your work.**
Accept any correct decomposition.
Possible answer:
$3 \times 8 = 24$
$2 \times 3 = 6$
$3 \times 7 = 21$
$24 + 6 + 21 = 51$

Answer The area of the walkway is 51 square feet.

MP2 **16.** Kevin decomposes the figure to find its area. He calculates the area as 44 square inches. What is the missing side length shown by the question mark? Possible answer:

4 in.
3 in.
?
8 in.

Answer The missing side length is 4 inches.

> **Justify your answer using words, drawings, or numbers.**
Possible justification:
The areas of the two rectangles add to 44 square inches. One rectangle has an area of 12 square inches, so find the difference. The other rectangle must have an area of 32 square inches.
$? \times 8 = 32$
$4 \times 8 = 32$

MP7 **17.** Beth puts 6 square stones in her garden. Each stone is the same size. What is the total area of the tops of the stones Beth put in her garden?

2 ft | Stone
2 ft

Answer The total area of the tops of the stones is 24 square feet.

> **Justify your answer using words, drawings, or numbers.**
Possible justifications:
The area of each stone is 4 square feet.
Then $6 \times 4 = 24$
or $2 \times 12 = 24$

12 ft
2 ft
$2 \times 12 = 24$

Teaching Tips

Item 15

Students will need to decompose the figure into at least three rectangles and add three or more areas to find the total area. Students should check their work to make sure they accounted for the entire area, that there are no overlapping parts, and that they determined the lengths of the side measures correctly.

Item 16

Help students decompose the figure into two rectangles (3×4 and $? \times 8$) so that they can find the area of one of the rectangles. Students will need to subtract that area from the total area of the figure. Discuss how they can then write an equation to find the missing side length.

Mathematical Practices	
MP1	**Make sense of problems and persevere in solving them.**
Item 15: Students analyze and plan a solution to a real-world problem.	
MP2	**Reason abstractly and quantitatively.**
Item 16: Students pay attention to all mathematical language in order to find the missing length.	
MP7	**Look for and make use of structure.**
Item 17: Students search for patterns in the drawing of the figure.	

Common Core Focus:

3.MD.2 Measure and estimate liquid volumes and masses of objects using standard units of grams (g), kilograms (kg), and liters (l). Add, subtract, multiply, or divide to solve one-step word problems involving masses or volumes that are given in the same units; **3.MD.7** Relate area to the operations of multiplication and addition; **3.OA.3** Use multiplication and division within 100 to solve word problems in situations involving equal groups, arrays, and measurement quantities.

OBJECTIVE
Use drawings to solve problems with measurement.

ESSENTIAL QUESTION
Ask students how drawing pictures has helped them solve problems in the past. Making a drawing is an effective strategy that can help students understand the information provided in a measurement word problem.

FLUENCY PRACTICE
Fluency practice is available at **sadlierconnect.com**.

Concept Development

Understand: Using a drawing to help solve a problem

■ Explain that a drawing must first be made to illustrate the original shape described in the problem. With each step of the problem, the original drawing is changed to show each detail.

■ Guide students through a different way to solve the problem by subtracting the area of the piece Sharon gave her sister (4 × 4 = 16) from the area of the piece Sharon started with (8 × 8 = 64); 64 − 16 = 48.

Lesson 32 — Problem Solving: Measurement

Essential Question: How can you make drawings to solve problems with measurements? 3.MD.2, 3.MD.7, 3.OA.3

Guided Instruction

In this lesson you will learn to make drawings to solve problems about measurement.

Understand: Using a drawing to help solve a problem

> Sharon has a square piece of cloth 8 feet long on each side. From the corner of the cloth, Sharon cuts out a square 4 feet long on each side. Sharon gives the small square piece to her sister. What is the area of the piece Sharon has left?

Draw a picture to show the information in the problem.

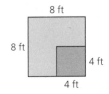

Decompose the piece of cloth that is left into squares. Label the side lengths.

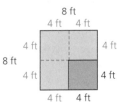

Find the area of each square in the piece Sharon has left.

Add the areas.

16 + 16 + 16 = 48

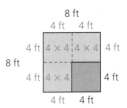

➤ The area of the piece of cloth Sharon has left is 48 square feet.

Support English Language Learners

There are many units of measurement used in this lesson, such as *liter, centimeter, foot, gram,* and *kilogram.* Help English language learners understand these units by presenting concrete examples. Give each student a sheet of drawing paper. Write the word *liter* on the board, say the word and have students repeat after you. Show them a 1-L bottle of water and tell them the bottle holds 1 *liter* of water. On their papers, have students write the word *liter* and draw a picture of the 1-L bottle. Repeat the procedure using different concrete examples, such as a 12-in. ruler to represent 1 *foot*; the width of a fingernail to represent 1 *centimeter*; a small button to represent 1 *gram*; and a whole, fresh pineapple to represent 1 *kilogram*.

Connect: Drawing a picture to solve a problem

> Eric stacks 4 books in a pile. Each book is 6 centimeters thick.
> How high is the stack of books?

Step 1

Make a drawing.

	6 cm
	6 cm
	6 cm
	6 cm

Step 2

Use the drawing to write and solve an equation for the problem.

$4 \times 6 = $ ▓

$4 \times 6 = \underline{24}$

➡ The stack of books is 24 centimeters high.

> Ben has a container with 6 liters of water. He uses the water to fill
> 2-liter bottles. How many bottles can he fill?

Step 1

Make a drawing.

6 L of water

1   2   3

Step 2

Use the drawing to solve the problem.

The drawing shows equal groups of 2 liters.

There are $\underline{3}$ equal groups of 2 liters.

➡ Ben can fill 3 bottles.

✏ What equation can you use to solve this problem? $6 \div 2 = 3$

Connect: Drawing a picture to solve a problem Use this page to help students strengthen their understanding of how using a drawing helps to solve a measurement problem.

■ A key understanding in this process lies within the necessary steps to solving such a word problem. First, students will make a drawing to show the information provided in the problem. Next, students will use the drawing to write and solve an equation for the problem.

✏ Explain to students that the quotient will be the solution to the problem.

Math-to-Architecture Connection

Designing a Floor Plan A strong understanding of determining the area of rectangular figures will enable students to design a floor plan. Have students create a floor plan for their own dream room using geometric shapes to create a figure that can be decomposed into rectangles. Students can calculate the area of each rectangular figure in the floor plan. Ask students to explain why they choose the floor plan they did to represent their dream room. Remind students that their floor plan must contain measurement units.

Observational Assessment

Use pages 290–291 to assess whether students are able to make drawings to solve word problems involving measurement. Identify students who have trouble deciding what type of drawing to use. Remind them that they can use area models, number lines, arrays, or make a drawing of the objects described in the word problem. In problem 1, encourage students to label the sides of the rectangular drawing and check that their drawing correctly represents the given measurements.

Guided Practice

Make a drawing. Solve the problem.

1. Jeff tapes together small paper squares that are 3 inches on each side to make a large square 6 inches on each side. How many small squares does he use?

   Show your work.
   Possible answer:

   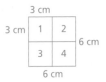

   Answer Jeff uses 4 small squares.

2. Ginger makes 15 liters of fruit punch. She pours all of the punch into some bowls. If each bowl has 3 liters of punch, how many bowls does Ginger fill?

   Show your work.
   Possible answer:

   Answer Ginger fills 5 bowls.

3. Ben uses 1 liter of water to fill 5 paper cups. How many liters of water will he use to fill 20 paper cups?

   Show your work.
   Possible answer:

   Answer Ben will use 4 liters of water.

Math-to-Science Connection

Weight on Celestial Bodies If a person were able to stand on any planet or moon in the solar system, his or her weight would be different from what it is on Earth. Weight is a force caused by the gravitational pull on an object. It depends on the mass of the object, the mass of the planet (or moon), and how far from the center of the planet (or moon) the object is. Share this word problem with students and have them make drawings to help find a solution.

Jasmine weighs 50 pounds on Earth. She learns that if she were to stand on Mars, she would weigh 31 pounds less than what she weighs on Earth. How much would Jasmine weigh on Mars?

4. Fluffy the cat has a mass of 8 kilograms. This is 2 kilograms more than the mass of Frisky the cat. What is the mass of Frisky the cat?

■■■ • **Show your work.**
Possible answer:

Fluffy [kg][kg][kg][kg][kg][kg][kg][kg]

Frisky [kg][kg][kg][kg][kg][kg]

Answer Frisky the cat has a mass of 6 kilograms.

5. Henry buys a sack of gravel. The mass is 900 grams. Henry pours 524 grams of the gravel into his turtle's tank. How much gravel is left in the sack?

■■■ • **Show your work.**
Possible answer:

```
                    524              900
    ├──────(                )──────  −524
         ?               900         376
```

Answer The mass of the gravel left in the sack is 376 grams.

Think•Pair•Share

MP3 6. Ann says that sometimes you can find the answer to a word problem by just using a drawing, but sometimes the drawing just helps you decide how to solve the problem. Do you agree? Explain your reasoning.
I agree. Possible explanation: For problem 4, I could actually use my drawing and count to find the answer. For problem 5, I made a drawing that helped me know to subtract.

Unit 5 ■ Focus on Measurement and Data/Geometry   **291**

Think•Pair•Share

Peer Collaboration Ask pairs to discuss how using a drawing can sometimes help solve a word problem and how it can sometimes help in deciding *how* to solve a problem.

Have pairs share their ideas with the class. For each pair of presenters, pose questions such as:

- *What is an example of a problem in which a drawing helps you solve?*

- *How does a drawing only sometimes help in planning how to solve a problem?*

- *What is the difference between the two uses for a drawing?*

Return to the Essential Question

Reread the Lesson 32 Essential Question on page 288: *How can you make drawings to solve problems with measurements?*

Ask volunteers to use what they learned in this lesson to answer this question. (Possible responses: I can draw a picture to show the information in the problem and make changes to the pictures with each step in the problem. I can illustrate what is being explained in the problem in order to better understand.)

Invite as many volunteers as possible to express ideas about making drawings to solve measurement problems.

Mathematical Practices

Mathematical Practice Standards underline the teaching and understanding of all concepts and skills presented. The emphasis of specific practices is noted throughout the guided and independent practice of this lesson.

MP3	**Construct viable arguments and critique the reasoning of others.**

Item 6: Students critique the reasoning of others and explain an approach to solving a problem.

Independent Practice

Concept Application

Students may work independently on these pages in the classroom or at home. They may refer to the first four pages of the lesson to revisit the instruction or to see a worked-out example.

Common Errors and **Teaching Tips** may help you support student learning either in the classroom or as a follow-up for work done at home.

Teaching Tips

Items 1–3

Remind students that there are many different kinds of drawings they can use to solve a problem. For example, they might draw an area model or a number line. Encourage students to think about the type of drawing that would be most helpful to illustrate each problem.

Independent Practice

Make a drawing for each problem. Solve the problem.

MP7 **1.** Sam has a rectangular sheet of cardboard with side lengths 11 inches and 9 inches. He cuts off a piece with side lengths 2 inches and 9 inches and uses that piece to make a bookmark. What is the area of the piece of cardboard left over?

✏ **Show your work.**
Possible answer:

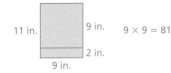

$9 \times 9 = 81$

Answer The area of the piece left over is 81 square inches.

MP4 **2.** How many 2-liter bottles can Glen fill from a container holding 18 liters of water?

✏ **Show your work.**
Possible answer:

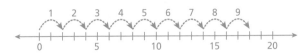

Answer Glen can fill 9 bottles.

MP5 **3.** How many books each 3 centimeters thick do you need to make a stack 9 centimeters high?

✏ **Show your work.**
Possible answer:

$$9 \left\{ \; 6 \left\{ \begin{array}{c} 3 \\ 3 \\ 3 \end{array} \right. \right.$$

Answer You need 3 books.

Mathematical Practices	
MP1	**Make sense of problems and persevere in solving them.**
Item 5: Students use a picture to solve a problem.	
MP4	**Model with mathematics.**
Items 2, 4, and 6: Students solve a measurement problem using a drawing.	
MP5	**Use appropriate tools strategically.**
Item 3: Students use a diagram to solve a problem.	
MP7	**Look for and make use of structure.**
Item 1: Students discuss geometric shapes in terms of their differences in area.	

MORE ONLINE sadlierconnect.com   Lesson 32

Independent Practice

MP4 **4.** Thomas cuts a 32-inch piece of rope into 4 equal length pieces.
What is the length of each piece?

     ✏ · **Show your work.**
     Possible answer:

     32 ÷ 4 = 8

     Answer Each piece is 8 inches long.

MP1 **5.** Five potatoes have a mass of 1 kilogram. What is the mass of
30 potatoes of the same size?

     ✏ · **Show your work.**
     Possible answer:

     ```
     ooooo  1 kg ⎫
     ooooo  1 kg ⎪
     ooooo  1 kg ⎬ 6 kgs
     ooooo  1 kg ⎪
     ooooo  1 kg ⎪
     ooooo  1 kg ⎭
     ```

     Answer The mass of 30 potatoes is 6 kilograms.

MP4 **6.** Adam's packed suitcase has a mass of 10 kilograms. This is
2 kilograms more than the mass of his sister's packed suitcase.
What is the mass of his sister's packed suitcase?

     ✏ · **Show your work.**
     Possible answer:

     | kg | kg | kg | kg | kg | kg | kg | kg | ⊠ | ⊠ |

     Answer The mass of his sister's packed suitcase is 8 kilograms.

Unit 5 ■ Focus on Measurement and Data/Geometry   **293**

Writing About Math

✏ · **Write a Word Problem** Ask students to create their own
measurement word problems. Explain to students that word problems
are organized into a series of sentences. First, the important information
in the problem is presented in complete sentences. Second, a question is
included to ask how the problem should be solved. Encourage students
to create a word problem that will enable the reader to make a drawing
and provide an equation to solve it.

Have students share their problems with a partner. The partner should
make a drawing and solve the problem. Have volunteers share their
problems with the rest of the class.

Independent Practice

Common Errors

Item 6

Students might add the two quantities
presented in the problem. Encourage
students to read every detail within the
problem and provide a detailed drawing
to organize facts.

Teaching Tips

Item 5

After students have shown their work,
ask them which operation and equation
is useful in solving this problem.

Independent Practice

Teaching Tips

Item 7
Have students literally follow the directions given by each student in the problem to test the accuracy of their suggested solutions.

Item 9
Have students read the question carefully and identify key words that indicate the correct operation to use when solving the problem.

Independent Practice

MP1 **7.** A nickel has a mass of 5 grams. Ben and Sarah want to know the mass of 3 nickels. Ben says the way to find out is by making a drawing. Sarah says you can just write and solve an equation. Who is right? Possible answer:
Both are right. You can make a drawing of 3 groups of 5 symbols and count the number of symbols, or you can write the equation $3 \times 5 = 15$.

MP7 **8.** The two drawings below both show a ribbon 12 feet long cut into 3 equal pieces.

Drawing A: ▭▭▭▭│▭▭▭▭│▭▭▭▭

Drawing B: ├────┼────┼────┤
12 ft

How are the drawings different? How can you use each drawing to find the length of one of the pieces of ribbon? Possible answer:
In Drawing A, each square shows 1 foot of ribbon. You can count the number of squares in each piece; each piece is 4 feet long. Drawing B helps you see that you can divide 12 by 3 to find the length of each piece. $12 \div 3 = 4$; each piece is 4 feet long.

Solve the problems.

MP2 **9.** Latisha's fish tank holds 65 liters of water. Pam's fish tank holds 48 liters of water. How much more water does Latisha's tank hold than Pam's tank?

▭▭▸ **Show your work.**
Possible answer: Latisha ___65 L___ $\begin{array}{r} 65 \\ -48 \\ \hline 17 \end{array}$
Pam ___48 L___ ?

Answer Latisha's tank holds 17 more liters of water.

MP5 **10.** An egg has a mass of 50 grams. What is the mass of 6 eggs that are the same size?

▭▭▸ **Show your work.**
Possible answer: [50 g] [50 g] [50 g] [50 g] [50 g] [50 g]
100 g   100 g   100 g

Answer The mass of 6 eggs is 300 grams.

Mathematical Practices

MP1	**Make sense of problems and persevere in solving them.**
Item 7:	Students assess the progress of two plans for solving a problem.
MP2	**Reason abstractly and quantitatively.**
Item 9:	Students consider units and compare numbers to solve a problem.
MP5	**Use appropriate tools strategically.**
Item 10:	Students use an appropriate drawing to solve a problem.
MP7	**Look for and make use of structure.**
Item 8:	Students evaluate two different drawings used to solve a problem.

Lesson 32

Independent Practice

MP6 **11.** Maria uses 2 cuts to cut a piece of yarn 18 feet long into pieces with equal lengths. How long is each piece?

▸ Show your work.
Possible answer:

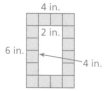

18 feet

2 cuts make 3 equal pieces.
$18 \div 3 = 6$

Answer Each piece of yarn is 6 feet long.

MP1 **12.** Ginger makes a craft project. She starts with a rectangular mirror with side lengths 6 inches and 4 inches. She glues 1-inch square tiles on the mirror along the edge to make a frame. What is the area of the mirror that is not covered with tiles?

Answer The area of the mirror that is not covered is 8 square inches.

▸ Justify your answer using words, drawings, or numbers.
Possible justification:

4 in.

2 in.

6 in.

4 in.

The side lengths of the uncovered mirror are 4 inches and 2 inches.
$4 \times 2 = 8$

MP7 **13.** Look back at exercise 12. Ginger does the project again using a larger mirror and the same 1-inch tiles. This mirror has side lengths 12 inches and 10 inches. What is the area of the mirror that is not covered with tiles?

Answer The area of the mirror that is not covered is 80 square inches.

▸ Justify your answer using words, drawings, or numbers.
Possible justification:
I know that each side length will be 2 inches less than its length at the start of the project. So, one side length will be 10 inches and the other side length will be 8 inches.
$10 \times 8 = 80$

Unit 5 ■ Focus on Measurement and Data/Geometry **295**

Common Errors

Item 11

Students may confuse two cuts for two pieces. Have students actually cut a piece of yarn or string twice and explain how many pieces are made from the two cuts.

Teaching Tips

Item 13

Encourage students to make a drawing using the directions given. Ask students how the drawing is similar to the one that could be used to solve problem 12.

Mathematical Practices	
MP1	**Make sense of problems and persevere in solving them.**
Item 12: Students use a picture to explain a solution.	
MP6	**Attend to precision.**
Item 11: Students use measurements appropriately to divide a larger length into three equal pieces.	
MP7	**Look for and make use of structure.**
Item 13: Students search for a pattern to apply to a similar problem with different measurements.	

Common Core Focus:

3.MD.8 Solve real world and mathematical problems involving perimeters of polygons, including finding the perimeter given the side lengths, finding an unknown side length, and exhibiting rectangles with the same perimeter and different areas or with the same area and different perimeters.

OBJECTIVE

Solve problems about the perimeters of polygons.

ESSENTIAL QUESTION

Now that students have learned about area, they make the transition to perimeter. Students may need to visualize the difference between the two terms and be told in what situations each should be used.

FLUENCY PRACTICE

Fluency practice is available at **sadlierconnect.com**.

Concept Development

Understand: The meaning of perimeter

■ In this presentation, students find the perimeter of a polygon given the side lengths. Tell students that perimeter is the distance around a figure. To find perimeter, you add the side lengths.

■ Remind students that you can add in any order and the sum does not change.

Understand: Finding an unknown side length of a polygon

■ In this presentation, students use the perimeter to find an unknown side length.

■ Have students identify the steps they should take to solve the problem.

■ Point out that 12 and 8 were added first because their sum is easy to calculate mentally.

Lesson 33 Problem Solving: **Perimeter**

Essential Question:
How can you solve problems about the perimeters of polygons?
3.MD.8

Words to Know:
closed figure
polygon
perimeter
quadrilateral

Guided Instruction

In this lesson you will learn about the perimeter of a polygon.

Understand: The meaning of perimeter

> William drew this triangle.
> What is the perimeter of the triangle?

5 in.   5 in.   6 in.

A closed figure has no breaks in its sides.
A polygon is a plane closed figure with straight sides.
The perimeter of a polygon is the sum of the lengths of its sides.

Add the side lengths to find the perimeter of the triangle.

$$5 + 5 + 6 = P$$
$$10 + 6 = 16$$

➡ The perimeter of the triangle is 16 inches.

Understand: Finding an unknown side length of a polygon

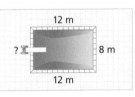

> The perimeter of the swimming pool is 40 meters.
> What is the unknown side length?

12 m   ?   8 m   12 m

Find the sum of the known side lengths.

$$12 + 8 + 12 = \blacksquare$$
$$20 + 12 = 32$$

Subtract the sum of the known side lengths from the perimeter.

$$40 - 32 = 8$$

➡ The unknown side length is 8 meters.

296   Unit 5 ■ Focus on Measurement and Data/Geometry

Words to Know

closed figure: a two-dimensional figure that has no breaks

polygon: a plane closed figure with straight sides

perimeter: the sum of the lengths of the sides of a polygon

quadrilateral: a polygon with four sides and four vertices or angles

Glossary can be found on pp. 347–350.

Connect: What you know about side lengths and perimeter

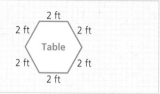

Mr. Green is making a table. This is a model of the tabletop. What is the perimeter of the tabletop?

Write and solve an addition equation.

$2 + 2 + 2 + 2 + 2 + 2 = P$
$2 + 2 + 2 + 2 + 2 + 2 = 12$

Or, since all side lengths are the same length, you can multiply to find the perimeter.

$6 \times 2 = 12$

➡ The perimeter of the tabletop is 12 feet.

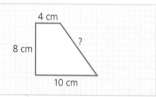

Sophia drew a quadrilateral, a polygon with four sides, with a perimeter of 32 centimeters. What is the unknown side length?

Step 1

Find the sum of the known side lengths.

$8 + 4 + 10 = $ ▧

$12 + 10 = \underline{22}$

Step 2

Subtract the sum of the known side lengths from the perimeter.

$32 - 22 = \underline{10}$

➡ The missing side length is $\underline{10}$ centimeters.

Guided Instruction

Connect: What you know about side lengths and perimeter Use this page to help students strengthen their understanding of how to solve problems involving perimeter.

■ Have students count the number of sides for the table. Encourage students to explain why they can skip count by 2s six times to find the perimeter.

■ Ask students if there is another way to find the perimeter of the table. Since the side lengths are equal, they can use multiplication to find the perimeter. Be sure students understand that multiplication is used here to represent repeated addition.

■ In the second problem, remind students that finding an unknown side length is a two-step process.

■ Students can check their answers to an unknown side length problem by adding all of the sides and comparing the sum to the given perimeter.

Support English Language Learners

English language learners may need additional help to understand the terms *closed figure, polygon, quadrilateral,* and *perimeter*. Distribute geoboards, rubber bands, and dot paper to students. Write the term *closed figure* on the board, have students repeat the word after you, and then use a rubber band to make a closed figure on the geoboard. Have them draw the closed figure they made on the dot paper and label it *closed figure*. Repeat this procedure for *polygon* and *quadrilateral*. Be sure that when they build, draw, and label a quadrilateral that it only has four straight sides and four angles. Once the figures are drawn, have them count the spaces around the figures and identify the number as the *perimeter* of each figure.

Guided Practice

Observational Assessment

Use pages 298–299 to assess whether students are able to determine the perimeters of various figures. Students must also demonstrate that they can determine unknown side lengths of polygons.

Students should develop a process to make sure they have accounted for all of the sides when finding perimeter. They might cross off the sides as they count them or determine a starting and stopping point. Careless errors may occur if students are not careful about adding the correct number of sides.

Guided Practice

Find the perimeter of each figure.

1.

6 in.   6 in.

6 in.

$6 + 6 + 6 = P$

$\underline{12} + \underline{6} = \underline{18}$

Perimeter: __18__ inches

2.

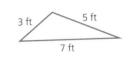

3 ft   5 ft

7 ft

$3 + 5 + 7 = P$

$\underline{8} + \underline{7} = \underline{15}$

Perimeter: __15__ feet

Solve the problems.

3. The model shows the shape of Mason's front lawn. Mason measures the side lengths of his front lawn. What is the perimeter?

   The perimeter is __56__ meters.

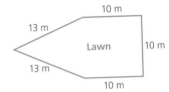

13 m   10 m

Lawn   10 m

13 m   10 m

4. Linda draws this "L." She wants to glue gold ribbon on the outline of the letter. How much gold ribbon does Linda need? How do you know?

   Linda needs __20__ inches of ribbon.
   Linda needs the same measure of ribbon as the perimeter of the letter L.

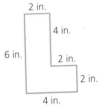

2 in.
4 in.
6 in.   2 in.
2 in.
4 in.

5. Stanley is painting a design on his wall that looks like an hourglass. He wants to outline the figure with tape before he paints. How much tape will he need?

   Stanley needs __31__ centimeters of tape.

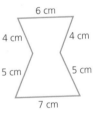

6 cm
4 cm   4 cm
5 cm   5 cm
7 cm

Math-to-Math Connection

Arithmetic and Algebra A strong understanding of the relationship between addition and unknown addends will be especially helpful when students work through this lesson. If they have a strong understanding of the methods of solving for unknown addends, they will be able to solve for unknown side lengths. Remind students that they can use a letter to represent an unknown addend.

Lesson 33

Guided Practice

Find each unknown side length.

6.

3 ft

<u>5</u> ft

4 ft

Perimeter: 12 feet

7.

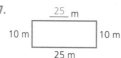

<u>25</u> m

10 m   10 m

25 m

Perimeter: 70 meters

8.

4 m   4 m

<u>4</u> m   4 m

4 m

Perimeter: 20 meters

9.

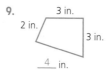

3 in.

2 in.

3 in.

<u>4</u> in.

Perimeter: 12 inches

Solve the problem.

10. Lisa measures a wall of her doll house. The perimeter of the wall is 60 centimeters. What is the unknown side length?

The unknown side length is <u>10</u> centimeters.

17 cm

18 cm

?

15 cm

⚇ Think·Pair·Share

MP3 11. Paul uses addition to find the perimeter of the square. Barbara uses multiplication to find the perimeter. Explain why both methods work.

Possible explanation: The perimeter is the sum of the side lengths of the square, so you can add the four side lengths. The side lengths are equal, so you can multiply 4 times a side length to find the perimeter of a square.

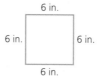

6 in.

6 in.   6 in.

6 in.

⚇ Think·Pair·Share

Peer Collaboration Ask each student to work with a partner and try to find the perimeter using both methods described. Ask:

- *Are the perimeters the same using both methods? Explain.*

- *Why can multiplication be used in this case?*

- *Can you always use multiplication when determining the perimeter of a figure? Explain why or why not.*

In summary, students should understand that they can only use multiplication as a strategy when the side lengths all have equal measures.

Return to the Essential Question

Reread the Lesson 33 Essential Question on page 296: *How can you solve problems about the perimeters of polygons?*

Ask volunteers to use what they learned in this lesson to answer this question. (Possible response: I can find the sum of all side lengths to determine the perimeter of a polygon. I can also multiply the side lengths if all the side lengths are equal.)

Mathematical Practices

Mathematical Practice Standards underline the teaching and understanding of all concepts and skills presented. The emphasis of specific practices is noted throughout the guided and independent practice of this lesson.

MP3	**Construct viable arguments and critique the reasoning of others.**

Item 11: Students explain different approaches to a problem and explain why both approaches are correct.

Independent Practice

Concept Application

Students may work independently on these pages in the classroom or at home. They may refer to the first four pages of the lesson to revisit the instruction or to see a worked-out example.

Common Errors and **Teaching Tips** may help you support student learning either in the classroom or as a follow-up for work done at home.

Common Errors

Item 7

Students may need to be reminded that a square has four equal-length sides. Encourage students to draw a diagram before solving the problem.

Teaching Tips

Items 1–4

Remind students that they can use multiplication to determine perimeter only if all the sides have the same length.

Independent Practice

Find the perimeter of each figure.

1.
25 m
14 m
25 m

Perimeter: __64__ meters

2.
3 ft
3 ft   3 ft
3 ft

Perimeter: __12__ feet

3.
9 in.   9 in.
9 in.   9 in.
9 in.

Perimeter: __45__ inches

4.
4 cm
5 cm   5 cm
10 cm

Perimeter: __24__ centimeters

Solve the problems.

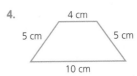

MP1 **5.** Rabbits are eating Mrs. Gianni's lettuce. She decides to put a fence around her lettuce patch. How much fencing should she buy?

8 ft
5 ft   5 ft
8 ft

Mrs. Gianni should buy __26__ feet of fencing.

MP6 **6.** Michael builds a frog pond. What is the perimeter of the pond?

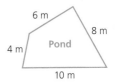

6 m
8 m
4 m   Pond
10 m

The perimeter of the pond is __28__ meters.

MP2 **7.** Emily is helping to build a platform for the school play. It is in the shape of a square with one side equal to 5 feet. The students plan to put a piece of fabric around the sides of the square. What length of fabric will they need?

The students will need a length of fabric __20__ feet long.

300 Unit 5 ▪ Focus on Measurement and Data/Geometry

Mathematical Practices

MP1	**Make sense of problems and persevere in solving them.**
Items 5 and 12: Students plan a solution.	
MP2	**Reason abstractly and quantitatively.**
Item 7: Students consider units in problem solving.	
MP4	**Model with mathematics.**
Item 14: Students relate mathematics to a real-world problem.	
MP6	**Attend to precision.**
Items 6 and 13: Students calculate accurately.	

Independent Practice

Find each unknown side length.

8.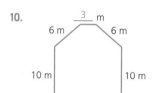

6 ft

_6_ ft   6 ft

Perimeter: 18 feet

9.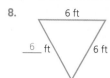

7 in.

3 in.   3 in.

_7_ in.

Perimeter: 20 inches

10.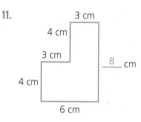

_3_ m

6 m   6 m

10 m   10 m

12 m

Perimeter: 47 meters

11.

3 cm

4 cm

3 cm

_8_ cm

4 cm

6 cm

Perimeter: 28 centimeters

Solve the problems.

MP1 **12.** This is the shape of the kite that Stan makes. The perimeter of the kite is 10 feet. What is the unknown side length?

The length of the unknown side is _3_ feet.

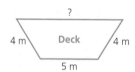

2 ft

2 ft   3 ft

?

MP6 **13.** This is the shape of Mr. Dean's deck. He measured the deck and found that the perimeter is 22 meters. What is the unknown side length?

The unknown side length is _9_ meters.

?

4 m   Deck   4 m

5 m

MP4 **14.** Jasman is cutting out stars for a science poster. The perimeter of each star is 30 centimeters and all the sides are equal. What is the length of each side?

The length of each side is _3_ centimeters.

Teaching Tips

Items 8–13

If students are struggling, remind them to represent an unknown side length with a letter and solve for that letter. Remind students to look for numbers that are easy to add mentally.

Writing About Math

▸ **Write an Opinion Text** Ask students to write a paragraph giving their opinion on when they might need to know the perimeter of a real-world figure. Have students give at least two different examples. Students should include illustrations to aid in comprehension. Ask volunteers to read their paragraphs aloud. Remind students that these are opinion paragraphs, so there are no right or wrong answers.

Independent Practice

Common Errors

Item 15
Students may be confused by the fact that there are no numbers or mathematical computations given. Emphasize that they can use words to explain the process, even with the absence of actual numbers.

Teaching Tips

Item 16
Some students might need to make a drawing of the problem before they can explain their answer.

Independent Practice

MP6 15. Mr. Peters wants to put weather stripping around a door. Explain how Mr. Peters can find out how much weather stripping he needs.
Possible answer: Mr. Peters needs to find the perimeter of the door. He should measure the four side lengths of the door and then find their sum.

MP3 16. Sharon knows the perimeter of a quadrilateral. She also knows three side lengths of the quadrilateral. Sharon says that she can find the unknown side length just by subtracting. Is she right?

Answer Yes, she is right.

· Justify your answer using words, drawings, or numbers.
Possible justification:
Sharon can subtract each side length, one by one, from the perimeter. The leftover amount is the unknown side length.

Solve the problems.

MP4 17. Ave drew this model of a soccer field. The perimeter of the real soccer field is 190 meters. What is the unknown side length?

· Show your work.
Possible answer:

```
   60        190
   60      − 155
+  35         35
  155
```

Answer The unknown side length is 35 meters.

Mathematical Practices

MP3	**Construct viable arguments and critique the reasoning of others.**
Item 16: Students share their reasoning with others.	
MP4	**Model with mathematics.**
Item 17: Students relate mathematics to real-world problems.	
MP6	**Attend to precision.**
Item 15: Students carefully formulate full explanations.	

MORE ONLINE sadlierconnect.com

Lesson 33

Independent Practice

Teaching Tips

Items 18–19
These are multi-step problems. Encourage students to write a plan for their solution and to draw the figures, if necessary, to visualize the problems and solutions.

Solve the problems.

MP5 **18.** Compare the perimeter of Rectangle A with the perimeter of Rectangle B. Write <, >, or =.

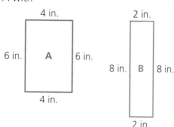

■■■ **Show your work.**
Possible answer:
Rectangle A
4 + 6 + 4 + 6 =?
(4 + 6) + (4 + 6) =?
10 + 10 = 20

Rectangle B
2 + 8 + 2 + 8 =?
(2 + 8) + (2 + 8) =?
10 + 10 = 20

The perimeter of Rectangle A __=__ the perimeter of Rectangle B.

MP7 **19.** Jill has two windows in her bedroom. The height of each window is 3 feet. The left window is 4 feet wide. The right window is 5 feet wide. How much greater is the perimeter of the right window than the perimeter of the left window?

Answer The perimeter of the right window is 2 feet more than the perimeter of the left window.

■■■ **Justify your answer using words, drawings, or numbers.**
Possible justification:
3 + 4 + 3 + 4 = 14
3 + 5 + 3 + 5 = 16
16 − 14 = 2

MP4 **20.** Jack bought 30 feet of fencing. He uses all of the fencing to make a pen for his goat. The pen is shaped like a triangle. Each of two sides is 9 feet long. What is the length of the third side?

Answer The third side of the fence is 12 feet long.

■■■ **Justify your answer using words, drawings, or numbers.**
Possible justification:
9 + 9 = 18
30 − 18 = 12

Mathematical Practices	
MP4	**Model with mathematics.**
Item 20: Students relate mathematics to real-world problems.	
MP5	**Use appropriate tools strategically.**
Item 18: Students carefully and strategically compare the figures.	
MP7	**Look for and make use of structure.**
Item 19: Students relate geometric shapes in terms of their similarities and differences.	

Common Core Focus:

3.MD.8 Solve real world and mathematical problems involving perimeters of polygons, including finding the perimeter given the side lengths, finding an unknown side length, and exhibiting rectangles with the same perimeter and different areas or with the same area and different perimeters.

OBJECTIVE

Solve problems by comparing the areas and perimeters of different rectangles.

ESSENTIAL QUESTION

Explain that different rectangles can have the same perimeter, but a different area. They can also have the same area, but different perimeters. Students will compare different rectangles to demonstrate this fact.

FLUENCY PRACTICE

Fluency practice is available at **sadlierconnect.com**.

Concept Development

Understand: Areas of different rectangles with the same perimeter

■ Students need to be able to determine the area of a rectangle by counting the number of square units in a rectangle and also by multiplying two adjacent side lengths.

■ As a demonstration, draw square units inside the rectangles to give students a visual representation and enhance understanding of both multiplication and area.

▬▬▶ Remind students to look back at the diagrams of Pen A and Pen B to see two ways to make the perimeter of a rectangle 14 feet. After solving the problem, have a volunteer draw and label the rectangle at the board.

Lesson 34

Problem Solving: Compare Perimeter and Area

Guided Instruction

In this lesson you will learn more about using perimeter and area to solve problems.

Understand: Areas of different rectangles with the same perimeter

> Angela has 14 feet of fencing. She wants to make a pen for her guinea pigs. She draws two models of rectangles that have a perimeter of 14 feet.
>
> | | 6 ft | |
> |---|---|---|
> | 1 ft | Pen A | 1 ft |
> | | 6 ft | |
>
> | | 5 ft | |
> |---|---|---|
> | 2 ft | Pen B | 2 ft |
> | | 5 ft | |
>
> Which pen will have the greater area?

Find the area of Pen A.

$1 \times 6 = 6$

The area of Pen A is 6 square feet.

Remember!
To find the area of a rectangle, you can multiply side lengths, or count unit squares.

Find the area of Pen B.

$2 \times 5 = 10$

The area of Pen B is 10 square feet.

Compare the areas of the two pens.

6 square feet < 10 square feet

➡ Pen B will have the greater area.

▬▬▶ Draw a rectangle with a perimeter of 14 feet that has an area greater than Pen B's area.

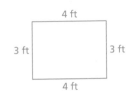

Support English Language Learners

The term *area* is used throughout this lesson. Some students may know the term *area* used in a different context.

Ask students to draw pictures or write sentences that show different understandings or meanings of the word *area*, such as *a place where you live* or *a room in your house*.

Mathematically speaking, *area* means *the number of square units needed to cover a figure without gaps or overlaps*. English language learners may need help understanding *square units* initially. Demonstrate fitting square units inside a rectangle and have students draw the model on an index card. Assist students in writing the definition of *area* in their own words under the model.

Lesson 34

Understand: Perimeters of different rectangles with the same area

Pedro is making a pen for his turtle. He wants the area of the floor of the pen to be 16 square feet. He draws two models.

Key: 1 square = 1 square foot

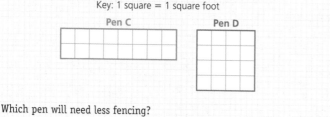

Pen C   Pen D

Which pen will need less fencing?

Find the perimeter of Pen C.

$$2 + 8 + 2 + 8 = ?$$
$$10 + 10 = 20$$

Remember!
To find the perimeter of a polygon, add the side lengths.

The perimeter of Pen C is 20 feet.

Find the perimeter of Pen D.

$$4 + 4 + 4 + 4 = 16$$

The perimeter of Pen D is 16 feet.

Compare the perimeters of the two pens.

$$20 \text{ feet} > 16 \text{ feet}$$

➡ Pen D will need less fencing.

✏ Can you draw a rectangle with an area of 16 square feet that would use less fencing than Pen D? No. This rectangle has an area of 16 square feet, but its perimeter is 34 feet.

Understand: Perimeters of different rectangles with the same area

■ In this presentation, students compare rectangles with the same area (16 square feet), but with different perimeters. This skill has a real-world application, similar to that used in the example. Extend students' thinking by asking for other instances when they might practically apply this math concept.

■ Help students see that the length of each side of each square unit of Pen C and Pen D is 1 foot. Be sure students understand how to determine the perimeter by putting hash marks on each length of square unit and counting them up, or by labeling the number of hash marks on each side with the correct number of feet.

✏ Ask students to list other possible combinations that would produce an area of 16 square feet. If students are struggling, have them make a list of the factors of 16. Students should discover that the only possible combination is 16 × 1. However, the perimeter is 34 feet, which is greater than 16 feet.

Math-to-Real-World Connection

Dog Kennel In some states, it is required by law for dog kennels to be a certain size for specific types of dogs. For example, in Pennsylvania, the law requires a dog kennel for a typical bird dog to be 6 ft by 15 ft. Tell students that they are to design a dog kennel that has an area of 100 ft². Ask students to determine the dimensions of a kennel that would require the least amount of fencing.

Guided Instruction

Connect: What you know about perimeter and area to solve problems Use this page to help students strengthen their understanding of area and perimeter and use that knowledge to solve problems.

■ Remind students that they are looking for the area, not the perimeter, and that they must multiply the side lengths of the rectangles to find the area.

■ Be sure students understand the term *least*.

■ When using < and >, remind students to put the open end of the symbol towards the larger quantity.

▸ Have students work in pairs or groups of three to determine the perimeter of each frame and place the appropriate symbol on each line. Ask students to explain how the frames can have different areas but the same perimeter.

Guided Instruction

Connect: What you know about perimeter and area to solve problems

Ms. Gonzalez has 12 inches of wood to make a picture frame. She draws three models. Which frame has the least area?

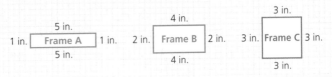

Step 1

Find the area of each frame.

Frame A
 1 × 5 = 5

The area of Frame A is 5 square inches.

Frame B
 2 × 4 = 8

The area of Frame B is 8 square inches.

Frame C
 3 × 3 = 9

The area of Frame C is 9 square inches.

Step 2

Compare the areas of the frames.

 5 square inches ___≤___ 8 square inches ___≤___ 9 square inches

➤ Frame A has the least area.

▸ Compare the perimeters of the frames.

	Frame A	Frame B	Frame C
Perimeter:	__12__ in.	__12__ in.	__12__ in.

Compare perimeters: Frame A __=__ Frame B __=__ Frame C

Math-to-Architecture Connection

Designing Houses Tell students that they are architects designing a house. The house they are designing must contain 10 rooms that are each 10 ft × 10 ft. Provide students with squares that represent the 10-ft × 10-ft rooms. Have students try different arrangements of the rooms by using the squares. Ask students to determine the area and perimeter for the house they have arranged.

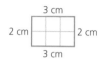

Lesson 34

Guided Practice

In exercises 1 and 2, draw a different rectangle with the same perimeter. Then find the area of each rectangle.

1. Perimeter: 10 centimeters

3 cm
2 cm · 2 cm
3 cm

Area: __6__ square cm

Key: 1 square = 1 square centimeter

4 cm
1 cm · 1 cm
4 cm

Area: __4__ square cm

2. Perimeter: 16 inches

Area: __15__ square in.

Key: 1 square = 1 square inch
Also accept 1 × 7 and 4 × 4 rectangles

with areas 7 or 16.

Area: __12__ square in.

Draw a different rectangle with the same area. Then find the perimeter of each rectangle.

3. Area = 12 square meters

Perimeter: __14__ meters

Key: 1 square = 1 square meter

Also accept 1 × 12 rectangle

with perimeter 26.

Perimeter: __16__ meters

✌ Think•Pair•Share

MP2 **4.** Manuel says that if two rectangles have the same area, they must have the same perimeter. Is he right? Explain your reasoning.
Possible answer: No. Rectangles with different side lengths can have the same area. Since they have different side lengths, their perimeters will be different.

Mathematical Practices

Mathematical Practice Standards underline the teaching and understanding of all concepts and skills presented. The emphasis of specific practices is noted throughout the guided and independent practice of this lesson.

MP2	Reason abstractly and quantitatively.

Item 4: Students use what they have learned about perimeter and area to answer the question and explain their reasoning.

Observational Assessment

Use page 307 to assess whether students are able to design rectangles with the same perimeters but different areas, and with the same areas, but different perimeters.

✌ Think•Pair•Share

Peer Collaboration Ask each student to demonstrate the thinking behind their answer by drawing a set of rectangles that supports their answer. Have students share their rectangles with a partner. Invite partners to the board to choose a set of rectangles to draw and explain to the class how their drawings support their answer to the question. Ask each pair of volunteers:

- *What are the lengths of the sides of your rectangles?*

- *Do your rectangles have the same area? Explain why or why not.*

- *Do your rectangles have the same perimeter? Explain why or why not.*

To summarize, tell students that they can draw several examples of two rectangles with the same area, but different perimeters.

Return to the Essential Question

Reread the Lesson 34 Essential Question on page 304: *How can you compare different rectangles with the same perimeter or the same area?*

Ask volunteers to use what they learned in this lesson to answer this question. (Possible response: I can draw rectangles with the same area, but different perimeters, or the same perimeter, but different areas. I can then compare the areas or perimeters to see which is greater.)

Independent Practice

Concept Application

Students may work independently on these pages in the classroom or at home. They may refer to the first four pages of the lesson to revisit the instruction or to see a worked-out example.

Common Errors and **Teaching Tips** may help you support student learning either in the classroom or as a follow-up for work done at home.

Common Errors

Item 3

Students may make a guess about which garden could grow the most strawberries, or may be confused about how to determine this. Remind them to find the area of each rectangle to determine the garden with the greatest area.

Independent Practice

In exercises 1 and 2, draw a different rectangle with the same perimeter. Then find the area of each rectangle.

1. Perimeter = 8 feet

Area: __3__ square feet

Key: 1 square = 1 square foot

Area: __4__ square feet

2. Perimeter: 18 inches

Area: __14__ square inches

Key: 1 square = 1 square inch
Also accept 1 × 8 and 3 × 6 rectangles

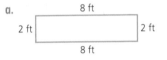

with areas 8 or 18.

Area: __20__ square inches

3. Fatima wants to grow strawberries. She has 20 feet of fencing to protect the plants. She draws four models of gardens with a perimeter of 20 feet. Choose the model for the garden that will let Fatima grow the most strawberries.

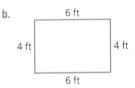

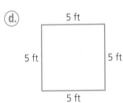

Writing About Math

▸ **Write an Opinion Text** Ask students to write a paragraph giving their opinion on which strategy for finding the area of a rectangle is most helpful to them. Have students provide reasons that support their opinion and use linking words such as *because, since,* and *for example* when writing their paragraphs.

Ask volunteers to read their paragraphs aloud. Remind students that these are opinion paragraphs, so there are no right or wrong answers.

MORE ONLINE sadlierconnect.com

Lesson 34

Independent Practice

In exercises 4 and 5, draw a different rectangle with the same area. Then find the perimeter of each rectangle.

4. Area: 10 square centimeters

Key: 1 square = 1 square centimeter

Perimeter: _14_ centimeters   Perimeter: _22_ centimeters

5. Area: 18 square inches

Key: 1 square = 1 square inch
Also accept 1 × 18 rectangle

with area 38.

Perimeter: _18_ inches   Perimeter: _22_ inches

Solve the problems.

MP4 6. Harry wants to make a corral for his toy dinosaur with an area of 24 square inches. He draws the model shown below. Draw another model of a corral that has a smaller perimeter. Then find the perimeter of each corral.

Harry's Dinosaur Corral

Perimeter: ___22 inches___   Perimeter: ___20 inches___

MP5 7. Draw a model for the coral floor from exercise 6 that will have a greater perimeter than Harry's model. Then find the perimeter of your model.

Also accept 24 × 1 model.

Perimeter: ___28 inches or 50 inches___

Teaching Tips

Items 4-7
Provide students with graph paper to provide visual support for drawing models with the same area but different perimeters.

Mathematical Practices	
MP4	**Model with mathematics.**
Item 6: Students relate mathematics to real-world problems.	
MP5	**Use appropriate tools strategically.**
Item 7: Students consider the range of available tools and decide on appropriate ones to solve the problem.	

Teaching Tips

Item 11

Point out to students that this is a two-step problem and they need to be sure to answer both questions. Some students may need to number or use hash marks on the side of each square unit to determine the lengths of each side.

Lesson 34   Problem Solving: **Compare Perimeter and Area**

Independent Practice

MP7 8. Compare the dinosaur corrals in exercise 6. How are they alike? How are they different?
Possible answer: They are both rectangles and they have the same area. But they have different perimeters. Harry's corral is longer and narrower than mine.

MP4 9. Andrew draws a rectangle with side lengths of 1 inch and 5 inches. How can Andrew draw a different rectangle with the same perimeter?
Possible answer: Andrew has to pick different side lengths that add to 6 inches, like 2 inches and 4 inches. Since the side lengths add to 6 inches, the perimeter will be the same.

MP6 10. Cheryl has 24 inches of ribbon. She wants to paste the ribbon around a birthday card for her mother. Cheryl draws two models of the card. Which card has the lesser area?

▮▬ · Show your work.
Possible answer:
8 × 4 = 32
6 × 6 = 36
32 < 36

Answer Card A has the lesser area.

MP1 11. Ms. Hansen is making a pen for her ducks. She wants the area of the floor of the pen to be 40 square meters. Ms. Hansen draws two models. Which model will need less fencing? How much less fencing will it need?

▮▬ · Show your work.

Key: 1 square = 1 square meter

Possible answer:
    4 + 10 + 4 + 10 = 28   5 + 8 + 5 + 8 = 26
    28 − 26 = 2
Answer Duck Pen B will need less fencing. It will need 2 feet less.

310   Unit 5 ▪ Focus on Measurement and Data/Geometry

Mathematical Practices

MP1	**Make sense of problems and persevere in solving them.**
Item 11: Students will analyze the problem and make a plan for solving it.	
MP4	**Model with mathematics.**
Item 9: Students explain how different rectangles have the same perimeter.	
MP6	**Attend to precision.**
Item 10: Students accurately calculate the areas of two rectangles.	
MP7	**Look for and make use of structure.**
Item 8: Students compare two rectangles.	

Lesson 34

Independent Practice

MP4 **12.** Cindy reads that the mouse family home is very dark with just one window. Draw a window with the same perimeter that will let in more light. How much greater is the area of your window than the area of the old window?

Key: 1 square = 1 square cm

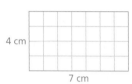

8 cm

3 cm   Mouse Window   3 cm

8 cm

🔲 **Show your work.**
Possible answer: 3 × 8 = 24
4 × 7 = 28
28 − 24 = 4

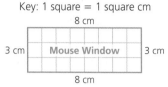

4 cm

7 cm

Also accept 5 × 6 rectangle with an area of 6 square cm more.

Answer The area of my window is 4 square cm more.

MP2 **13.** Abel has two desks in his attic. Each desktop is a different rectangle shape with an area of 6 square feet. If Abel puts glow-in-the-dark tape around the edges of both desktops, how much tape will he need?

Answer Abel will need 24 feet of tape.

🔲 **Justify your answer using words, drawings, or numbers.**
Possible justification:
1 + 6 + 1 + 6 = 14

2 + 3 + 2 + 3 = 10

14 + 10 = 24

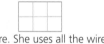

MP7 **14.** Vicky has 20 inches of wire. She uses all the wire to make a rectangle. What is the least possible area of the rectangle? What is the greatest possible area?

Answer The least possible area is 9 square inches. The greatest possible area is 25 square inches.

🔲 **Justify your answer using words, drawings, or numbers.**
Possible justification:

1 × 9 = 9
5 × 5 = 25

Common Errors

Item 12
Students may mistakenly answer the problem with a *greater than* or *less than* symbol. Be sure they understand they need to determine how much greater the area of their window is than that of the previous window.

Item 13
Students may mistakenly add the areas and get an answer of 12 square feet. Point out that the area of each desk is 6 square feet. Students must draw two different rectangles with an area of 6 square feet, find the perimeter of each rectangle, and then add the perimeters to find how much tape will be needed.

Teaching Tips

Items 12–14
It may be helpful for students to use graph paper to draw their rectangles.

Mathematical Practices

MP2	**Reason abstractly and quantitatively.**

Item 13: Students pay attention to the mathematical language in the problem to complete all steps.

MP4	**Model with mathematics.**

Item 12: Students interpret the solution to the problem in the context of the situation that is presented.

MP7	**Look for and make use of structure.**

Item 14: Students will evaluate different designs for a rectangle with a perimeter of 20 to determine the least and greatest areas.

Common Core Focus:

3.G.1 Understand that shapes in different categories may share attributes, and that the shared attributes can define a larger category. Recognize rhombuses, rectangles, and squares as examples of quadrilaterals, and draw examples of quadrilaterals that do not belong to any of these subcategories.

OBJECTIVE
Use attributes to identify shapes.

ESSENTIAL QUESTION
An attribute is a defining characteristic of a shape, such as the number of sides or the number of vertices. Shapes can easily be defined and categorized according to their defining attributes.

PREREQUISITE SKILLS
Use Item K on page 342 of the Foundational Skills Handbook to review using sides and angles to identify two-dimensional shapes.

FLUENCY PRACTICE
Fluency practice is available at **sadlierconnect.com**.

Concept Development

Understand: Using number of sides and number of vertices to identify polygons

■ Students learn how to use attributes to identify two-dimensional shapes and that shapes in different categories may share some attributes.

■ Remind students that a polygon is a two-dimensional closed figure with straight sides.

■ Shapes that are not quadrilaterals should also be discussed. If a polygon does not have 4 sides and 4 vertices, then it is not a quadrilateral. Encourage students to sort shapes according to attributes.

Lesson 35 — Understand Shapes and Attributes

Essential Question:
How do you use attributes to identify shapes?
3.G.1

Words to Know:
vertex (vertices)
angle
right angle
rhombus

Guided Instruction

In this lesson you will learn how to use attributes to identify shapes.

Understand: Using number of sides and number of vertices to identify polygons

Look at these shapes.

Which ones are quadrilaterals?

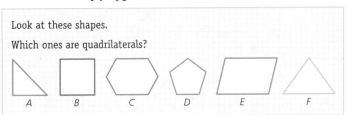

A B C D E F

Two sides of a polygon meet at a **vertex** and form an **angle**.
You can identify a polygon by counting its sides and its **vertices**.

vertex

A quadrilateral is a polygon that has 4 straight sides and 4 vertices.
Count the number of sides and vertices of each shape above.
Shapes B and E each have 4 sides and 4 vertices.
They are quadrilaterals.

➡ Shapes B and E are quadrilaterals.

▸ Name each shape if you can. Tell how many sides and vertices each has.
Shape A–triangle: 3 sides and 3 vertices; Shape B–quadrilateral or square: 4 sides and 4 vertices; Shape C–hexagon: 6 sides and 6 vertices; Shape D–pentagon: 5 sides and 5 vertices; Shape E–quadrilateral, 4 sides and 4 vertices; Shape F–triangle: 3 sides and 3 vertices.

Words to Know

vertex (vertices): the point at which two sides meet to form an angle

angle: formed when two sides extend from a common endpoint called the vertex

right angle: an angle that forms a square corner

rhombus: a quadrilateral that has sides of equal length

Glossary can be found on pp. 347–350.

Understand: Using lengths of sides and right angles to identify special quadrilaterals

> Look at these three special quadrilaterals.
>
>
>
>   A   B   C
>
> What is the name of each special quadrilateral?

Look at the sides and the angles.

    Quadrilateral A has opposite sides that are the same length. It has 4 angles that are square corners. Each of these angles is called a right angle.

Quadrilateral A is a rectangle.

    All 4 sides of Quadrilateral B are the same length.

Quadrilateral B is a rhombus.

    All 4 sides of Quadrilateral C are the same length. It has 4 right angles.

Since Quadrilateral C has the attributes of both a rhombus and a rectangle, Quadrilateral C is a square.

➡ Quadrilateral A is a rectangle; Quadrilateral B is a rhombus; Quadrilateral C is a square.

 Draw a quadrilateral that is NOT a rectangle, a rhombus, or a square.
Check students' drawings.
A possible quadrilateral is shown.

Understand: Using lengths of sides and right angles to identify special quadrilaterals

■ You may wish to review attributes of quadrilaterals such as number of sides and number of angles.

■ Students should recognize rhombuses, rectangles, and squares as examples of special quadrilaterals, and draw an example of a quadrilateral that does not belong to any of these subcategories.

■ Emphasize that shapes in different categories may share attributes, and that the attributes can define a larger category. Have students identify the shared attributes they see on this page, such as rectangles and squares both have four right angles.

■ Have students explain why a square has attributes of both a rectangle and a rhombus.

■ Students should have an opportunity to draw multiple examples of each special quadrilateral. Ask students to describe the similarities and differences among special quadrilaterals.

 Have students share their drawings. Have the rest of the class check to make sure the drawing shows a quadrilateral, but does not have all of the same attributes of a rectangle, rhombus, or square.

Support English Language Learners

English language learners may need additional support with the names and meanings of the following terms: *quadrilateral, vertex, angle, right angle,* and *rhombus*. Have students create a picture book. To make the book, type the five terms and simplified definitions and make copies for students. Use a drawing tool to make pictures to illustrate each term, print the pictures, and make copies. Have students cut and paste the terms into a booklet made of folded construction paper. Work with students as they match and paste the definitions and pictures with the correct terms.

Students might look online or in magazines for real-world examples of the terms. They can add these pictures to their picture books.

Guided Instruction

Connect: **What you know about attributes of polygons** Use this page to help students strengthen their understanding of attributes of polygons.

■ Remind students that the number of sides and vertices will determine what type of polygon each shape is.

■ Students can measure the sides of the shapes by placing a piece of paper next to a side and marking the endpoints on the paper. Then, they can hold the paper next to each side to verify that the sides are the same length.

■ Tell students that if a quadrilateral is a special quadrilateral, they should name it as a square, rectangle, or rhombus. They should use the most specific name.

■ Allow students to sort the names of the polygons from their responses according to attributes.

Guided Instruction

Connect: **What you know about attributes of polygons**

> Clara used polygons to make this drawing. What polygons did Clara use?

To identify the polygons, first count the number of sides and vertices. If the polygon is a quadrilateral, check to see if it is a special quadrilateral.

Step 1

The head has 4 sides and 4 vertices. The head is a quadrilateral. Check to see if the quadrilateral is a special quadrilateral. The head has 4 equal sides and 4 right angles.

The head is a ____square____.

Step 2

Each ear has 6 sides and 6 vertices.

Each ear is a ____hexagon____.

> **Remember!**
> A polygon with 6 sides and 6 vertices is a hexagon.

Step 3

The body has 3 sides and 3 vertices.

The body is a ____triangle____.

Step 4

Each leg has 4 sides and 4 vertices.
Each leg is a quadrilateral.
Each leg has opposite sides that are equal and 4 right angles.

Each leg is a ____rectangle____.

> **Remember!**
> Check if the quadrilateral is a special quadrilateral.

➡ To make the drawing, Clara used ____1 square____, ____2 hexagons____, ____1 triangle____, and ____2 rectangles____.

Math-to-Science Connection

Snowflakes A strong understanding of attributes of shapes will enable students to develop a stronger understanding of geometric concepts.

Snowflakes are very unique natural occurrences, as some scientists claim that no two snowflakes are alike. However, snowflakes can be classified by shape, though most snowflakes are hexagonal. Search on the Internet or in other resources for a chart that shows the types of snowflakes and provide copies for students. Allow students to name and label shapes found within each snowflake. Additionally, students can create their own snowflakes with construction paper. Encourage students to try to cut as many different shapes as possible.

MORE ONLINE sadlierconnect.com   Lesson 35

For each polygon, write the number of sides and the number of vertices. Write triangle, quadrilateral, pentagon, or hexagon to name each figure.

1.

___3___ sides
___3___ vertices
____triangle____

2.

___5___ sides
___5___ vertices
____pentagon____

3.

___4___ sides
___4___ vertices
____quadrilateral____

Use the quadrilateral at the right for exercises 4–7.

4. Are the opposite sides the same length? ___yes___

5. Are all 4 sides the same length? ___yes___

6. Does the quadrilateral have 4 right angles? ___no___

7. Is the quadrilateral a rectangle, rhombus, or square? ___rhombus___

Solve the problem.

8. Orlando has a garden in the shape of a quadrilateral. Each side of the garden is 6 feet long. The garden has four right angles. Draw and label a picture to show Orlando's garden. What is the best name for the shape of the garden? square

6 ft
6 ft

★ Think·Pair·Share

MP3 9. Irene says that a rectangle is always a quadrilateral. Jamie says that a rectangle is sometimes a square. Are both students correct? Explain your reasoning.
Possible explanation: Yes. A rectangle always has 4 sides so it is always a quadrilateral. If the length of each side of a rectangle is equal, then the rectangle is a square.

Unit 5 ■ Focus on Measurement and Data/Geometry **315**

Observational Assessment

Use page 315 to assess whether students are able to identify and categorize shapes. If students struggle, they may require additional practice identifying attributes of shapes.

★ Think·Pair·Share

Peer Collaboration Ask students to determine why each claim in the problem is correct. Then break the students into pairs. Pairs should share whether they agree or disagree with the students in the problem and why. Guide students with questions such as:

• *Why is a rectangle always a quadrilateral?*

• *Why is a square always a rectangle?*

• *Is a rectangle always a square? Why or why not?*

Return to the Essential Question

Reread the Lesson 35 Essential Question on page 312: *How do you use attributes to identify shapes?*

Ask volunteers to use what they learned in this lesson to answer this question. (Possible responses: I can use attributes, such as the number of sides and the number of vertices, to identify shapes. I can use the lengths of sides and right angles to identify special quadrilaterals.)

Mathematical Practices

Mathematical Practice Standards underline the teaching and understanding of all concepts and skills presented. The emphasis of specific practices is noted throughout the guided and independent practice of this lesson.

MP3	**Construct viable arguments and critique the reasoning of others.**

Item 9: Students explain two different approaches to a problem.

Independent Practice

Concept Application

Students may work independently on these pages in the classroom or at home. They may refer to the first four pages of the lesson to revisit the instruction or to see a worked-out example.

Common Errors and **Teaching Tips** may help you support student learning either in the classroom or as a follow-up for work done at home.

Teaching Tips

Items 1-7

Review this lesson's *Words to Know* to better enable students to understand the problems.

Item 1

The drawing shown is not a typical representation of a pentagon. Remind students that pentagons must have 5 sides, but they may have different shapes. The lengths of the sides of a pentagon may not be equal.

Independent Practice

Write the name for the figure. Choose triangle, quadrilateral, rectangle, rhombus, square, pentagon, or hexagon.

1.
_____pentagon_____

2.
_____rectangle_____

3.
_____quadrilateral_____

4.
_____triangle_____

5.
_____rhombus_____

6.
_____square_____

7. Are any of the quadrilaterals in exercises 1–6 special quadrilaterals? If so, write the problem number and the special name.
2. rectangle; 5. rhombus; 6. square

Draw each figure.

8. rectangle
Check students' drawings.

9. rhombus
Check students' drawings.

10. square
Check students' drawings.

11. quadrilateral that is not a rectangle, a rhombus, or a square
Check students' drawings.

Writing About Math

 · **Use Descriptive Details** Ask students to write a description of a 'mystery shape' for others to figure out. Require students to include at least four details written in complete sentences. The details will include defining attributes of the shape without naming the shape.

Students will share their 'mystery shape' paragraphs with the class. Classmates should name the shape described.

Lesson 35

Independent Practice

12. Which figure is a rectangle?

a.

b.

c.

d.

Teaching Tips

Item 12

Encourage students to explain why answer choice d is correct. Have them explain why answer choice b is not a rectangle.

13. Which figure is a rhombus?

a.

b.

c.

d.

14. Which figure is NOT a quadrilateral?

a.

b.

c.

d.

Unit 5 ■ Focus on Measurement and Data/Geometry **317**

Digital Connection

Painting Software Use drawing or paint software on a computer to create artwork containing various shapes and patterns. Encourage students to create patterns with as many different shapes as possible. Print students' artwork and use it as a discussion tool in locating and defining attributes of various shapes.

Independent Practice

Common Errors

Item 15

Students might draw shapes that are not quadrilaterals. If so, take some time to review the attributes of quadrilaterals. Illustrate some examples and non-examples of quadrilaterals for students to identify.

Teaching Tips

Item 16

There are several questions to answer for this item. Encourage students to think about one question at a time to better understand the problem.

Independent Practice

MP7 **15.** Draw two different quadrilaterals. Check students' drawings.

How are the quadrilaterals you drew alike? How are they different?
Possible answer: Both quadrilaterals have 4 sides and 4 vertices. The quadrilaterals are different shapes and different sizes.

MP6 **16.** A window has 6 panes of glass.

What is the shape of the window?
What is the shape of each pane of glass?
How did you identify the shapes?
The window is a rectangle. Each pane of glass is a square. The window has opposite sides that are the same length and 4 right angles. Each pane of glass has equal side lengths and 4 right angles.

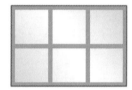

MP4 **17.** Lance made this drawing of his kite.

What is the shape of the kite?
How do you know?
The kite is a quadrilateral because it has 4 straight sides and 4 vertices.

Mathematical Practices

MP4	**Model with mathematics.**

Item 17: Students explain the attributes of a two-dimensional shape.

MP6	**Attend to precision.**

Item 16: Students carefully formulate a full explanation of the attributes of the object shown in the problem.

MP7	**Look for and make use of structure.**

Item 15: Students discuss the similarities and differences between two different quadrilaterals.

Lesson 35

Independent Practice

MP6 **18.** Christine thinks that both of these figures are quadrilaterals.

Is she correct?

Answer <u>No, Christine is not correct.</u>

▶ **Justify your answer using words, drawings, or numbers.**
Possible justification: The figures do not have 4 straight sides.

MP3 **19.** Juan says that any square is also a rhombus. Clay says that any rhombus is also a square. Who is correct?

Answer <u>Juan is correct that any square is also a rhombus.</u>

▶ **Justify your answer using words, drawings, or numbers.**
Possible justification: Both are quadrilaterals. Any square is also a rhombus since all 4 sides are the same length. A rhombus is not always a square since it may not have 4 right angles.

MP6 **20.** Victoria says that a quadrilateral can have more than one name. Is she correct?

Answer <u>Yes, Victoria is correct.</u>

▶ **Justify your answer using words, drawings, or numbers.**
Possible justification: A closed figure with 4 straight sides and 4 vertices is a quadrilateral. A rectangle, a rhombus, and a square are also quadrilaterals. A square is a quadrilateral that is both a rhombus and a rectangle.

Unit 5 ■ Focus on Measurement and Data/Geometry **319**

Common Errors

Item 18

Students may assume that both figures are quadrilaterals because they are closed and appear to have four sides. Review the attributes of quadrilaterals with students.

Teaching Tips

Item 20

If students have difficulties naming subcategories of quadrilaterals, draw a rectangle, a rhombus, and a square for all to see. Discuss the attributes that make a shape a quadrilateral, a rhombus, a square, and a rectangle.

Mathematical Practices	
MP3	**Construct viable arguments and critique the reasoning of others.**
Item 19: Students share reasoning to explain which answer is correct.	
MP6	**Attend to precision.**
Item 18: Students accurately communicate the attributes of a true quadrilateral.	
Item 20: Students carefully formulate a full explanation as to why a quadrilateral can have more than one name.	

Common Core Focus:

3.G.2 Partition shapes into parts with equal areas. Express the area of each part as a unit fraction of the whole.

OBJECTIVE

Understand how to partition shapes into parts with equal areas.

ESSENTIAL QUESTION

Students have learned about unit fractions and the concept of area. In this final lesson, students will learn how to partition shapes into equal parts, or areas. They will then express each area as a unit fraction of the whole.

PREREQUISITE SKILLS

Use Item L on page 342 of the Foundational Skills Handbook to review counting to find the number of same-size squares in a rectangle.

FLUENCY PRACTICE

Fluency practice is available at **sadlierconnect.com**.

Concept Development

Understand: Partitioning a circle into 4 parts with equal area

■ Help students understand the connection between unit fractions and partitioning a circle into equal parts.

■ Remind students what the numerator and denominator of a unit fraction represent.

■ To solidify the connection between partitioning and unit fractions, model breaking a circle apart into 4 equal parts.

When students have finished, discuss which words in the prompt they found most helpful in creating their answer. Help them recognize that phrases such as *4 equal parts* and *each part of the whole* were helpful in identifying the fraction.

Lesson 36 — Partition Shapes to Make Equal Areas

Essential Question: How do you partition shapes to make equal areas?

3.G.2

Guided Instruction

In this lesson you will learn how to partition shapes to make equal areas.

Understand: Partitioning a circle into 4 parts with equal area

Amos has a pizza that he wants to cut into 4 slices. He wants each slice to have the same area. How can Amos cut the pizza? What fraction or part of the pizza does each slice represent?

You can draw lines to partition a whole into 4 equal parts. Use a horizontal line and a vertical line. Or use two diagonal lines.

Remember!
Write a unit fraction to identify one equal part of the whole. The whole has 4 equal parts. One equal part is $\frac{1}{4}$ of the whole.

The pizza is now cut into four equal parts. Each part of the pizza has the same area. The area of each part is $\frac{1}{4}$ of the area of the whole pizza.

➤ Amos can cut the pizza into fourths as shown above. Each slice of the pizza is $\frac{1}{4}$ the area of the whole pizza.

Draw a rectangle. Partition the whole rectangle into 4 equal parts. What fraction is each part of the whole rectangle?
Possible answer:

Each part is $\frac{1}{4}$ of the whole rectangle.

Support English Language Learners

The terms *partition* and *part*, as they are used in this lesson, may be confusing for some students. Model the correct pronunciation of each term, paying special attention to the *-tion* ending of *partition* as many languages do not have an equivalent sound. Tell students that in this lesson, the term *part* is a noun, it is a piece of something. The term *partition* is a verb, it is something that they can do to separate an object into pieces. Give students a sheet of construction paper. Tell them they will *partition* the paper by folding it. Have them fold the paper so the long edges touch and then fold it again so the short edges touch. Have them unfold the paper and write "1 part" in each smaller rectangle. Tell them they partitioned the paper into four equal parts.

Lesson 36

Guided Instruction

Understand: Partitioning a rectangle into 8 parts with equal area

Rachel has a rectangular garden. She wants to partition the garden into 8 equal parts. She will plant different vegetables in each part, including carrots.

How can Rachel partition her garden? What fraction represents the area of each part of the garden? What part of the garden will Rachel plant with carrots?

Partition a rectangle into 8 equal parts.

Partition a rectangle into 8 equal parts in another way.

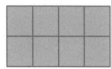

There are 8 equal parts. Each section of the garden is 1 equal part of the garden. The area of each part of the garden is $\frac{1}{8}$ of the whole garden.

Remember!
Write a unit fraction to show one equal part of the whole.

➡ Rachel can partition her garden into 8 equal parts as shown above. The area of each part of the garden is $\frac{1}{8}$ the area of the whole garden. She will plant $\frac{1}{8}$ of the garden with carrots.

✏ Show another way that Rachel could partition her garden into 8 equal parts. Check students' work. A possible answer is shown.

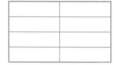

Understand: Partitioning a rectangle into 8 parts with equal area

■ This presentation shows how partitioning a rectangle into 8 equal parts can be done in many ways, but one part always represents the unit fraction $\frac{1}{8}$.

■ Help students understand that the word problem does not tell them how the rectangle should be partitioned. Have them underline or highlight the important words, *8 equal parts*, in the first paragraph.

■ Have students identify and highlight the important words in the second paragraph and discuss as a class what the problem is asking them to find.

✏ Have volunteers share their work. Then analyze as a class whether the answers are accurate. Ask the class if they would have partitioned the rectangle differently if it were taller than it is wide.

Math-to-Cooking Connection

Equal Portions Most students have seen what can happen when a snack, such as an apple or granola bar, isn't partitioned into equal parts. Someone may be upset if given the smaller piece.

Have students use the mathematical language from this lesson to describe a time when they had to partition food into equal parts and what unit fraction each part represented. Alternatively, they could tell about a time when food was not partitioned in this way and what the results were. As time allows, have students talk, write, draw, or act out their descriptions.

Connect: What you know about partitioning shapes to make equal areas Use this page to help students strengthen their understanding of how partitioning shapes into equal areas and unit fractions are related.

■ Students should understand the concept of area and how to calculate it. Remind students that area is the number of unit squares needed to cover a shape. They can also think of area as the interior of a shape.

■ Explain that when Step 3 asks, *What is the area of each pane of glass?* it is not asking them to calculate the area in terms of number of unit squares. They should describe the equal part (the pane of glass) as a unit fraction of the whole area (the entire window).

✏️ ▸ Have volunteers share their work and discuss the shape of the equal parts of their partitioned squares. Point out how these equal parts are not unit squares. Then discuss which shape(s) could be partitioned into equal parts so that the equal parts are the same kind of shape as the whole. Students should see that a particular shape may have to have a specific number of equal parts for this to be true.

Guided Instruction

Connect: What you know about partitioning shapes to make equal areas

A designer partitions a square stained glass window into equal parts. Each part of the window has a pane of glass that is a different color. What fraction represents the area of each pane of glass?

Stained Glass Window Design

Step 1

The square is partitioned into equal parts. Count the number of equal parts.

How many equal parts is the square partitioned into? __6__

Step 2

A unit fraction shows one equal part of the whole. What unit fraction represents one equal part of the whole window?
$\frac{1}{6}$

Step 3

The area of each pane of glass is one equal part of the area of the window.

What is the area of each pane of glass?
$\frac{1}{6}$ of the area of the window.

➡ The area of each pane of glass in the stained glass window is $\frac{1}{6}$ of the area of the window.

✏️ ▸ Draw a square. Show another way to partition your square into six equal parts. Check students' work. A possible answer is shown.

Math-to-Art Connection

Modern Art Many forms of art make use of partitioning shapes into equal parts to create interesting compositions and striking patterns. Have each student choose a shape such as a circle, rectangle, or square. Then assign each student a number from 2 to 10. Have them create their own modern art by drawing their shape and partitioning it into their assigned number of equal parts. Let them use any colors they wish to color in the equal parts with the exception of one part. They should then title their artwork using that unit fraction. Display the artwork for the remainder of the lesson.

MORE ONLINE sadlierconnect.com

Lesson 36

Guided Practice

In exercises 1–3, each shape is partitioned into parts with equal areas. Express the area of one equal part of each as a unit fraction of the whole area.

1. $\frac{1}{3}$ 2.  $\frac{1}{6}$ 3. $\frac{1}{8}$

Use the circles below for exercises 4–8.

Circle A   Circle B

4. Partition each circle into two equal parts in different ways.

5. Look at Circle A. What unit fraction represents each equal part of the circle? $\frac{1}{2}$

6. Look at Circle B. What unit fraction represents each equal part of the circle? $\frac{1}{2}$

7. What is the area of each part of Circle A?
   $\frac{1}{2}$ the area of the whole circle

8. What is the area of each part of Circle B?
   $\frac{1}{2}$ the area of the whole circle

Think•Pair•Share

MP7 9. Both of these squares are partitioned into equal parts. Are the areas of each part of these squares the same? Explain your reasoning.
Possible explanation: Yes. For both squares the area of each equal part is $\frac{1}{4}$ the area of the whole square.

Observational Assessment

Use page 323 to assess whether students can partition shapes into equal areas, and express the area of one equal part as a unit fraction.

Think•Pair•Share

Peer Collaboration Break students into pairs. Have students discuss their conclusions with their partners. Ensure each student justifies his or her reasoning. Then, have pairs share their reasoning with the class. Encourage class discussion and student participation by asking questions such as:

- *What do you think "same" means in the question?*

- *How would you describe each square and each square's equal parts?*

Return to the Essential Question

Reread the Lesson 36 Essential Question on page 320: *How do you partition shapes to make equal areas?*

Ask volunteers to use what they learned in this lesson to answer this question. (Possible response: I draw lines vertically, horizontally, or diagonally so that each part is of equal size.)

Invite volunteers to share their ideas about partitioning a shape to make equal areas in different ways.

Mathematical Practices

Mathematical Practice Standards underline the teaching and understanding of all concepts and skills presented. The emphasis of specific practices is noted throughout the guided and independent practice of this lesson.

MP7	**Look for and make use of structure.**

Item 9: Students discuss the similarities and differences of geometric shapes that have been partitioned.

Independent Practice

Concept Application

Students may work independently on these pages in the classroom or at home. They may refer to the first four pages of the lesson to revisit the instruction or to see a worked-out example.

Common Errors and **Teaching Tips** may help you support student learning either in the classroom or as a follow-up for work done at home.

Common Errors

Item 6

Some students may incorrectly compare the unit fractions. Determine what aspect they are struggling with, the symbols or the fractions themselves. If it's the symbols, remind them that these are *less than* symbols, and therefore the fractions should be listed from least to greatest. If it's the fractions, tell students to imagine each rectangle is a plate of their favorite food. Which rectangle would give them the biggest part?

Teaching Tips

Item 5

If students struggle with the meaning and usage of the phrases *equal parts* versus *equal area*, explain that if a whole is partitioned into equal parts, it is also partitioned into equal areas.

Independent Practice

In exercises 1–3, each shape is partitioned into parts with equal areas. Express the area of each part as a unit fraction of the whole area.

1.

$\frac{1}{6}$

2.

$\frac{1}{2}$

3.

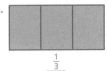

$\frac{1}{3}$

4. Which rectangle is partitioned into 6 parts with equal areas?

a.

b.

  c.

d.

5. What unit fraction represents each equal area of the circle?

  a. $\frac{1}{8}$ b. 1

  c. $\frac{8}{8}$ d. 8

6. Look at the rectangles in exercises 4 a, b, and c. The rectangles are all the same size and area. Find the unit fraction for one part of each of the rectangles. Write the unit fraction next to the rectangle. Compare the unit fractions here.

$$\frac{1}{6} < \frac{1}{5} < \frac{1}{3}$$

Writing About Math

▸ **Write a Narrative Text** Have students write a short story using imagined events and characters who make use of a shape that has been partitioned into equal parts, and one equal area is consumed or used. For example, a football player could run $\frac{1}{3}$ of the field to score a touchdown.

Have pairs of students read each other's stories and then draw and write the shape, the equal parts, and the unit fraction described.

Lesson 36

Independent Practice

Teaching Tips

Items 7–9

These shapes can be partitioned in more than two ways. Challenge students to draw all of the ways each shape can be partitioned on a separate sheet of paper.

In exercises 7–9, show two different ways to partition each figure into the given number of equal parts. Then write the fraction that represents each equal part of the whole area.
Check students' drawings. Possible answers are shown.

7. 4 equal parts

Answer $\frac{1}{4}$

Answer $\frac{1}{4}$

8. 6 equal parts

Answer $\frac{1}{6}$

Answer $\frac{1}{6}$

9. 8 equal parts

Answer $\frac{1}{8}$

Answer $\frac{1}{8}$

10. Draw two matching rectangles. Show two different ways to partition the rectangle into thirds. Check students' drawings.

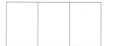 

Unit 5 ■ Focus on Measurement and Data/Geometry **325**

Digital Connection

Partitioning Shapes Have students use drawing software to draw a polygon or circle. Then have each student use an online random number generator to determine the number of equal parts to partition the shape into. Finally, students should type or draw the unit fraction that represents the area of one part and print their work for display for the class.

Independent Practice

Teaching Tips

Item 12

Students may be confused by the use of the term *unit fraction* in the first question, and the use of the term *fraction* in the second question. Remind them that each equal part can be expressed as a unit fraction of the whole, and the unit fraction can also be used to express the area of each part of the whole. Help students realize that the questions are asking for the same fraction.

Independent Practice

MP7 **11.** Look back at your drawings for exercise 9. Compare your drawings with those of a partner. What can you say about the area of each part in your drawings and in your partner's drawings?
Possible answer: Even though the drawings are different, each part of the rectangle is $\frac{1}{8}$ of the area of the whole rectangle.

Solve the problems.

MP4 **12.** Zach has a piece of carpet. He plans to cut the carpet into 3 equal size pieces. What unit fraction represents each equal size piece of the carpet? What fraction represents the area of each piece of the carpet?

▭ · **Make a drawing.**
Check students' drawings.

Answer The fraction is $\frac{1}{3}$; each piece is $\frac{1}{3}$ the area of the whole carpet.

MP4 **13.** Jessica has a tablecloth. She folds it into 8 equal parts. What fraction represents each of the folded parts of the tablecloth? What fraction represents the area of each of the folded parts?

▭ · **Make a drawing.**
Check students' drawings.

Answer The fraction is $\frac{1}{8}$; each folded part is $\frac{1}{8}$ the area of the whole tablecloth.

MP4 **14.** Carl has a large piece of cotton fabric. He wants to cut it into 6 equal, smaller pieces. What fraction represents each smaller piece of the fabric? What fraction represents the area of each of the smaller pieces?

▭ · **Make a drawing.**
Check students' drawings.

Answer The fraction is $\frac{1}{6}$; each smaller piece is $\frac{1}{6}$ the area of the whole piece of cotton fabric.

Mathematical Practices	
MP4	**Model with mathematics.**
Items 12–14: Students model partitioning shapes into equal parts and then explain the relationship of each equal part to a unit fraction.	
MP7	**Look for and make use of structure.**
Item 11: Students evaluate the structure of solutions to a previous problem to describe how partitioning the rectangles are similar and different.	

Independent Practice

Solve the problems.

MP7 **15.** Ron has a large poster board for a report he is doing. He partitions the poster board into parts with equal-size areas. The area of each part is $\frac{1}{6}$ of the area of the whole poster board. Ron will put a picture of a different animal in each part. How many animals can Ron put on his poster?

Answer Ron can put 6 animals on his poster.

🖉 · **Justify your answer using words, drawings, or numbers.**
Possible justification: Each part is $\frac{1}{6}$ of the whole so there are 6 parts with equal areas in the whole.

MP3 **16.** Mr. Drake cut construction paper into 8 triangles for his students to make flags. Each triangle has an equal area. The area of each triangle is $\frac{1}{4}$ of the area of the whole sheet of construction paper. How many pieces of construction paper did Mr. Drake cut? How many triangles did he make from each piece of construction paper?

Answer Mr. Drake cut 2 pieces of construction paper, each cut into 4 equal-size triangles.

🖉 · **Justify your answer using words, drawings, or numbers.**
Possible justification: Each piece of construction paper must be cut into fourths since the area of each triangle is $\frac{1}{4}$ of a whole. Since there are 8 triangles, he must have cut 2 pieces of paper.

MP6 **17.** Delia has a sheet of plastic shaped like a hexagon. She needs to cut the plastic into pieces with equal areas. She says that she can use both of these patterns to cut the plastic. Do you agree? Explain your reasoning.

Answer No, she can only use the left pattern to cut the hexagon into equal areas.

🖉 · **Justify your answer using words, drawings, or numbers.**
Possible justification: The left hexagon is cut into fourths and each piece has the same area. The right hexagon is not cut into equal-size pieces so the areas of the pieces are not the same.

Unit 5 ■ Focus on Measurement and Data/Geometry   **327**

Common Errors

Item 16

Students may reach an incorrect answer if they are misinterpreting the relationship between 8 equal triangles and each triangle being $\frac{1}{4}$ of a whole sheet of construction paper.

Point out that the first part of the problem is to determine how many pieces of construction paper Mr. Drake cut. Since each triangle is $\frac{1}{4}$ of a whole sheet, and there are $\frac{4}{4}$ in a whole, Mr. Drake can cut out only 4 triangles from each sheet. Since he has 8 triangles, he needed to have 2 sheets of paper.

Alternatively, allow students to model the word problem with actual construction paper.

Return to the

Progress Check

Remind students to return to the Progress Check self-assessment, page 253, to check off additional items they have mastered during the unit.

Mathematical Practices	
MP3	**Construct viable arguments and critique the reasoning of others.**
Item 16: Students construct a viable argument to justify their reasoning.	
MP6	**Attend to precision.**
Item 17: Students formulate explanations to justify their analysis.	
MP7	**Look for and make use of structure.**
Item 15: Students partition a shape to solve a problem.	

The Common Core Review covers all the standards presented in the unit. Use it to assess your students' mastery of the unit's concepts and skills.

Depth of Knowledge

The depth of knowledge is a ranking of the content complexity of assessment items based on Webb's Depth of Knowledge (DOK) levels. The levels increase in complexity as shown below.

Level 1: Recall and Reproduction
Level 2: Basic Skills and Concepts
Level 3: Strategic Reasoning and Thinking
Level 4: Extended Thinking

Item	Standard	DOK
1	3.G.1	1
2	3.G.1	1
3	3.MD.6	2
4	3.MD.6	2
5	3.MD.8	2
6	3.MD.7a	1
7	3.MD.7a	2
8	3.MD.8	2
9	3.MD.8	2
10	3.MD.7c	2
11	3.G.2	2
12	3.MD.7a	2
13	3.MD.7d	2
14	3.MD.8	2
15	3.MD.7b	2
16	3.MD.7	3
17	3.G.1	3
18	3.MD.8	4
19	3.MD.7c	3

For exercises 1 and 2, draw an example of the shape.
Drawings may vary. Possible shapes shown.

1. rhombus

2. quadrilateral that is not a rectangle or rhombus

For exercises 3–5, use the figure at the right.

3. What is the area of the shaded figure?
   __10__ square units

4. What is the area of the part of the figure that is not shaded? __20__ square units

5. What is the perimeter of the shaded figure?
   __18__ units

For exercises 6–9, use the rectangle at the right.

3 in.
4 in.

6. Shade one unit square in the rectangle. What is the area of the square you shaded? __1 square inch__

7. How many 1-inch square tiles would you need to cover the rectangle completely? __12 tiles__

8. What is the perimeter of the rectangle? __14 inches__

9. What is the area of the rectangle? __12 square inches__

Circle the correct answers.

10. A rectangle has side lengths of 6 meters and 14 meters. Wei-Yin wants to use the Distributive Property to find the area of the rectangle. Which equations could Wei-Yin use?

    (a.) $(6 \times 4) + (6 \times 10)$ b. $(6 \times 4) \times (6 \times 10)$

    (c.) $6 \times (4 + 10)$ (d.) $(2 \times 14) + (4 \times 14)$

UNIT 5 Common Core Review

11. Partition the pie into eight equal slices.

Write the fraction that represents one slice.

$\frac{1}{8}$

12. This is a model of Kim's garden. What is the area of Kim's garden in square feet?

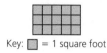

Key: ▢ = 1 square foot

_____15 square feet_____

13. This is a model of the floor in Delma's room. What is the area of the floor?

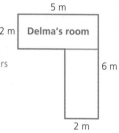

5 m

2 m   Delma's room

6 m

2 m

▬▬ · **Show your work.** Students' work may vary.
Possible answer shown. I partitioned the floor into two
rectangles. Top rectangle area: 2 × 5 = 10 square meters
Bottom rectangle: length: 6 m − 2 m = 4 m;
area: 4 × 2 = 8 square meters
10 sq. meters + 8 sq. meters = 18 sq. meters

Answer 18 square meters

For exercises 14–16, use the model of the closet floor.

14. Mike measures the distance around the floor. What is the distance?

The distance around the floor is 32 feet.

Closet   7 ft

9 ft

15. What is the area of the floor?

The area is 63 square feet.

16. A carpet tile is 1-foot square. Each box contains 10 tiles. How many boxes of tiles should Mike buy to cover the floor with tiles?

▬▬ · **Show your work.** Possible answer:
Each tile covers 1 square foot. Since the area of the floor is 63 square feet,
Mike needs 63 tiles.
6 boxes × 10 = 60 tiles; 60 tiles is not enough.
Mike needs to buy 1 more box.

Answer Mike should buy 7 boxes of tiles.

This chart correlates the Common Core Review items with the lessons in which the concepts and skills are presented.

Item	Lesson
1	35
2	35
3	28
4	28
5	33
6	29
7	29
8	33
9	29
10	30
11	36
12	29
13	31
14	33
15	29
16	32
17	35
18	34
19	30

Writing About Math

✏️ Direct students to respond to the Unit 5 Essential Question. (This can also be found on student page 255.)

Essential Question:
How can you find the area and perimeter of geometric shapes?

Possible responses:
- I can tile and multiply the length and width to find the area of a rectangle.
- I can use the Distributive Property to find the area.
- I can add the lengths of all sides of a figure to find the perimeter.

Unit Assessment

- Unit 5 Common Core Review, *pp. 328–330*
- Unit 5 Performance Task ONLINE

Additional Assessment Options

- Performance Task 2, *pp. 331–336* ALSO ONLINE

Optional Purchase:

- iProgress Monitor ONLINE
- Progress Monitor Student Benchmark Assessment Booklet

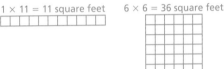

UNIT 5 Common Core Review

Solve the problems.

MP3 **17.** Ciro says that a rectangle is always a square. Rewrite his statement to make it correct.

Answer Answers may vary. Possible answers: A rectangle is sometimes a square. A square is always a rectangle.

✏️ **Justify your answer using words, drawings, or numbers.**
Possible justifications: A rectangle has opposite sides that are the same length and 4 right angles. When all 4 sides are the same length, a rectangle is also a square.

MP4 **18.** Krissa has 24 feet of fencing. She wants to make a pen in the shape of a rectangle for her turtles. What is the least possible area of a rectangle Krissa can make? What is the greatest possible area?

Answer The least possible area of a rectangle Krissa can make is 11 square feet. The greatest possible area is 36 square feet.

✏️ **Justify your answer using words, drawings, or numbers.**

$1 \times 11 = 11$ square feet $6 \times 6 = 36$ square feet

MP8 **19.** The tray on Mr. Garth's desk is shaped like a rectangle. The tray has two sections. Mr. Garth measures the tray in inches. He wants to find the area of the tray and writes $9 \times (3 + 5)$. What is the area of the tray?

Answer The area of the tray is 72 square inches.

✏️ **Justify your answer using words, drawings, or numbers.**
Possible justification:

9 in.
9×3 9×5
3 in.   5 in.

Area of left rectangle: 27 sq. in.
Area of right rectangle: 45 sq. in.
Area of tray: $27 + 45 = 72$ sq. in.

330 Unit 5 ■ Focus on Measurement and Data/Geometry

Mathematical Practices

MP3	Construct viable arguments and critique the reasoning of others.
Item 17:	Students share their reasoning with others.
MP4	**Model with mathematics.**
Item 18:	Students explain the relationship of quantities.
MP8	**Look for and express regularity in repeated reasoning.**
Item 19:	Students use patterns to relate operations.

Performance Task 2

3.OA.3, 3.OA.5, 3.NF.3b, 3.NF.3d,
3.MD.1, 3.MD.4, 3.MD.5a, 3.MD.5b,
3.MD.6, 3.MD.7a, 3.MD.7b, 3.MD.7d,
3.MD.8, 3.G.1, 3.G.2

Performance Tasks

Performance Tasks show your understanding of the Math that you have learned. You will be doing various Performance Tasks as you complete your work in this text, **Common Core Progress Mathematics**.

Beginning This Task

The next five pages provide you with the beginning of a Performance Task. You will be given 5 items to complete, and each item will have two or more parts. As you complete these items you will:

 I Demonstrate that you have mastered mathematical skills and concepts

 II Reason through a problem to a solution, and explain your reasoning

 III Use models and apply them to real-world situations.

Extending This Task

Your teacher may extend this Performance Task with additional items provided in our online resources at sadlierconnect.com.

Scoring This Task

Your response to each item will be assessed against a rubric, or scoring guide. Some items will be worth 1 or 2 points, and others will be worth more. In each item you will show your work or explain your reasoning.

Performance Task 2   331

ONLINE Customize Performance Task 2

Performance Task 2 in *Common Core Progress Mathematics* also provides students with additional practice. You can use the online items of Performance Task 2 to customize the amount and kind of performance task practice based on your ongoing evaluation of your students. You may choose to challenge some students, to give extra experience with a particular kind of task for other students, or to extend exposure to performance assessments for the entire class.

Go to **sadlierconnect.com** to download the following resources for Performance Task 2.

• Additional Items

• Additional Teacher Support

• Additional Scoring Rubrics

Performance Task 2 Overview

Performance Task 2 in *Common Core Progress Mathematics* provides students with practice for the types of items that may be found on standardized performance assessments.

Various item formats, including short- and extended-response items and technology-enhanced items, are included in the tasks. All items connect mathematical content correlated to the mathematical practices.

Items in Performance Task 2 are based on three primary types of tasks.

Type I Mastery of mathematical concepts, skills and procedures

Type II Using and explaining mathematical reasoning

Type III Modeling problem situations in a real-world context

Performance Task 2 begins with a collection of five self-contained items in the Student Book and continues with additional items online at **sadlierconnect.com**.

Introduce Performance Task 2 Read student page 331 with the class. Explain that Performance Task 2 may cover any of the math they have learned in Units 1–5. Orient students to each item and communicate helpful reminders that will enable students to approach each item successfully. Once students have completed each item, go over the correct responses with them.

Recommended Pacing Administer Performance Task 2 on Student Book pages 332–336 over five 20-minute sessions.

Teacher Resources For each task, the teacher materials include:

• Item types and purposes

• Correlations to Common Core State Standards for Mathematical Content and Practice and Depth of Knowledge (DOK) levels

• Suggested Administration procedure

• Scoring Rubric

Item 1: Planning a Mural

Item	Type	Purpose
1.a.	I	Plot a time on a number line.
1.b.	II	Explain the location for the time on the number line.
1.c.	III	Use a number line to solve a time problem.
1.d.	II	Explain an error related to telling time.

Item	CCSS	MP	DOK
1.a.	3.MD.1	4	Level 1
1.b.	3.MD.1	3	Level 2
1.c.	3.MD.1	4	Level 2
1.d.	3.MD.1	3	Level 3

Administering Item 1 (Pacing: 20 minutes)

Ask a volunteer to read the introductory paragraph. Have others describe the situation in their own words.

Item 1.a. (2 minutes)

Discuss how the number line represents time. Have students explain that each point on the number line represents a time.

Item 1.b. (5 minutes)

Remind students that each tick mark represents an equal amount of time.

Item 1.c. (8 minutes)

Some students may know that five spaces represent 50 minutes, but for others, encourage them to use skip counting to find the ending time of the meeting.

Item 1.d. (5 minutes)

Remind students what each tick mark on the face of a clock represents. Discuss how many tick marks are on a clock.

Planning a Mural

1. The students at Foster Park School are planning to paint a wall mural. The principal explains the project at a 50-minute all-school meeting.

   a. The meeting starts at 1:20 P.M. Draw a point on the number line to show 1:20 P.M.

   b. Explain how you decided where to place the point on the number line.

   The number line shows 3 equal parts from 1:00 to 1:30. So, each equal part represents 10 minutes. I counted by 10s from 1:00 and placed the point for 1:20 on the second tick mark to the right of 1:00.

   c. The all-school meeting lasts 50 minutes. Use the number line above to find when the meeting ends. What time does the meeting end?

   Modeling may vary. Students might draw curved arrows showing jumps from 1:20 to 1:30, from 1:30 to 1:40, and so on to 2:10, with each jump labeled "10 minutes."
   The meeting ends at 2:10 P.M.

   d. Isabella says that the meeting ends at 1:70 P.M. What mistake did Isabella make?

   Possible response: Isabella added 50 minutes to 1:20. She did not understand that there are only 60 minutes in one hour, so the number of minutes after any hour cannot be more than 59.

Scoring Rubric

Item	Points	Student Responses
1.a.	2	Correctly plots the time.
	0	Incorrectly plots the time.
1.b.	2	Correctly explains how to locate the time on the number line.
	1	Partially explains how to locate the time on the number line.
	0	Does not explain how to plot the time.
1.c.	2	Correctly uses the number line to find the time.
	0	Does not find the correct time.
1.d.	2	Shows clear understanding of the mistake made.
	1	Shows some understanding of the mistake made.
	0	Does not explain the mistake.

Performance Task 2

Gathering Paintbrushes

2. Teresa and Joel gather paintbrushes from the supply closet. They measure the lengths of the paintbrushes and record the measurements in the chart below.

Paintbrush Lengths (in.)

11	$10\frac{1}{4}$	11
$10\frac{1}{2}$	$10\frac{3}{4}$	$11\frac{1}{4}$
10	11	$10\frac{1}{4}$
$10\frac{3}{4}$	$11\frac{1}{4}$	$10\frac{3}{4}$

a. Use the data in the chart to make a line plot of the paintbrush lengths.

Title: _____ Brush Lengths (in.)

```
            X       X
    X   X   X   X   X
X   X   X   X   X   X
+---+---+---+---+---+---+
10  10¼ 10½ 10¾ 11  11¼
```

b. How did you know where to place the point for $10\frac{1}{2}$ inches on the number line?

Possible explanation: The number line shows $\frac{1}{4}$ inches. $10\frac{1}{2}$ inches is the same as $10\frac{2}{4}$ inches. So, $10\frac{1}{2}$ is between $10\frac{1}{4}$ and $10\frac{3}{4}$.

c. What is the length of the shortest paintbrush? What is the length of the longest paintbrush?

The shortest paintbrush is 10 inches long.
The longest paintbrush is $11\frac{1}{4}$ inches long.

d. How will the line plot change if Teresa and Joel find a long brush that is $11\frac{3}{4}$ inches long?

The number line would be extended to include two more points, $11\frac{1}{2}$ and $11\frac{3}{4}$. There would be one X above $11\frac{3}{4}$.

Scoring Rubric

Item	Points	Student Responses
2.a.	2	Correctly makes the line plot and displays all data.
	1	Creates a line plot with few errors.
	0	Does not complete the line plot.
2.b.	2	Correctly describes a data point.
	1	Provides a partial explanation of how to plot a data point.
	0	Incorrect answer.
2.c.	2	States shortest and longest lengths.
	1	Correctly identifies either the shortest or the longest lengths.
	0	Incorrect answer.
2.d.	2	Correctly describes all changes to the line plot.
	1	Describes some changes to the line plot, but misses information.
	0	Incorrect answer.

Item 2: Gathering Paintbrushes

Item	Type	Purpose
2.a.	I	Display data on a line plot.
2.b.	II	Describe how to find the location of a point on the line plot.
2.c.	II	Interpret the line plot.
2.d.	III	Describe how new data would change the line plot.

Item	CCSS	MP	DOK
2.a.	3.NF.3d	2	Level 1
2.b.	3.MD.4	4	Level 2
2.c.	3.NF.3b	3	Level 4
2.d.	3.MD.4	8	Level 4

Administering Item 2 (Pacing: 20 minutes)

Ask a volunteer to read the introductory paragraph. Have others describe the problem situation in their own words.

Item 2.a. (8 minutes)

Students need to first determine the intervals they will use. Then they need to determine the number for each point and plot the data.

Item 2.b. (5 minutes)

Students should describe the intervals of their line plots, and how they are used to find a specific value.

Item 2.c. (2 minutes)

Students should use their line plots to determine the shortest and longest paint brush lengths.

Item 2.d. (5 minutes)

Students may need to sketch the new line plot to be able to visualize the changes. They could make the changes to the current line plot using a different color pencil.

Item 3: Drawing Rectangles

Item	Type	Purpose
3.a.	I	Use tiling to find area.
3.b.	I	Use multiplication to find area.
3.c.	II	Explains why two rectangles have the same area.
3.d.	III	Identify a rectangle with same area and different perimeter.

Item	CCSS	MP	DOK
3.a.	3.MD.5a, 3.MD.5b	5	Level 1
3.b.	3.MD.7b	1	Level 1
3.c.	3.MD.7a	3	Level 3
3.d.	3.MD.7b, 3.MD.8	2	Level 3

Administering Item 3 (Pacing: 20 minutes)

Ask a volunteer to read the introductory paragraph. Have others describe the situation in their own words.

Item 3.a. (3 minutes)

Review the difference between area and perimeter. Remind students to use units in their answers.

Item 3.b. (4 minutes)

Tell students that they should write the equation that represents the multiplication they used to find the area.

Item 3.c. (5 minutes)

If needed, have students trace Steven's rectangle onto tracing paper and lay it over Sonia's rectangle. They will see that the rectangles are the same size.

Item 3.d. (8 minutes)

Ask students to explain how two rectangles might have the same area and different perimeters. Discuss solution strategies.

Drawing Rectangles

3. Sonia, Steven, and Sam draw rectangles for a large wall mural at their school.

   a. Sonia draws this rectangle. Use tiling to find the area.

   Sonia's Rectangle

   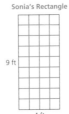

   9 ft

   4 ft

   Thirty-six 1-foot squares cover the rectangle. The area of Sonia's rectangle is 36 square feet.

   b. Steven draws this rectangle. Use multiplication to find the area.

   Steven's Rectangle

   4 ft

   9 ft

   $4 \times 9 = 36$
   The area of Steven's rectangle is 36 square feet.

   c. Compare the areas of Sonia's and Steven's rectangles. Explain why the areas are the same or different.

   The areas are the same. Possible explanation: The side lengths of the two rectangles are the same. Steven's rectangle has exactly the same side lengths as Sonia's rectangle; it is just turned. Also, if you find the area of a rectangle by counting unit squares you get the same area as when you find the area by multiplying side lengths.

   d. Sam draws a rectangle that has the same area as Steven's rectangle but Sam's rectangle has a different perimeter. Draw a rectangle that could be Sam's.

   Possible side lengths for rectangles: 1 foot and 36 feet; 2 feet and 18 feet; 3 feet and 12 feet; 6 feet (a square).

Scoring Rubric

Item	Points	Student Responses
3.a.	2	Correctly finds the area by tiling.
	0	Finds the incorrect area.
3.b.	2	Correctly finds the area by multiplication.
	0	Finds the incorrect area.
3.c.	2	Accurately compares the areas and explains how orientation is different.
	1	Explains that the areas are the same, but does not identify difference in orientation.
	0	Does not provide an explanation.
3.d.	2	Draws a rectangle with the same area and a different perimeter.
	1	Draws a rectangle with the same area and perimeter.
	0	Does not draw a rectangle.

Performance Task 2

The Class Painting

4. The students in Pedro's class paint a picture of a mountain range. The diagram below shows the shape and size of the painting.

a. What is the best name for the shape of the painting? Explain.
   The painting is a hexagon. It has 6 straight sides.

b. What is the area of the painting?
   Possible decomposition and solution:

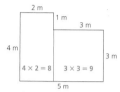

8 + 9 = 17
The area of the painting is 17 square meters.

c. Explain how you found the area of the painting.
   Possible response: I decomposed the figure into two shapes—one rectangle with side lengths 4 m and 2 m and one square with side length 3 m. I found the area of each shape, and then added the areas.

d. Paint costs 8¢ for each square meter of the picture. What is the total cost of the paint?
   Possible solution: $8 \times 17 = 8 \times (10 + 7)$
   $= (8 \times 10) + (8 \times 7)$
   $= 80 + 56$
   $= 136$
   The total cost of the paint is 136¢, or $1.36.

Performance Task 2   335

Item 4: The Class Painting

Item	Type	Purpose
4.a.	I	Identifies the name of a shape.
4.b.	II	Finds the area by decomposing into rectangles.
4.c.	I	Describes how to find area.
4.d.	I	Finds the cost based on the area.

Item	CCSS	MP	DOK
4.a.	3.G.1	1	Level 1
4.b.	3.MD.7d	6	Level 2
4.c.	3.MD.7d	3	Level 2
4.d.	3.OA.3, 3.OA.5	7	Level 2

Administering Item 4 (Pacing: 20 minutes)

Ask a volunteer to read the introductory paragraph. Have others describe the situation in their own words.

Item 4.a. (2 minutes)
Have students highlight each side as they count them.

Item 4.b. (6 minutes)
Tell students to look for shapes for which they can find the area. Remind them that there is more than one way to decompose the shape, so theirs may not look like their classmates'.

Item 4.c. (7 minutes)
Encourage students to use the word *decompose* in their explanations. Remind them to include the dimensions of any rectangle that they describe.

Item 4.d. (5 minutes)
Review how to write money in cents and in dollars and cents. Solutions may or may not include the use of the Distributive Property.

Scoring Rubric

Item	Points	Student Responses
4.a.	2	Identifies the shape as a hexagon and explains why.
	1	Identifies the shape as a hexagon with no explanation.
	0	Incorrectly names the shape.
4.b.	2	Correctly finds the area.
	0	Finds the incorrect area.
4.c.	2	Correctly explains how to decompose the shape and find the area.
	1	Correctly explains how to decompose the shape or how to find the area.
	0	Does not provide an explanation.
4.d.	2	Correctly finds the total cost of the paint.
	0	Shows no understanding of how to find the total cost of the paint.

Item 5: Heidi's Hexagon

Item	Type	Purpose
5.a.	I	Adds to find perimeter.
5.b.	I	Multiplies to find perimeter.
5.c.	II	Explains why perimeter is used to solve the problem.
5.d.	II	Analyzes the area of the shape to see if it is decomposed into equal regions.

Item	CCSS	MP	DOK
5.a.	3.MD.8	1	Level 1
5.b.	3.MD.8	1	Level 2
5.c.	3.MD.8	3	Level 2
5.d.	3.G.2	6	Level 2

Administering Item 5 (Pacing: 20 minutes)

Ask a volunteer to read the introductory paragraph. Have others describe the situation in their own words.

Item 5.a. (5 minutes)

Ask students what mathematical concept represents how much tape she will use. Have students highlight where the tape will go.

Item 5.b. (5 minutes)

Ask students to look at the equation they wrote to solve for the perimeter. Tell them to find a way to write the same work using one operation.

Item 5.c. (6 minutes)

Understanding the difference between perimeter and area is important. If students struggle, ask them to color the part of the hexagon that represents its area and trace the part that represents its perimeter.

Item 5.d. (4 minutes)

Guide students to recognize that the areas are equal by asking them to think about whether the same amount of each color of paint would be used.

Heidi's Hexagon

5. A hexagon is Heidi's favorite polygon. She draws a hexagon to hang in her room and paints it.

   a. Before Heidi paints the hexagon, she outlines the border with masking tape. Use addition to show how much tape Heidi uses.

   8 in.
   8 in.   8 in.
   8 in.   8 in.
   8 in.

   8 + 8 + 8 + 8 + 8 + 8 = 48
   Heidi uses 48 inches of tape.

   b. Use multiplication to find how much tape Heidi uses. Compare adding and multiplying to find how much tape Heidi uses.
   6 × 8 = 48
   Heidi uses 48 inches of tape.
   Since adding 8 six times is the same as multiplying 6 × 8, the answer is the same.

   c. To find the amount of tape Heidi needs, did you find the perimeter or the area of Heidi's hexagon? Explain.
   I found the perimeter. Possible explanation: The perimeter is the distance around a polygon. The tape went around the outside edge of the hexagon.

   d. Heidi will use three different colors to paint the inside of her hexagon. She outlines the areas that she will paint as shown below. Is each part $\frac{1}{3}$ of the area of the shape? Explain.

   No. Each part is not $\frac{1}{3}$ of the shape because the 3 parts do not all have equal areas.

Scoring Rubric

Item	Points	Student Responses
5.a.	2	Adds to find perimeter.
	1	Writes the correct equation, but adds incorrectly.
	0	Incorrect answer.
5.b.	2	Multiplies to find perimeter.
	1	Writes the correct equation, but multiplies incorrectly.
	0	Incorrect answer.
5.c.	2	Identifies perimeter and describes why.
	1	Identifies perimeter with no explanation.
	0	Does not identify perimeter.
5.d.	2	States the 3 regions are not equal in area with an explanation.
	1	States each region is not the given fraction without explanation.
	0	Incorrect answer.

A review of prerequisite mathematics needed to understand the concepts and skills of Grade 3.

A. Understand: Using an array to find how many in all

When you arrange things in equal rows, you make an array.

Row 1 ⟶ ●●●●   There are 4 counters in Row 1.
Row 2 ⟶ ●●●●   There are 4 counters in Row 2.
Row 3 ⟶ ●●●●   There are 4 counters in Row 3.

Write an equation to find how many counters in all.

You can add to find how many in all. $4 + 4 + 4 = 12$

There are 12 counters in all.

B. Understand: Using related addition and subtraction equations to solve subtraction problems

There were some apples on a tray.
Steve takes 20 apples.
Then 18 apples are left.
How many apples were on the tray at the start?

Make a drawing to show the problem.

⬚ apples on the tray at start	
20 apples that Steve takes	18 apples left

Use the drawing to write an equation.

⬚   −   20   =   18
apples on tray at start   apples that Steve takes   apples left

Write a related addition equation.
$18 + 20 = ⬚$ Add: $18 + 20 = 38$

There were 38 apples on the tray at the start.

Foundational Skills Handbook   **337**

Foundational Skills Handbook Contents

To review content for:		Go to:		Grade 2
Unit	**Lesson(s)**	**Page**	**Item**	**Standard**
1	1	337	A.	2.OA.4
1	5	337	B.	2.OA.1
2	13	338	C.	2.NBT.1
2	14	338	D.	2.NBT.5
3	16, 17	339	E.	2.G.3
3	18	339	F.	2.MD.6
4	24	340	G.	2.MD.7
4	25	340	H.	2.MD.5
4	26	341	I.	2.MD.10
4	27	341	J.	2.MD.9
5	35	342	K.	2.G.1
5	36	342	L.	2.G.2

The Foundational Skills Handbook:
Use to provide review of prerequisite content and skills needed for Grade 3.

Item A.

Understand: Using an array to find how many in all.

■ Explain that an array is not just any group of objects but is a group of objects that is arranged in equal rows.

Group of 12:

●   ●   ●
●   ●   ●   ●
●   ●   ●
●

Array of 12:

●   ●   ●   ●
●   ●   ●   ●
●   ●   ●   ●

■ Point out that the addition equation has the numbers in the rows as addends.

Item B.

Understand: Using related addition and subtraction equations to solve subtraction problems

■ Emphasize that making a drawing to represent the problem shows how to write an equation for the problem.

■ For the related addition equation, help students see that the amount left plus the amount taken away is equal to the amount at the start.

■ Some students may suggest that they can write the addition equation directly from the drawing. If so, say that is another way to solve the problem and praise them for their good mathematical thinking.

Item C.

Understand: Models can show that 10 tens is the same as 1 hundred

■ Students should be able to recognize that 10 ones is the same as 1 ten. When they use place-value models, they can see the 10 model is 10 ones that are put together.

■ Applying the base-ten number system structure to tens leads students to see that when they put 10 tens together, they get 100 ones or 100. This helps students visualize the concept that 10 tens is the same as 1 hundred.

■ Students who develop a firm understanding that each new place value is 10 of the preceding place value can extend this understanding to greater place values.

■ Relate the models to the places in the place-value chart to help students connect the models with using the 10 digits to represent a number symbolically.

Item D.

Understand: Adding two 2-digit numbers using place value

■ Guide students through the process of first writing an addition equation and then using place-value materials to model the equation.

■ Adding the ones first and then the tens helps prepare students for using the standard algorithm. Students combine the partial sums of the tens and the ones to find the sum. Be sure that students write the tens first when writing the sum. A common error would be writing, for this example, 9 ones 3 tens = 93.

■ Reinforce the concept by asking students to rewrite the addition equation with the sum.

■ If you have place-value materials, provide other addition exercises, including some with regrouping.

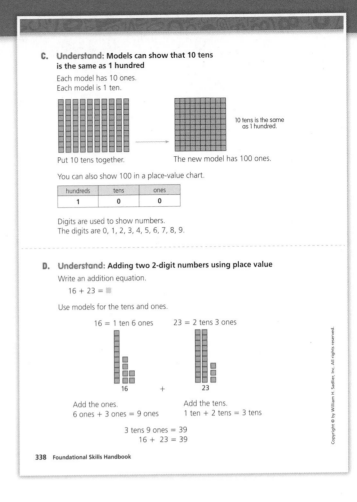

C. Understand: Models can show that 10 tens is the same as 1 hundred

Each model has 10 ones.
Each model is 1 ten.

Put 10 tens together.   The new model has 100 ones.

10 tens is the same as 1 hundred.

You can also show 100 in a place-value chart.

hundreds	tens	ones
1	0	0

Digits are used to show numbers.
The digits are 0, 1, 2, 3, 4, 5, 6, 7, 8, 9.

D. Understand: Adding two 2-digit numbers using place value

Write an addition equation.

16 + 23 = ■

Use models for the tens and ones.

16 = 1 ten 6 ones   23 = 2 tens 3 ones

16   +   23

Add the ones.   Add the tens.
6 ones + 3 ones = 9 ones   1 ten + 2 tens = 3 tens

3 tens 9 ones = 39
16 + 23 = 39

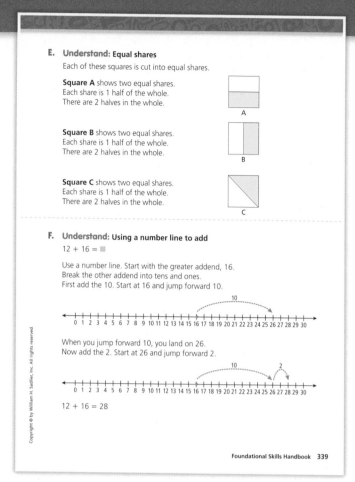

E. Understand: Equal shares

Each of these squares is cut into equal shares.

Square A shows two equal shares.
Each share is 1 half of the whole.
There are 2 halves in the whole.

Square B shows two equal shares.
Each share is 1 half of the whole.
There are 2 halves in the whole.

Square C shows two equal shares.
Each share is 1 half of the whole.
There are 2 halves in the whole.

F. Understand: Using a number line to add

$12 + 16 = $ ■

Use a number line. Start with the greater addend, 16.
Break the other addend into tens and ones.
First add the 10. Start at 16 and jump forward 10.

When you jump forward 10, you land on 26.
Now add the 2. Start at 26 and jump forward 2.

$12 + 16 = 28$

Foundational Skills Handbook **339**

Item E.

Understand: Equal shares

■ Emphasize the importance of identifying the parts that make up the whole. If the shading prevents some students from seeing the whole, have them trace around the whole with a dark marker.

■ In these examples, students see three same-size squares cut into equal shares three different ways. Ask students if the halves in the first square are the same size as the halves in the other squares. Stress that equal shares of identical wholes need not have the same shape.

■ Recognizing equal shares is fundamental to students understanding fractional parts. A solid foundation will lead to greater success in future mathematical topics such as ratios and percents.

Item F.

Understand: Using a number line to add

■ Students should recognize that the points on a number line are equally spaced. The numbers represent a distance from zero.

■ Ask why the first number plotted was 16 even though 12 is the first in the equation. Remind students that the Commutative Property of Addition allows them to start with either addend.

Item G.

Understand: Reading time to the nearest five minutes

■ Skip count by 5s from 0 to 100 with the class several times. Do so in a rhythmic pattern so that those who are less confident can hear the pattern.

■ Review the features of the clock with the students. If possible, give each small group of students a model clock they can use to identify each feature as it is discussed.

■ Remind students that there are different ways to write, display, and refer to the same time. Remind them that 30 minutes is the same as *half past,* and on the hour is called *o'clock.*

Item H.

Understand: Using an inch ruler to find the length of an object

■ Show students a ruler marked with inches and centimeters. Discuss ways to make sure the correct side of the ruler is being used when measuring.

■ Review the procedure for measuring length, emphasizing the need to align one end of the object being measured with the 0 mark on the ruler. Remind students that the 0 mark may not be the very end of the ruler.

■ Discuss how to estimate the length of an object. Have students identify an object that is about 1 inch long that could be used to approximate measurements in inches. Discuss how this is one way to check their work.

G. Understand: Reading time to the nearest five minutes

What time does the clock show?

The short hand is the hour hand.
The long hand is the minute hand.

The hour hand is between the 9 and the 10. This means that the time is past 9 o'clock, but not yet 10 o'clock.

Look at the marks around the clock face. Each of them stands for one of the 60 minutes that make up 1 hour. There are 5 marks between each number and the next.

Start at 12. Skip count by 5s until you reach the minute hand. It is 20 minutes past 9 o'clock.

The time on the clock is 9:20.

H. Understand: Using an inch ruler to find the length of an object

How long is the pencil?

An inch is a unit of measure used to measure lengths. You can measure the length of the pencil using inches.

Use an inch ruler. Line up one end of the pencil with the 0-mark on the ruler.

inches

Find the number of inches that lines up with the tip of the pencil. The pencil is 5 inches long.

I. Understand: Making a bar graph

The table shows how many flowers four children picked.

Make a bar graph to show the data.

Use the title Flowers Picked.

Make the scale on the left side of the graph go from 0 to 10.

Label the columns with the names of the children.

Make the bars show the number of flowers each child picked.

Flowers Picked	
Name	Number of Flowers
Joey	6
Zoe	8
Anna	5
Pat	9

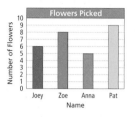

J. Understand: Making a line plot

Make a line plot of the heights of the tomato plants. Use the data in the table.

Tomato Plants				
Height (inches)	5	6	7	8
Number of Plants	3	2	4	3

Draw a number line.

Label it with the heights of the plants.

Place an X above the label for the height of each plant.

Give the line plot a title.

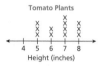

Foundational Skills Handbook 341

Item I.

Understand: Making a bar graph

■ Have students identify the title, scale, categories, and bars on the bar graph. Explain that without each part, the data might be misleading or even impossible to read.

■ Encourage students to use a ruler to mark where the top of each bar should be. This allows for the precision necessary for a well-constructed bar graph.

■ Review some of the types of problems that can be solved using bar graphs. Challenge students to write their own *put-together, take-apart,* and *compare* problems using this bar graph.

Item J.

Understand: Making a line plot

■ Ask students to describe the process of making a line plot. They should identify the first step as drawing a number line. Once the number line is drawn, an X is placed above the appropriate label for each data point.

■ This measurement data is easily displayed on a line plot because each piece of data is a number.

■ Encourage students to use appropriate tools when making a line plot. A ruler can be used to form a good foundational line upon which to build the line plot.

■ The Xs on a line plot should be the same size. Also, the Xs should form straight vertical columns. If students struggle to establish this consistency, encourage them to use grid paper when they make line plots. Apply the rule: *One X per grid square.*

Item K.

Understand: Using sides and angles to identify a flat shape

■ Create a mini-scavenger hunt in the classroom where each student looks for a triangle, quadrilateral, pentagon, and hexagon. For each shape, have students count sides and angles aloud to reinforce the connection between the number of sides and angles and the name of the shape.

■ Create flash cards with a shape on one side and its name on the other. Review flat shapes with the students by showing them either the shape or the name of the shape and having them provide the other.

■ Ask students if it is possible to draw a closed, flat shape with a given number of sides and either fewer or more angles. Remind students that flat shapes have the same number of sides as they do angles.

Item L.

Understand: Counting to find the number of same-size squares in a rectangle

■ Remind students that the same-size squares represent square units. The total number of squares represents the area. Challenge students to recall and name some square unit measurements, such as square feet.

■ Encourage students to take the process one step further and explain how they could use multiplication to find the number of same-size squares. Review that repeated addition is just another way to do multiplication.

■ Explain that the same-size squares are just one way to partition a rectangle. They may recall partitioning rectangles in other ways.

K. Understand: Using sides and angles to identify a flat shape

	Shape	Number of Sides	Number of Angles
Triangle		3	3
Quadrilateral		4	4
Pentagon		5	5
Hexagon		6	6

L. Understand: Counting to find the number of same-size squares in a rectangle

Find the number of same-size squares in the rectangle.

One way: Add the squares in the rows.

4
4
4

There are 4 same-size squares in each row.

There are three rows.

Use repeated addition.

Add 4 three times.

4 + 4 + 4 = 12

Another way: Add the squares in the columns.

3 3 3 3

There are 3 same-size squares in each row.

There are four columns.

Use repeated addition.

Add 3 four times.

3 + 3 + 3 + 3 = 12

There are 12 same-size squares in the rectangle.

You can use this model to solve problems.

Problem-Solving Model

Read
Read the problem.
Focus on the facts and the questions.
- What facts do you know?
- What do you need to find out?

Plan
Outline a plan.
Plan how to solve the problem.
- What operation will you use?
- Do I need to use 1 step or 2 steps?
- Will you draw a picture?
- How have you solved similar problems?

Solve
Follow your plan to solve the problem.
- Did you answer the question?
- Did you label your answer?

Check
Test that the solution is reasonable.
- Does your answer make sense? If not, review and revise your plan.
- How can you solve the problem a different way? Is the answer the same?
- How can you estimate to check your answer?

Problem-Solving Model   343

Introducing the Problem-Solving Model

You can use the Problem-Solving Model pages to encourage students to think problems through and solve them successfully.

The Problem-Solving Model is just one way to help students master the art of problem solving. Many students intuitively see alternative methods or solutions. Their intuitive grasp of the problem/situation should not be impeded or slowed by having to use the model. Students should be asked only to demonstrate that they solved a problem using some logical plan, and not necessarily this specific model. Students should be able to explain the method they have used.

Problem-Solving Model

A Number Pattern Problem

Finding a pattern that leads to a problem's solution provides students with other opportunities to think about math in nonroutine situations. To solve A Number Pattern Problem, students must understand addition and subtraction, and use logical reasoning to find missing terms in a number pattern.

A Number Pattern Problem

Rita made up this number pattern.
1, 5, 4, 8, 7, 11, 10, ▪, ▪, 17
What are the unknown eighth and ninth terms in Rita's pattern?

Read

Visualize the pattern on the number line.

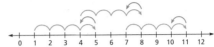

Facts: The number pattern has 10 terms.
The numbers in the pattern increase, then decrease.

Question: What are the missing eighth and ninth terms?

Plan

Look at the numbers in Rita's pattern.
Since the second number is greater and the third number is less, try adding first, subtracting next, and so on.

$$1, \quad 5, \quad 4, \quad 8, \quad 7, \quad 11, \quad 10$$
$$+4 \quad -1 \quad +4 \quad -1 \quad +4 \quad -1$$

The pattern is: Start at 1. Add 4, subtract 1.

Solve

Use the pattern.
$10 + 4 = 14$ eighth term
$14 - 1 = 13$ ninth term

➡ The missing eighth and ninth terms are 14 and 13.

Check

The tenth term in the pattern is 17.
Check your computation.
Does $13 + 4 = 17$? Yes.

344 Problem-Solving Model

A Spending Problem

To solve multistep problems, such as A Spending Problem, students must be able to perceive and understand the interrelatedness of the multiple parts. By following the problem-solving model, students can analyze the problem and not only choose the correct operations, but plan the correct sequence in which to do each operation.

A Spending Problem

Aiden and Max are shopping for a greeting card. Aiden has 50¢. Max has 30¢ more than Aiden. Do they have enough money altogether to buy a card that costs $1?

Read

Visualize the problem as you reread it.
Focus on the facts and the question.

Facts: Aiden—50¢
Max—30¢ more than Aiden
card—costs $1

Question: Do they have enough money to buy a card that costs $1?

Plan

To find if Aiden and Max have enough money, first add together the amounts of money they have. Then compare the total amount with the cost of the card.
Is more than one step needed? Yes.

Solve

Find the amount Max has.

50¢	50¢ Aiden's money
+30¢	+80¢ Max's Money
80¢ Max's money	130¢ altogether

Remember!
$1 = 100¢

$130¢ > 100¢$

➡ Aiden and Max have enough money.

Check

Does your answer make sense?
Aiden has 50¢. Since Max has more than 50¢, they have enough money.
$50¢ + 50¢ = 100¢ = \$1$
The answer is reasonable.

Problem-Solving Model **345**

The Standards for Mathematical Practice, identified here, are an important part of learning mathematics. They are covered in every lesson in this book.

MP1 Make sense of problems and persevere in solving them.

- Analyze and plan a solution
- Relate to a similar problem
- Assess progress
- Use concrete objects or pictures
- Check solutions

MP2 Reason abstractly and quantitatively.

- Pay attention to all mathematical language
- Represent problems using symbols
- Consider units in problem solving
- Use properties of operations and objects

MP3 Construct viable arguments and critique the reasoning of others.

- Analyze a problem situation
- Share reasoning with others
- Explain an approach to a problem
- Construct arguments by using drawings or concrete objects

MP4 Model with mathematics.

- Relate mathematics to everyday problems
- Make assumptions and estimations
- Explain the relationship of quantities
- Use concrete tools to explain operations
- Interpret the solution in the context of a situation

MP5 Use appropriate tools strategically.

- Consider the range of available tools (e.g., place-value charts, graphs, clocks, etc.)
- Decide on appropriate tools to use for each situation
- Use tools carefully and strategically

MP6 Attend to precision.

- Communicate with precision
- Identify the meaning of symbols
- Use measurement units appropriately
- Calculate accurately
- Carefully formulate full explanations

MP7 Look for and make use of structure.

- Search for patterns or structure
- Evaluate the structure or design of a problem
- Discuss geometric shapes in terms of their similarities and differences

MP8 Look for and express regularity in repeated reasoning.

- Make generalizations in computation
- Obtain fluency using patterns
- Look for patterns with shapes and designs
- Use patterns to relate operations
- Evaluate reasonableness of answers

Key: MP = Mathematical Practice

Glossary

A

angle Formed when two sides extend from a common endpoint called the vertex.

area The number of unit squares needed to cover the figure without gaps or overlaps.

array An arrangement of objects or symbols in equal rows and equal columns.

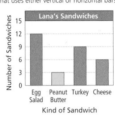

Associative Property of Addition Changing the grouping of addends does not change the sum.

For example, $50 + (90 + 7) = (50 + 90) + 7$

Associative Property of Multiplication Changing the grouping of factors does not change the product.

For example, $2 \times 3 \times 2 = (2 \times 3) \times 2$
$2 \times 3 \times 2 = 2 \times (3 \times 2)$

B

bar graph A display of data, or information, that uses either vertical or horizontal bars.

C

closed figure A two-dimensional figure that has no breaks.

Commutative Property of Addition Changing the order of addends does not change the sum.

For example, $50 + (7 + 90) + 4 = 50 + (90 + 7) + 4$

Commutative Property of Multiplication Changing the order of factors does not change the product.

For example, $2 \times 3 = 6$
$3 \times 2 = 6$

compatible numbers Numbers that can be easily added, subtracted, multiplied, or divided.

D

data Facts or information.

decompose Breaking apart a plane figure into simpler plane figures to find the area of the entire figure.

denominator The number of equal parts in the whole, shown below the bar in a fraction.

For example, $\frac{1}{3}$ ← denominator

Distributive Property The product of a number and the sum of two numbers is equal to the sum of the two products. Multiplication can be distributed over addition.

For example, $7 \times 9 = 7 \times (5 + 4)$
$= (7 \times 5) + (7 \times 4)$.

divide Perform a division with two numbers.

dividend The number to be divided.

---

division An operation used when partitioning a group of objects to find either the number of equal shares or the number in each equal share.

divisor The number by which the dividend is divided.

E

elapsed time The amount of time between two given times.

equation A number sentence that includes an equal sign.

For example, $4 \times 8 = 32$

equivalent fractions Fractions that have different names but are at the same point on the number line.

For example, $\frac{1}{3} = \frac{2}{6}$

estimation A strategy used to determine an approximate answer.

even Any number that can be divided by 2 with no remainder.

F

fact family A set of equations that shows related addition and subtraction facts or related multiplication and division facts.

For example, fact family for 3, 7, and 21:
$3 \times 7 = 21 \qquad 7 \times 3 = 21$
$21 \div 3 = 7 \qquad 21 \div 7 = 3$

factor Each of the numbers being multiplied that will result in a product.

fraction A number that names part of a whole, an area, or a group. It can be expressed in the form $\frac{a}{b}$.

G

gram (g) A metric unit of mass. A paper clip has a mass of about 1 gram.

H

half inch A customary unit of length.

hexagon A polygon with six sides and six vertices or angles.

hour (h) A unit of time. 1 hour = 60 minutes

I

Identity Property of Multiplication The product of any number and 1 is that number.

For example, $5 \times 1 = 5$

K

key Tells what each symbol in a picture graph stands for.

Ms. Brown's Fruit	
Bananas	◆ ◆
Pears	◆ ◆ ◆
Apples	◆ ◆ ◆ ◆ ◆
Mangos	◆
Key: ◆ = 2 fruits	

kilogram (kg) A metric unit of mass. A textbook has a mass of about 1 kilogram. 1 kilogram = 1000 grams

L

line plot A graph that uses a number line and symbols to represent data.

Carrot Lengths (in.)

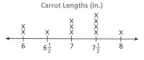

liquid volume The amount of liquid a container can hold.

liter (L) A metric unit of liquid volume. A tall water bottle can hold about 1 liter of liquid.

M

mass The measure of the amount of matter an object contains.

minute (min) A unit of time.
60 minutes = 1 hour

multiple The product of a given whole number and another whole number.

multiplication A joining operation on two or more numbers to find a total for equal groups.

multiply Perform multiplication with two or more numbers.

N

number line A line used to show the order of numbers. The numbers are represented by points that are spaced equally.

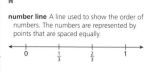

numerator The number of equal parts being considered in a fraction, shown above the bar in a fraction.
For example, $\frac{1}{3}$ ← numerator

O

odd Any number that when divided by 2 has a remainder of 1.

operations Mathematical processes, such as addition, subtraction, multiplication, and division.

P

parentheses ( ) Symbols used to show grouping within equations.
For example, $(2 \times 3) \times 2 = \blacksquare$

partition Separate into equal parts.

pattern A predictable sequence.
For example, 123123123

perimeter The sum of the lengths of the sides of a polygon.

picture graph A display of data, or information, that uses symbols or pictures.

Favorite Fruit	
Peaches	🍹 🍹 🍹 🍹
Strawberries	🍹 🍹 🍹
Bananas	🍹 🍹
Oranges	🍹 🍹 🍹 🍹
Key: 🍹 = 2 students	

plane figure A two-dimensional figure.

polygon A plane closed figure with straight sides.

---

product The answer in multiplication.

property A mathematical rule.

Q

quadrilateral A polygon with four sides and four vertices or angles.

quarter inch A customary unit of length.

quotient The answer in division.

R

rhombus A quadrilateral that has sides of equal length.

right angle An angle that forms a square corner.

round A method to estimate by changing numbers to the nearest 10 or 100.

rule Tells the number to start with and how to find the next number in an arithmetic pattern.

S

scale On a bar graph, it tells how many are represented by the length of a bar.

square centimeter The area of a square whose side lengths measure 1 centimeter. Can be written as *square cm*.

square foot The area of a square whose side lengths measure 1 foot. Can be written as *square ft*.

square inch The area of a square whose side lengths measure 1 inch. Can be written as *square in*.

square meter The area of a square whose side lengths measure 1 meter. Can be written as *square m*.

T

tile A method of determining area by joining unit squares along their edges to cover a figure.

time A quantity that can be measured using years, months, days, hours, minutes, and/or seconds.

time interval A segment of time.

U

unit fraction Represents the quantity, or amount, in one of the equal parts of a whole.

unit square A square with side lengths of 1 unit.

unknown A value in a mathematical problem that is not known.

V

vertex (vertices) The point at which two sides meet to form an angle.

W

whole number Any of the numbers 0, 1, 2, 3, 4, 5, and so on.

Z

Zero Property The product of any number and 0 is 0.
For example, $5 \times 0 = 0$

A

Addition
addend, 120–127
Associative Property of Addition, 120–127
Commutative Property of Addition, 120–127
fluently within 1,000, 120–127
in measurement, 288–295
sum, 120–127

Area
as a fraction, 256–263, 304–311
of composite figures, 280–287
decompose to find, 280–287, 320–327
use Distributive Property to find, 272–279
partitioning and equal areas, 320–327
of rectangles, 264–271, 272–279
tile to find, 264–271
units of, 256–263

Arithmetic patterns, 104–111

C

Common Core Review, 74–76, 136–138, 206–208, 250–252, 328–330

Common Core State Standards for Mathematical Practice, 346

Compatible numbers, 88–95

D

Data
categorical, 234–241
measurement, 242–249

Decompose to find area, 280–287

Division
arrays, 34–41
dividend, 18–25
divisor, 18–25
equal groups, 26–33
equations, 42–49
fact families, 66–73
in measurement, 288–295
partition, 18–25
quotients, 18–25
unknown factors, 66–73
unknown numbers, 42–49
strategies, 80–87
of whole numbers, 18–25

E

Equations
division, 42–49
multiplication, 42–49
use of, 96–103

Essential Question—Unit, 9, 79, 141, 217, 255

Estimation
and compatible numbers, 88–95
of liquid volume, 226–233
of mass, 226–233
and rounding, 112–119

F

Foundational Skills Handbook
addition and subtraction equations, 337
addition on a number line, 339
area, 342
array, 337
bar graph, 341
fractions, 342
geometric figures, 342
line plot, 341
measurement, 340
place value, 338
time, 340

Fractions
areas as, 320–327
compare, 190–197, 198–205
denominators, 142–149
and equal areas, 320–327
equivalent, 166–173, 174–181
on a number line, 158–165
numerators, 142–149
as quantities, 142–149, 150–157
relation to whole numbers, 182–189
concept of, 142–149, 150–157
unit fractions, 142–149
whole numbers and, 182–189

G

Geometry
closed figures, 296–303
equal areas, 320–327
use decomposition to find area, 320–327
hexagon, 312–319
pentagon, 312–319
plane figures, 256–263
polygon, 296–303
right angle, 312–319
rhombus, 312–319
shapes and attributes, 312–319
vertex, 312–319

Graphs
bar, 234–241
of categorical data, 234–241
line plot, 242–249
and measurement, 242–249
picture, 234–241
scale, 234–241

H

Home Connect, 8, 78, 140, 216, 254

L

Liquid volume, 226–233

M

Measurement
area, 256–263, 264–271, 304–311
gram, 226–233
hour, minute, 218–225
inch, half-inch, quarter inch, 242–249
liquid volume, 226–233

liter, 226–233
mass, 226–233
perimeter, 304–311
square centimeter, square meter, 256–263
square inch, square foot, 256–263
unit square, 256–263

Measurement and Data
area, 256–263, 264–271, 272–279, 280–287
graphing, 234–241, 242–249
liquid volumes and masses, 226–233
perimeter, 296–303, 304–311
time, 218–225

Multiplication
array, 34–41
Associative Property of, 50–57
Commutative Property of, 50–57, 104–111
Distributive Property, 58–65
equal groups, 26–33
equations, 42–49
fact families, 66–73
factor, 10–17
finding unknown factors in, 66–73
Identity Property of, 80–87
in measurement, 288–295
by multiples of 10, 128–135
product, 10–17, 26–33, 42–49
strategies, 80–87
of whole numbers, 10–17, 128–135
Zero Property, 80–87

N

Number and Operations— Fractions
comparing, 190–205
equivalent, 166–181
on the number line, 158–165
as quantities, 142–149, 150–157
related to whole numbers, 182–189

Number and Operations in Base Ten
add and subtract within 1,000, 120–127
multiply by multiples of 10, 128–135
round whole numbers, 112–119

Number line
fractions, 158–165

O

Operations and Algebraic Thinking
division equations, 42–49
multiplication and division, 10–17, 18–25, 26–33, 34–41, 66–73, 80–87
patterns, 104–111
properties of operations, 50–57, 58–65
unknown factors, 26–33

P

Patterns, 104–111

Performance Task, 209–214, 331–336

Perimeter, 296–303, 304–311

Problem solving
arrays, 34–41
equal groups, 26–33
equations, 96–103
liquid volumes and masses, 226–233
measurement, 288–295
multiplication and division, 26–33, 42–49
perimeter, 296–303
perimeter and area, 304–311
time, 218–225
two–step problems, 88–95

Problem–Solving Model, 343–345

Progress Check, 7, 77, 139, 215, 253

Properties of Operations
Associative Property of Addition, 120–127
Associative Property of Multiplication, 50–57
Commutative Property of Addition, 120–127
Commutative Property of Multiplication, 50–57
Distributive Property, 58–65, 272–279
Identity Property of Multiplication, 80–87
Zero Property, 80–87

Q

Quadrilateral, 296–303

Quotient, 18–25, 26–33, 34–41, 42–49, 66–73

R

Rectilinear figure, 280–287

Rhombus, 312–319

Right angle, 312–319

Rounding, 112–119

Rule, 104–111

S

Scale, 234–241

Subtraction
fluent within 1,000, 120–127
and problem solving, 96–103

T

Tile to find area, 264–271

Time
elapsed, 218–225
hour, 218–225
interval, 218–225
minute, 218–225

Notes